Science and Innovation for Development

by Gordon Conway and Jeff Waage
with Sara Delaney

Published by:

UK CDS
UK Collaborative on Development Sciences

Production funded by:

DFID Department for
International
Development

i

UK Collaborative on Development Sciences (UKCDS)
Gibbs Building
215 Euston Road
London
NW1 2BE
Email: info@ukcds.org.uk

Disclaimer: Every effort has been made to ensure that all the information in this edition of *Science and Innovation for Development* is correct at the time of going to press. However, the authors and publisher do not accept liability for any error or omission in the content. Nothing in the publication shall be taken as warranty that any product or technique mentioned herein is not the subject of patent rights and UKCDS does not hold itself responsible for any infringement of the said right.

British Library Cataloguing in Publication Data. A catalogue record for this book is available from the British Library.

ISBN 978 1 84129 0829

Further copies of this book can be ordered direct from BCPC Publications Ltd, 7 Omni Business Centre, Omega Park, Alton, Hampshire GU34 2QD, UK

Tel: +44 (0) 1420 593 200 Fax: +44 (0) 1420 593 209 Email: publications@bcpc.org

For fast order processing and secure payment order online at www.bcpcbookshop.co.uk

The production of this book is funded by the UK Department for International Development (DFID) for the benefit of developing countries. The views expressed are not necessarily those of DFID.

Design and typesetting by: m360° Ltd, Nottingham, UK

Edited and project managed by: Moira Hart, Dewpoint Marketing, Long Clawson, UK

Printed by: Latimer Trend and Company Ltd, Plymouth, UK

© Cover images:
Dominic Sansoni – World Bank
Wellcome Images
USDA

Ray Witlin – World Bank
Hu Wei – Greenpeace International
Sewaburkina – Flickr

DFID
Environmental Education Media Project for China
Ken Banks – kiwanja.net

Contents

Part Two - Science and the Millennium Development Goals

Part Three - The Challenge of Climate Change

Box titles

Chapter 5

Chapter 6

Chapter 7

Chapter 8

Chapter 9

Chapter 10

List of tables

Foreword

Professor Calestous Juma FRS

Belfer Center for Science and International Affairs
Harvard Kennedy School, Harvard University

Science and Innovation for Development is a path-breaking book that reconnects development practice with the fundamental, technical processes of development outlined more than 50 years ago. It is a refreshing reminder that development is a knowledge-intensive activity that cannot be imposed from the outside. It is consistent with leading theories that define development as an expression of the endogenous capabilities of people.

The book is written in a clear and accessible way and will go a long way in demystifying the view that science and technology is irrelevant to development. It elegantly demonstrates that even the most basic of daily activities of local communities are based on science and innovation. Even the most stubborn critics of the role of science and innovation in development can hardly miss the glaring power of the core message and the sparkling examples.

But to appreciate the importance of this book one has to revisit history. The late 1950s were a turning point in the history of economic thought. In the process of mapping out the economic future of emerging nations, many industrialised countries have recognised the role that science and innovation have played in their own development. For example, in a seminal paper published in 1957, Nobel laureate Robert Solow showed that over the previous 40 years technical change had contributed more than 87 % of gross output per person while the increase in capital investment explained only about 12 %. [1]

But as such studies laid the foundation for our current understanding of the role of science and innovation in economic growth, new organisations, guided by the experiences of post-World War II relief efforts in Europe, were charting out strategies for extending their work to emerging developing nations. The 1960s saw a clear divergence where industrialized countries increasingly adopted innovation-oriented policies while development cooperation programmes focused on relief efforts.

One of the most damaging legacies of this divergence was the consistent downplaying of technological innovation as a force in economic development. In fact, many development agencies exhibited outright hostility towards proposals that sought to integrate innovation in development cooperation strategies. *Science and Innovation for Development* is not just an effort to add a new dimension to development cooperation activities. It is a challenge to the international community to jettison traditional development approaches that focus on financial flows without attention to the role of science and innovation in economic transformation.

There have been many exhortations of the importance of science and innovation in development. But this book differs from previous studies in at least four fundamental ways. First, it uses clear and practical examples to illustrate the importance of science and innovation in development. Second, the examples provided in the book are not just compelling, but they are inspirational and demonstrate the practical utility of putting science and innovation to the service of development. Third, unlike other studies on "appropriate technology", the book takes into account the important role that institutional innovation plays in economic growth. Finally, the book recognizes emerging critical challenges such as climate change. Concern over global warming has moved from the level of scientific debate to a challenge of epochal proportions and addressing its consequences will require equally extraordinary efforts to deploy the most relevant scientific and technical knowledge available in the shortest time possible. This opens the door for a more pragmatic view of the role of engineering in development, a field that has so far received little attention in development cooperation activities.[2]

But above all, the importance of this book lies in its timing. The traditional relief-based model of development assistance no longer works except in emergency situations. But even here the pressure to move from emergency to sustainable economic recovery calls for greater investment in science and innovation. Recent challenges, such as rising food prices, are focusing international attention on the importance of increasing investment in science and innovation. But more importantly, the entry of new role models such as China, India, Brazil and Israel are helping to underscore the importance of innovation in development. Indeed, developing countries are increasingly seeking to place science and innovation at the centre of their development strategies.

The recent financial crisis has forced a large number of industrialized countries to introduce stimulus packages which include emphasis on infrastructure, technical training, business incubation and international trade. These priorities are similar to the technology-led policies that are increasingly being pursued by developing countries. In effect, economic growth policies in industrialized and developing countries are converging around the idea of science and innovation. This book will therefore provide guideposts for international cooperation in the application of science and innovation and help support ongoing efforts to incorporate science and innovation in the activities of international development programmes.[3]

The book will play a key role in helping the development community relate their work more closely to the pioneering concepts laid out by Robert Solow and others 50 years ago. It is only by doing so that the community can bring reasoned practicality to their otherwise worthy efforts. *Science and Innovation for Development* is the most important book on development since Fritz Schumacher's 1973 classic book, *Small is Beautiful*. It will silence the critics of the role of technology in development and embolden its champions.

1   Solow, R., (1957) "Technical Change and the Aggregate Production Function," *The Review of Economics and Statistics*, **39**, 3, 312-320.

2   Juma, C., (2006) *Redesigning African Economies: The Role of Engineering in International Development.* Hinton Lecture, Royal Academy of Engineering, London.

3   House of Commons Science and Technology Committee. (2004) *The Use of Science in UK International Development Policy*, Vol. 1, Stationery Office Limited, London; National Research Council. (2006). *The Fundamental Role of Science and Technology in International Development: An Imperative for the US Agency for International Development,* National Academies Press, Washington, DC.

About the authors

Professor Sir Gordon Conway

Gordon Conway is Professor of International Development at Imperial College. He trained in agricultural ecology, attending the universities of Bangor, Cambridge, West Indies (Trinidad) and California (Davis).

In the 1960's he was a pioneer of sustainable agriculture, developing integrated pest management programmes for the State of Sabah in Malaysia. He joined Imperial College in 1970 setting up the Centre for Environmental Technology in 1976. In the 1970s and 1980s he lived and worked extensively in Asia and the Middle East, for the Ford Foundation, the World Bank and USAID. He directed the Sustainable Agriculture Programme at IIED and then became representative of the Ford Foundation in New Delhi. Subsequently he became Vice-Chancellor of the University of Sussex and Chair of the Institute of Development Studies.

From 1998-2004 he was President of the Rockefeller Foundation and from 2004-2009 Chief Scientific Adviser to DFID and President of the Royal Geographical Society. Between 2006 and 2009 he was Chairman of the UK Collaborative on Development Sciences (UKCDS) and is now currently heading the Gates funded project 'Africa and Europe: Partnerships in Food and Farming.'

He is a KCMG, Deputy Lieutenant of East Sussex, Hon Fell RAEng and FRS. He holds five honorary degrees and fellowships. He is the author of *'The Doubly Green Revolution: Food for all in the 21st Century'*, published by Penguin and Cornell.

Professor Jeff Waage

Jeff Waage is the Director of the London International Development Centre (LIDC), a Professor at the School of Oriental and African Studies (SOAS), University of London and a Visiting Professor at Imperial College London, the London School of Hygiene and Tropical Medicine (LSHTM) and the Royal Veterinary College (RVC).

He trained in entomology, and taught ecology at Imperial College London before joining CABI in 1986 where he headed the International Institute of Biological Control and later CABI Bioscience. At Imperial and CABI he contributed to ecological theory in integrated pest management, helped the spread of farmer field schools in Asia and Africa, and led the successful development of a biological pesticide for the desert locust.

He has been President of the International Organisation of Biological Control and Chair of the Global Invasive Species Programme. Jeff returned as Director of Imperial College at Wye in 2001, contributing to UK agricultural research through advisory roles with BBSRC and Defra, and joined

LIDC as its first Director in 2007. Today his passion is stimulating inter-disciplinary and inter-sectoral research to address complex development issues, including the integration of health and agricultural research sectors.

Sara Delaney

Sara Delaney joined Imperial College in July 2009 to work on the Gates Foundation funded project 'Africa and Europe: Partnerships in Food and Farming.' She studied biological and environmental engineering at Cornell University and 'Science, Society and Development' at the Institute of Development Studies (IDS).

From 2005-2007 she served as a US Peace Corps volunteer in Mali working in the water and sanitation sector. Since leaving IDS she has worked for the London International Development Centre (LIDC) and the UK Collaborative on Development Sciences (UKCDS).

About the publisher

UK Collaborative on Development Sciences (UKCDS) and its members work together to maximise the impact of UK research funding on international development outcomes. It prioritises facilitation and networking activities that lead to better coordination of development relevant research and encourages UK funders to reflect good practice in development in their research policies and practices. UKCDS is committed to ensuring that the UK is a global leader in development sciences and their impact.

UKCDS members are currently:

Research Councils UK

Biotechnology and Biological Sciences Research Council (BBSRC)

Economic and Social Research Council (ESRC)

Engineering and Physical Sciences Research Council (EPSRC)

Medical Research Council (MRC)

Natural Environment Research Council (NERC)

Departments of State and Government

Department for Business Innovation and Skills (BIS)

Department for Environment, Food and Rural Affairs (DEFRA)

Department for International Development (DFID)

Department of Energy and Climate Change (DECC)

Department of Health (DH)

The Scottish Government

UK Charity

Wellcome Trust

In partnership with the Bill & Melinda Gates Foundation

www.ukcds.org.uk

Preface and acknowledgments

We have written this book to help people understand how science can contribute to international development. People interested in international development often have very different views about the value of science. At one extreme, some see science and technology providing the principle means for reducing poverty, eliminating disease and improving well being. At another extreme, science is seen as part of an imposed, external regime, associated with industrial exploitation and suppression of indigenous knowledge.

Fluctuations over recent decades in perspectives on development create a similar diversity of roles for science. When development theory and practice have focused on generating economic growth, as in the days of the Washington Consensus, we have seen support for programmes that extend technological advances to poor countries which would make a workforce more efficient, raise GDP and improve incomes. When, instead, theory and practice swing towards the view that development is being prevented largely by social and political forces, e.g. education, social exclusion, poor governance and corruption, we see the agronomists, engineers and health specialists vacate their development advisor's offices, to be replaced by social scientists. Development policy makers seem to listen to social scientists or natural scientists, but rarely both.

Today the issue of the role of science could not be more alive, as we sit between cycles of development thinking. Having pursued a welfare-oriented agenda in the Millennium Development Goals (MDGs), we now face a global economic crisis which is focusing attention again on economic growth. Foundations, businesses and civil society organisations are becoming more important development players, and we are seeing them take very different views on the role of science. One needs only to look at recent dialogue on genetically modified (GM) crops to see how polarized communities have become, in both rich and poor countries, about the value of science and innovation in a development context.

We hope that this book will give anyone who is interested in international development a clearer picture of the role that science and innovation can play. We firmly believe that science is only one of many factors which can contribute to development, but we want that factor to be well understood, particularly as science is often presented in a way which is not easily accessible to the non-specialist. We have used the MDGs as a framework for our exploration, because they address a wide range of development issues where science is particularly active: agriculture, health, and the environment.

This book would not have been possible without the help and support of a large number of individuals and organisations. In particular, we would like to thank staff at DFID, UKCDS and LIDC who helped with gathering material and administering the project; Steve Hillier, Mandy Cook, Angela May, Kate O'Shea, Charlie McLaren and Guy Collender. Special thanks to Andrée Carter for providing the persistent leadership to make sure we did indeed deliver a book in the end! In addition, we would like to acknowledge the work of Rebecca Pankhurst and Hayaatun Sillem, who assisted with earlier versions of the manuscript. The text of this book was reviewed and enriched by a number of busy colleagues to whom we are most grateful, including John Mumford, Paul van Gardingen, Steve Hillier, Camilla Toulmin, Peter Piot, Chris Whitty, Jonathan Wadsworth, Tim Wheeler, Hayaatun Sillemand and Calestous Juma. Finally, we are grateful to Moira Hart of Dewpoint Marketing for her tireless and skilful management of editing and logistics, and to the team at m360° Ltd for their patience, hard work and brilliant, colourful presentation of the material.

A very large number of people contributed resources to this book, checking our stories and correcting our facts and figures. Thank you, your time helped to make our examples as up-to-date and as detailed as possible. Any errors or omissions are however the responsibility of the authors alone.

As we ranged across agriculture, health and environment, we found ourselves constantly making use of SciDev.net. They are an extraordinarily valuable and authoritative resource for development science, and we would like to thank them for being there. Finally, we thank DFID for providing funding for much of this book's production.

Gordon Conway, Jeff Waage and Sara Delaney

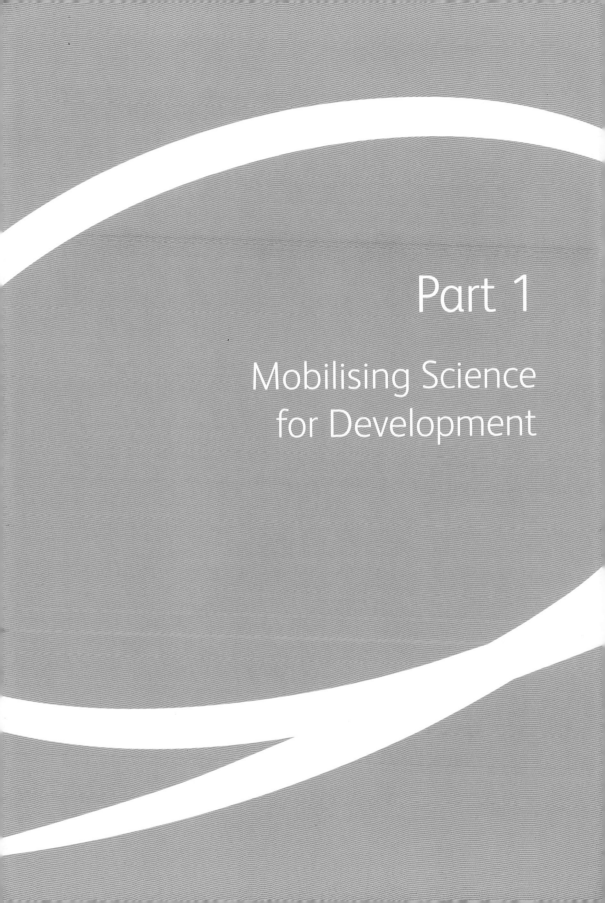

Part 1

Mobilising Science for Development

The Nature of Science and Innovation

A NERICA rice variety developed by the Africa Rice Center. © Gordon Conway

1. Why is science important?

Why is science important? Science underpins improvements in human welfare, through technologies which it develops for health, food production, engineering and communication. Science is also important in solving problems created by human activity, such as environmental degradation and climate change. Science allows us to move forward through incremental improvements in technology, adapted for particular needs and situations. But it also sometimes allows us to leap forward, through fundamental scientific discoveries that entirely change our sets of tools for human improvement, and create new platforms for technology, such as the genetic revolution and the consequent development of biotechnologies for improving health and agriculture.

The terms we use to describe science are explained in Box 1.1.

Box 1.1   What do we mean by science, technology and innovation?

Science is the process of generating knowledge based on evidence.[1] While it implicitly includes both natural sciences (biology, chemistry, physics, mathematics and related disciplines) and social sciences (economics, sociology, anthropology, politics, law), we will focus in this book largely on natural science disciplines.

Technology is the application of scientific knowledge, and frequently involves invention, i.e, the creation of a novel object, process or technique.

Innovation is the process by which inventions are produced, which may involve the bringing together of new ideas and technology, or finding novel applications of existing technologies. Generally, innovation means developing new ways of doing things in a place or by people where they have not been used before. Modern innovation is usually stimulated by **innovation systems and pathways**.

The phrase **'Science and Innovation'** in this book implicitly includes science, engineering, technology and the production systems which deliver them.

People who live in developed countries sometimes forget how scientific innovations have transformed their lives. They live much longer than their predecessors, they have access to a dependable supply and a great variety of foods and other goods, they can travel easily and quickly around the world and they have a myriad of electronic gadgets designed for work and pleasure. Much of this success is due to sound economic policies and to forms of governance that promote equality, justice and freedom of choice, but much is also due to advances in scientific innovation (Box 1.2).

How does scientific innovation work?

Scientific innovation involves the successful exploitation of new ideas to generate new techniques, products and processes. Traditionally, scientific innovation has been viewed as a process starting with curiosity-driven, basic research which generates new understanding. This then leads to translational research, which relates this fundamental understanding to systems we want to improve, and then to applied research, which produces the products which we can use. Private enterprise plays a key role in successful innovation – without business investment and marketing, inventions such as penicillin, computers and mobile phones would not exist today.

Box 1.2   Inventors past and present

The 20th century witnessed dramatic medical inventions – a vaccine against yellow fever, Fleming's discovery of penicillin, Salk's development of the oral polio vaccine, Barnard's first heart transplant. These and other discoveries have had widespread benefits unimaginable a century before and the pace of discovery shows no signs of abating. In 2005, the average UK life expectancy for men was 78 years, compared to 66 in 1950 and 48 in 1900.[2] The next wave of discoveries is likely to be treatments and cures for cancers and for the diseases of ageing, such as Alzheimer's.

© Imperial College Archive

Figure 1.1 – Alexander Fleming in his laboratory in 1909 at St Mary's Hospital, London

But today it is inventions in electronics and communications that catch the imagination – Jobs' and Wozniak's development of the Apple computer, Berners-Lee's invention of the World Wide Web and its exploitation by Page and Brin in the form of Google, and by Omidyar's eBay.

Arguably the biggest recent impact has come from the mobile phone, but here it is difficult to identify a single inventor. The nature of invention has significantly changed: modern inventions are largely the result of team work.

As an example of innovation, consider how new knowledge of the genetics of disease resistance, gained from basic research on a laboratory animal, may lead to translational research on livestock to determine whether similar genes exist that convey useful resistance. If this research is successful, industry may use it to develop products, in this case using livestock breeding methods to incorporate genes conferring resistance into specific commercial breeds for sale to farmers (Figure 1.2).

Figure 1.2 – A linear process of scientific innovation

Basic Research	**Translational Research**	**Product Development**
Studying genetics of disease resistance using a laboratory animal	Identifying similar genes in livestock	Breeding to incorporate relevant genes into new livestock breeds for sale

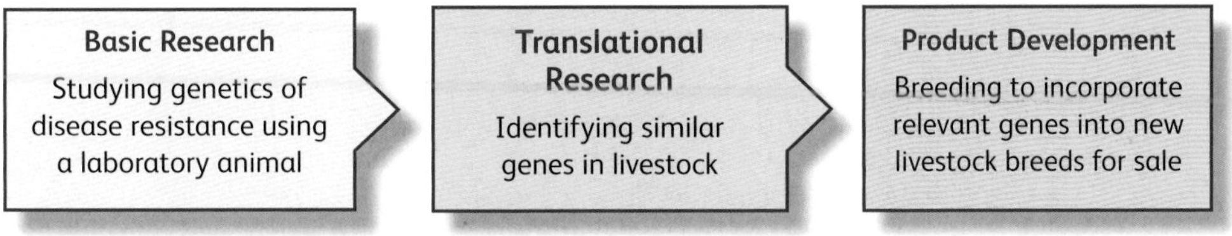

However, today we recognise that scientific innovation is not always a linear process, and that it often involves an interplay back-and-forth between basic, translational and applied research stages. It is possible, for example, for applied research to identify a need for more basic research in a new area. Going back to the example above, if new breeds exhibit only patchy resistance to the disease in question, farmers may choose not to buy the product. This may stimulate applied research into the causes of breakdown of resistance, which in turn may stimulate more basic research into resistance mechanisms, so as to generate new solutions.

This research interaction involves a diverse system of players and institutions that influence its progress and success. Together, these are often called a **science innovation system**. The players may come from companies, universities, government and civil society. Scientists play a key role, of course, but so do other stakeholders, such as policy makers, banks and investors. Involving policy makers allows for a conducive policy and regulatory environment for the development and use of new technologies, while banks and investors provide security and capital for product development. Figure 1.4 shows the framework for a basic science innovation system.

Figure 1.3 – Scientists from around the world collaborate to access best expertise

© Derek Mann – Wellcome Images

This concept of science innovation systems helps us to understand what is necessary for scientific progress to occur. Where science does not lead to innovation and new products, key players may be absent, or something may be blocking the two-way flow of ideas. In particular, it shows us that a range of elements must be in place and functioning before locally valuable technologies can result from scientific innovation.

Figure 1.4 – A science innovation system

Enabling Environment

Policies, Regulation, Instititions, Finance, Intellectual Property Rights etc

Translational Research

Government Laboratories
Public-Private Partnerships

Product Development and Use

Private Laboratories
Entrepreneurs

Basic Sciences

Universities
Advanced Laboratories

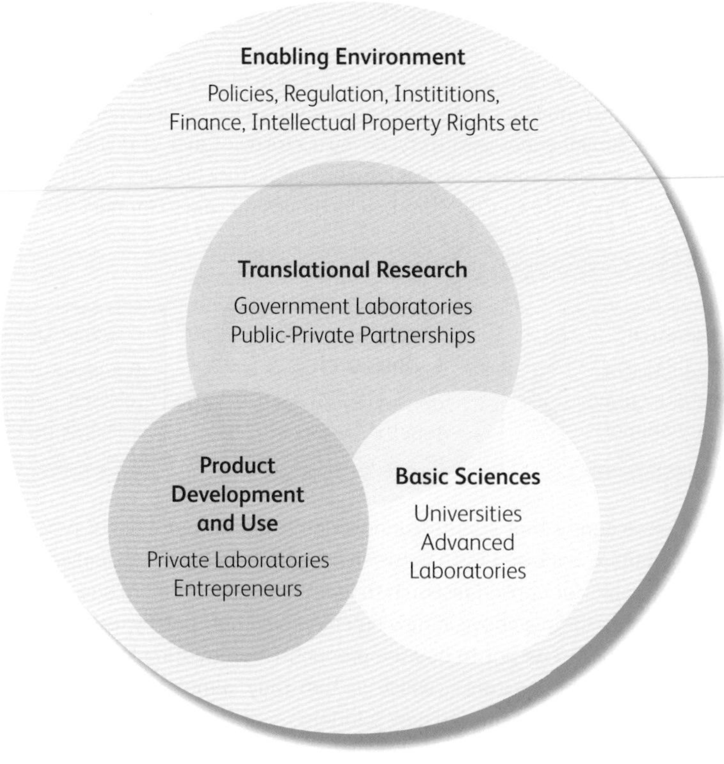

A striking feature of science innovation systems today is that they are becoming increasingly international, with groups from different countries bringing specific expertise to the innovation process. Science no longer functions in isolation at a national level as it did with the large-scale emergence of nationally funded science during the 20th century, when it was seen as a way of ensuring national security and productivity. Scientists from around the world now collaborate with each other for a variety of reasons, but particularly to access the best expertise, resources and partnerships, and funding and institutions have adapted accordingly.[3] Importantly, certain scientists, institutes and countries participate much more actively in the system than others, thus influencing the direction and benefits of research and outputs.

2. The role of science in international development

The goal of international development is to reduce poverty and to help poor people build a better life for themselves. It recognises the profound inequities which exist between countries in the ability of their citizens to make lasting, positive changes in their health, environment, opportunities and security. Poverty is often described in terms of income per capita, with US $1 or $2 a day being used as thresholds below which people are considered to be impoverished. But poverty is as much about lack of opportunity for betterment as it is about income.

Poverty and inequity exists to some degree in all countries. International development programmes make a distinction between countries which are highly industrialised where citizens enjoy relatively high incomes – developed countries – and countries which are generally poorly or moderately industrialised where citizens generally have low incomes, with many living in poverty – developing countries. The terms 'developed' and 'developing' are not official designations but the United Nations (UN) and other bodies use them as convenient shorthand for classifying countries for investment (Box 1.3).

Science can make a valuable contribution to this goal. Scientific knowledge and technology can be applied to specific technical challenges like achieving the Millennium Development Goals (MDGs) – see Chapter 4. More generally, it can provide countries with the tools needed to reason, innovate and participate in the ever-expanding global science network, thus supporting national economic growth and sustainable development.

The contribution of science to development challenges

The challenges of improving the lives of those in developing countries are large and diverse, and will not be achievable without the contribution of scientific knowledge and innovative technologies. Many technologies have already made significant impacts:

- Vaccines have eradicated smallpox, are near to eradicating polio and have significantly reduced child and adult mortality;

- Oral rehydration therapy has saved the lives of millions of children with diarrhoea;

- Integrated Pest Management (IPM) has increased rice yields and reduced the use of pesticides;

- Breeding of high yielding varieties of wheat and rice has transformed food security in South Asia;

- Using a vaccine to eliminate rinderpest has removed a major risk to pastoralists and livestock farmers;

- Minimum tillage systems have reduced water loss and soil erosion;

- Treadle pumps have opened up opportunities for irrigation for small farmers;

- Water purification technologies have reduced the risk of epidemics after natural disasters;

- Mobile phones have improved access to markets and helped strengthen urban-rural family links.

Box 1.3   Designations of developed and developing countries[4]

Regional groupings

● Developed regions	● Oceania
● Commonwealth of Independent States (CIS)	● Eastern Asia
● North Africa	● Southern Asia
● Sub-Saharan Africa	● Western Asia
● South-Eastern Asia	● Latin America & the Caribbean

Source: UN

Figure 1.5 – UN regional country groupings

The developed regions comprise Europe (including the transition countries but not the CIS), Australia, Canada, Japan, New Zealand and the United States (US), shown in blue.

The CIS (Commonwealth of Independent States) which include the areas in Europe and Asia highlighted in orange above, are sometimes included in the developing regions.

However, in this report the developing regions are the rest of the world and can be subdivided into:

Middle income countries – such as Brazil, Vietnam and South Korea and including the 'Emerging Economies' or BRICs (a term derived from the first letters of Brazil, Russia, India, China, but now used generally to describe countries with rapidly emerging industry and improving per capita wealth);

Low income countries – such as Kenya, Ghana and Honduras, and including the **least developed countries** such as Cambodia, Mali and Haiti;

Fragile States include those who are conflict ridden or recently emerging from conflict such as Afghanistan, Sierra Leone and Nepal.

Successes such as these have been achieved through years of experimentation by groups of scientists, often collaborating across countries and disciplines. It is therefore very important that scientific research and development, aimed at solving the problems facing the poor, is continued and given the funding and support it needs.

The benefits of scientific capacity

Developing countries face particular challenges in applying science and technology to their own development needs, because their science innovation systems are often weak or lack key elements, and their scientists have little access to global science networks. Strengthening national scientific capacity can bring a huge range of social and economic benefits to developing countries (Box 1.4).

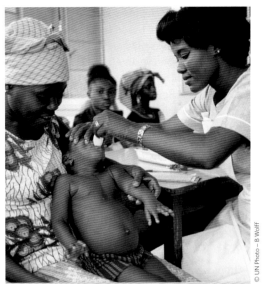

Figure 1.6 – A nurse administering oral polio vaccine at a clinic in Freetown, Sierra Leone

© UN Photo – B Wolff

Besides delivering new and valuable technologies, a strong national scientific capacity provides an evidence base to underpin sound political decisions and to challenge unsound ones. The central feature of the scientific revolution that began in Britain in the early 17th century was that hypotheses and assertions had to be scientifically tested. It was not good enough to base policy on theory, supposition or political ideology. This is as true and essential today as it was then.

Box 1.4   The importance of strengthening national scientific capacity

"Africa's ability to meet its human welfare needs, participate in the global economy and protect its environment will require considerable investment in science and innovation, in general, and engineering, in particular."[5]

Professor Calestous Juma, lead author of the Report of the Task Force on Science, Technology and Innovation of the UN Millennium Project

"There is one thing developing countries cannot do without: home-grown capacity for scientific research and technological know-how. Increasingly, a nation's wealth will depend on the knowledge it accrues and how it applies it, rather than the resources it controls. The "haves" and the "have-nots" will be synonymous with the "knows" and "know-nots.""[6]

Ismail Serageldin, Director of the Library of Alexandria.

"In the world of the 21st century, critical issues related to science and technology confront every nation…Today, no nation that wants to shape informed policies and take effective action on such issues can be without its own independent capacity in science and technology."[7]

Kofi Annan, former Secretary-General of the UN.

Policies aimed at combating climate change or controlling disease pandemics are only going to be successful if they are based on convincing scientific evidence. Scientists and scientific institutions can play a particularly important role by providing the government with independent and authoritative expertise. In Africa, for example, the Network of African Science Academies (NASAC), has recently voiced its commitment to achieving this goal and working more closely with national policy makers.[8] Box 1.5 highlights work being done by the science academies in the US and UK to help African academies strengthen their capacity in this area.

Besides the contribution that strong science innovation systems make to delivering services to society, it also creates an ability at the national level to:

• Articulate and prioritise research needs;

• Absorb, learn from and put to use the technologies being developed in other countries;

• Develop unique technologies specifically suited for local problems;

• Add higher value to natural resource, agricultural and mineral exports;

• Improve learning and production in both small and large businesses and develop new enterprises;

• Establish effective domestic regulations to control the release of new technologies;

• Participate in the international scientific network, learning from, contributing to, and influencing the direction of research and technology development;

• Engage fully in international debate and negotiations on, for instance: climate change; intellectual property rights; biotechnology and nanotechnology;

• Benefit more from foreign direct investment; particularly in high technology, value-added sectors.

While each of these benefits is distinct, it is clear they are also linked and mutually-reinforcing. For example, well chosen research priorities influence the efficiency of the firms which are using outputs from national research. Improving national science capacity thus has a widespread and positive effect not only on national science innovation systems, but also on society as a whole.

Science capacity and economic growth

The changes which come from a stronger national scientific capacity have positive system-wide economic effects. As stated in a recent document produced by the New Economic Partnership for Economic Development (NEPAD):

Nations' economic change and sustainable development are to a large measure accounted for by investments in science, technology and innovation. It is not the mere accumulation of physical capital and natural endowment that transform economies and stimulate human development but the ability of countries to produce, harness and wisely use scientific knowledge and related technological innovations. The economic history of the industrialised and newly industrializing countries vividly shows that economic improvement in these countries has been a result of the application of knowledge in productive activities. Indeed there is an explicit correlation between a country's scientific and technological capabilities and its economic performance and affluence.[9]

Box 1.5   Helping scientists provide the evidence

Begun in 2004 by the United States National Academy of Sciences, and funded by the Bill and Melinda Gates Foundation, the African Science Academy Development Initiative (ASADI) brings together the expertise of science academies in the US to work with national academies in Nigeria, South Africa and Uganda, chosen for their potential as well as the receptiveness of their governments. The initiative, which will run for

© The National Academy of Sciences

Figure 1.7 – A presenter at the 2008 ASADI conference in London

ten years, focuses on building the capacity of the academies to work in a public service role, and act as liaisons between their country's scientists and the policy makers in the government.

Activities include:

- Training of academy staff in key skills areas, by linking counterparts in the US in different areas such as management, research and administration with those in Africa;

- In-depth policy studies by committees to explore important issues such as the link between AIDS and nutrition, or mosquito resistance to insecticides, in order to offer formal guidance to national decision makers;

- Organised gatherings of specialists for discussion on particular subjects of interest;

- Conferences, workshops and fora both nationally and between the various academies in Africa.

The initiative has also set up an electronic database of African scientists, which can be shared across countries to help academies and governments to recruit experts and find appropriate knowledge.[10,11]

Similarly, the Royal Society (UK), the Network of African Science Academies (NASAC) and Pfizer (US) have recently formed a partnership to build capacity in four national scientific academies in Ghana, Zambia, Tanzania and Ethiopia. The Royal Society Pfizer African Academies Programme aims to extend the broader skills base within these academies whilst building vital policy links and understanding between institutions, scientists and policy makers. The academies are at various stages of development and so the multi-year programme of mentoring, training and project support will be flexible to fit each academy's needs. The Royal Society and NASAC are working closely with each academy to maximise and tailor the impact of the programme to individual country contexts.[12]

At the most basic level, science can be linked to economic growth because science innovation contributes to productivity growth, which in turn drives capital accumulation, output growth and general economic growth.[13] For this to happen, there must be investment, public and private, in science innovation, as well as access to finance for those businesses that will produce and market the resulting new products and services. Purchased by individuals and businesses ranging from small farms to major industries, these products and services enable customers to increase productivity, so contributing to economic growth.

It is often difficult to establish or prove a direct link between these steps because of the complexity of the national economic systems into which new science and technology feeds.[14] Factors like effective accountable government, political stability and a commitment to appropriate economic policies also make important contributions to economic growth. Nonetheless, a number of nations have recently provided affirmation of the close relationship between investment in science and technology and economic growth.

Strong evidence for the contribution of science to growth comes from the newly industrialised countries of East Asia. Some of these countries have exhibited in recent decades the fastest rates of both economic growth and poverty reduction in the world. This has been associated with policy commitments to improve education in science and technology, to provide public sector funding and to encourage private sector development.

Investment in science has led to these countries becoming participants in global science systems. Today, we acknowledge that leading scientific innovation is not only coming from traditionally wealthy countries, but from a number of rapidly growing economies in the developing world, including China, India, Brazil and South Africa – 'the so-called emerging economies'.

The Chinese experience is particularly worth highlighting. China's recent growth in scientific research activity is impressive. Authorship of papers in international, peer-reviewed scientific journals by Chinese researchers has increased from 828 papers in 1990 to over 80,000 in 2007, second only now to the US.[15] China has made highly visible investments in engineering to develop the basic infrastructure for growth – especially transportation, irrigation, power generation and distribution. But what is particularly impressive in China is not just its phenomenal technological growth in the large eastern and south-eastern cities, but also the growth in the poorer areas to the north-west such as the Loess Plateau.

© Wellcome images

Figure 1.8 – China has seen an impressive growth in scientific activity

Poverty reduction in the Loess Plateau

In the early 1990s, the Loess Plateau was a vast area of extremely degraded and eroded land, and the hundreds of thousands of farming families living there worked hard for very little return. This, however, was completely turned around with an extensive and long-term World Bank project which ran from 1994 – 2005. World Bank experts collaborated with Chinese scientists and the local community to devise a watershed rehabilitation plan for the area which was highly successful.[16,17] Although funded by the Bank this would not have been possible were it not for the Chinese investment in science educatio allowed for the contribution of local scientists, as well as the investment in the necessary infrastructure and markets which allowed the local farmers to profit from their new agricultural surplus. Box 1.6 below describes some of the benefits of this project in more detail. The specific technologies used will be expanded upon in the next chapter.

Box 1.6   Science and innovation on the Loess Plateau watershed in China

The Loess Plateau covers a vast area of north-west China, some 640,000 square kilometres extending over six provinces and home to some 90 million people. It is distinguished primarily by its soil – a very fine, yet very deep, silt – blown from the west over millennia. The soil is easily worked and fertile yet readily prone to erosion. Following years of over-cultivation and misuse it was left highly degraded.

Before the start of the World Bank Watershed Rehabilitation project in 1994 the area had the highest erosion rate in the world, and 1.6 billion tonnes of sediment was being deposited annually into the Yellow River.

The project team began what became a nine year investment to work with local communities to rehabilitate the local ecosystem, reduce erosion and improve agricultural yields.

© Environmental Education Media Project for China, 2005

Figure 1.9 – A farmer on his degraded field on the Loess Plateau

Over the first two years experts from the World Bank, together with a large group of scientists from the Yang Ling Soil and Water Institute and the Chinese Academy of Sciences, worked to assess the situation and discuss options. The team included specialists in areas such as: agriculture; water resources management; forestry and environmental science. The scientists collaborated with social scientists from Beijing University, local government officials and the watershed committees they formed in over 2,000 villages.

The team used both micro and macro-level assessment techniques in order to get a complete and accurate picture of the situation. The results of participatory surveys and activities were compiled into a database, and combined with the scientists' observations and Geographic Information System (GIS) maps of the area. From this, a comprehensive package of interventions was developed with the farmers, which could be implemented in each community.[16]

The first goal was to restore the infiltration and retention of rainfall. With the support of the farmers, grazing was banned on all upper slopes to allow for the restoration of vegetation.

Figure 1.10 – Modern terraces on the Loess Plateau

A variety of technical interventions were then implemented which included improved modern terracing, sediment traps and dams and new tree transplantation techniques. The UK Department for International Development (DFID) became involved in 2003, adding support to the watershed management and monitoring process.

As a result, the landscape has been remarkably transformed. With the restoration of healthy water-cycling, arable land has been recreated and farmers are now getting higher yields of wheat and maize, and additional income from fruit harvesting. And, the changes have resulted in significant labour savings. Families are now able to pursue increased livestock production and other enterprises such as growing vegetables and flowers in greenhouses. This has all led to an increase in resources held and incomes earned by farmers, with an estimated 2.5 million people able to rise above the poverty level as an immediate result of the project, and even more long-term positive change expected.[18]

As this example demonstrates, investment in local scientific capacity can make possible effective collaboration aimed at solving local problems. And, at the household level the adoption and adaptation of technologies can increase incomes and productivity, both by increasing the productivity of existing employment, for example in agriculture and domestic labour, and by freeing up labour for additional income-generating employment. It can also help to upgrade skills, increasing the ability of the poor to either start up new income-generating activities, or enter new forms of employment. Initiatives like this have contributed to China's excellent record of poverty reduction: a remarkable 628 million people have crossed over the poverty line since 1981.[19]

3. The challenge ahead

Strengthening science capacity

While there is evidence that emerging economies have used science and technology to reduce poverty and achieve economic growth, the majority of poor countries have yet to go down this path. In fact, there is a huge range in scientific capacity and investment in countries throughout the world, with those countries who are most in need of its benefits usually the ones who are most lacking. Figure 1.11 for example, shows gross domestic expenditure on research and development (R&D) as a fraction of national Gross Domestic Product (GDP) for a number of countries over the last decade, revealing both substantial gaps between nations and impressive progress in some.

Figure 1.11 – R&D spending as a percent of GDP in various countries[20]

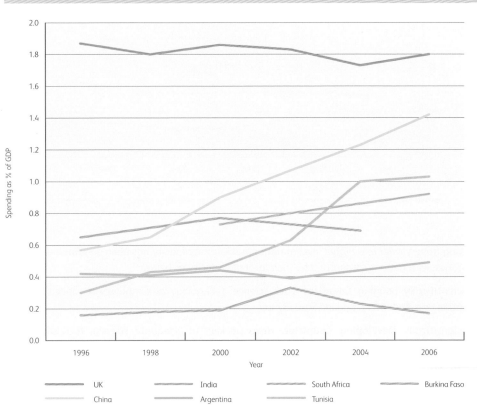

Of course, this investment, as discussed above, cannot always be directly correlated to economic success or poverty reduction. However, one can look at indicators such as the number of researchers, journal articles published or patents issued in a nation in order to get an idea of local scientific capacity and the likelihood of a society being able to benefit from it.

Figure 1.12 shows the number of scientific researchers per capita in the same set of countries as Figure 1.11. As one can see, investment by countries, like China, can translate into a growing number of researchers while, in a small country like Burkina Faso, there has been little investment and no increase in capacity.

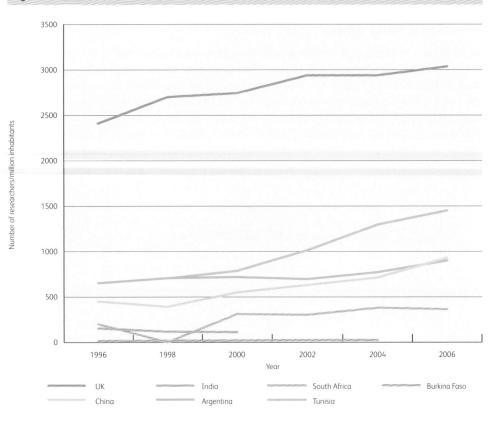

Figure 1.12 – Number of scientific researchers in various countries[20]

Moving from a lower to a higher level of national scientific capacity has been described as a series of stages, with nations categorised by their level of capacity as below:[3,21]

- **Scientifically Lagging Countries**: Lack science, technology and innovation capacity almost entirely e.g. Indonesia, Burkina Faso, Syria;

- **Scientifically Developing Countries**: Have pockets of adequate science, technology and innovation capacity amidst general scarcity, e.g. Portugal, India, Iran, Pakistan, Uganda;

- **Scientifically Proficient Countries**: Display world class capacity in science, technology and innovation in some areas e.g. Singapore, Estonia, Korea, China;

- **Scientifically Advanced Countries**: With advanced science, technology and innovating capacity in all major areas; publish most of the articles in the internationally recognised journals and fund 80 % of the world's R&D. e.g. US, UK, Germany, Japan, Australia.

But how can countries best build up their scientific capacity? Studies of successful national scientific development suggest that countries need to first be willing to adopt and learn from other, more scientifically advanced countries. Once this investment is made, countries then invest in national capacity to manage scientific innovation and eventually to adapt technology to their own settings, to innovate and link to markets.[22-26] With a critical mass of national capacity in a particular area of science, these countries can then enter the global scientific network. As Caroline Wagner, Calestous Juma and others have pointed out, being a part of this global system can be extremely beneficial for a developing country, allowing it to quickly access scientific information and ideas and to further strengthen its national capacity in new areas.[3,24-28]

Governments must therefore aim to work investment in strengthening scientific capacity into national development plans. In doing so, a government may set priorities for investment based on its current strengths and local needs, and decide to outsource or collaborate on other important areas where it chooses not to invest directly. This allows a country to take advantage of the strengths of others and avoiding a duplication of effort. Wagner calls this strategy 'link and sink,' as each nation decides when to link with others, and where to 'sink' their resources.[3]

© Commonwealth Secretariat

Figure 1.13 – Scientific capacity in countries such as Jamaica is still developing

Creating an enabling environment for science innovation

Investing in strengthening scientific capacity is only part of what is needed to produce successful innovation systems. Conditions must be created which make it profitable for the private sector to participate in innovation systems and to turn technology into valued products and services. This involves creating an effective enabling environment, including supportive regulatory frameworks, the protection of intellectual property rights, and banking and finance systems to facilitate and protect investments. Ultimately, it also requires the right infrastructure such as transport and energy supply systems, on which new products and services will depend.

Investment in scientific capacity building, therefore, must address both the supply and demand sides. An example of such investment is the recent Science, Technology and Innovation for Results (STIR) programme between the UK Department for International Development (DFID) and the Government of Rwanda. This £700,000 investment is contributing to the establishment of science capacity, including the establishment of a National Commission for Science, Technology and Innovation and a National Research Fund. The support helps build the legal and institutional frameworks that ensure that science and technology lead to practical, commercial innovations that benefit local industry.[29]

Signs of progress

Recently a number of developing country governments have made new commitments to strengthening science and technology capacity in order to address national development needs and to participate more effectively in the global economy and policy process.

Countries across Asia are making large-scale investments. Malaysia, for instance, is investing US $10m, and then $1.2m annually, in a new International Centre for South-South cooperation in Science, Technology and Innovation based in Kuala Lumpur.[30,31] In Latin America, countries like Brazil, Chile and Argentina are making substantial new investments in scientific research and development – in 2006, the region invested around $18 billion in R&D, a 60 % increase since 1997.[32] In January 2007, an African Union Summit endorsed a new focus on supporting national scientific research and development, including improving science education and revitalizing universities. Initiatives to strengthen science capacity and education have also been launched by the African Development Bank and several African nations. Nigeria, for instance, allocated $25 million in late 2006 to establish an African Institute of Science and Technology.[33]

This promising investment in strengthening national and regional scientific capacity will need to be sustained. It has been estimated that, even with political commitment and funding, it takes a scientifically "lagging" country between ten and 20 years to fulfil the criteria of a scientifically "developing" country.[3]

4. Scientific success in developing countries

In Section 2 of this chapter, we cited nine scientific advances which have contributed to international development over the past 50 years. In this last section, we look in detail at two quite recent examples of scientific innovation from Africa which illustrate some of the features of successful science for development, and particularly the value of global innovation systems.

One relates to improving the food supply for communities across Africa and the other to the reduction of the burden of disease.

New Rices for Africa (NERICAs)

Rice consumption is growing dramatically in West Africa, fuelled by population growth, rising incomes and a shift in consumer preferences, especially in urban areas. Local production, while increasing, is falling ever further behind demand. The region is now importing over half its requirements, some six million tonnes annually at a cost of over one billion dollars.[34]

The traditional African species of rice (*Oryza glaberrima*) has very low yields of about one tonne per hectare, compared with five tonnes or more for the Asian species (*Oryza sativa*). But, using tissue culture technology, Monty Jones, a Sierra Leone scientist working at the Africa Rice Center (WARDA), was able to cross the two species, producing hundreds of new varieties. At first the technique did not work well, but collaboration with Chinese scientists provided a new tissue culture method, involving the use of coconut oil, which proved highly successful.

The rice varieties produced in this manner, known as the New Rices for Africa (NERICAs), share many of the characteristics of their African ancestors. They grow well in drought-prone, upland conditions. Their early vigorous growth crowds out weeds. They are resistant to local pests and disease and tolerant of poor nutrient conditions and mineral toxicity. Yet as they mature, they take on some of the characteristics of their Asian ancestors, producing more erect leaves and full panicles of grain. And they are ready for harvesting in 90 to 100 days, that is 30 to 50 days earlier than current varieties. Under low inputs they yield up to four tonnes per hectare.[34]

NERICA rice has the potential to help meet the huge and growing demand for rice in Africa, and this can be achieved by increasing yields rather than through expansion onto ever more marginalised lands. There is also evidence that the need for less weed control and the shorter growing season is reducing the burden of child labour and improving school attendance in the areas it is being grown.[34]

Figure 1.14 – Panicles of NERICA rice

NERICA rice production has been steadily increasingly since the new seeds were first introduced in 1996, thanks largely to the pro-active approach taken by WARDA. Setting up partnerships across the region, WARDA has been able to work directly with farmers at all stages of the process, from varietal selection to seed dissemination. The process is not only participatory, ensuring that the priorities of a wide range of farmers are taken into account, but also efficient, speeding up the experimentation phase by an average of seven years, and streamlining seed dissemination by using the traditional farmer networks already in place. Farmers in west, central and eastern Africa are now growing some 200,000 ha of NERICAs.[34]

Figure 1.15 – Farmers in Benin happy with their harvest of NERICA rice

Insecticide treated mosquito nets

Another example of scientific innovation in Africa is the development of long lasting, insecticide-treated mosquito nets that kill mosquitoes, reducing the incidence of malaria. For several decades after the Second World War the preferred method for controlling the mosquitoes that transmit malaria was to spray the walls of dwellings, where mosquitoes rested, usually with the highly persistent insecticide DDT. However, the method required good logistics and infrastructure, and was never widely implemented in most African countries.

Moreover, DDT was found to be environmentally damaging and mosquitoes eventually became resistant, forcing a switch to less effective and more expensive insecticides.

A new approach to mosquito control in homes involved the use of mosquito nets treated with a pyrethroid insecticide. Early development of insecticide-treated nets (ITNs) was explored by researchers from the French *L'Institut de Recherche pour le Développement* (IRD, then ORSTOM) in 1983 in Burkina Faso, and later progressed in other parts of Africa by UK researchers from the London School of Hygiene and Tropical Medicine (LSHTM), the Medical Research Council (MRC), and others. Trials showed that treated nets give far better epidemiological protection than untreated nets, significantly reducing child mortality. Studies done by the MRC in the Gambia in 1986 and 1989, for example, confirmed that the use of ITNs resulted in a 63 % reduction in deaths of children under five.[35]

Encouraging initial results led to innovation in treatment of the nets, including 'dip-it-yourself' kits, more durable nets and finally nets where the fibres are coated with an insecticide coated resin and hence last for four to five years without re-dipping (known as long-lasting insecticide nets (LLINs). The insecticides used are photo-stable synthetic pyrethroids, fast acting yet safe to humans.

Since 1995, insecticide-treated nets have been used in the WHO's Global Malaria Programme with great success. But use varies from country to country, and there are still many African countries where less than 20 % of children are sleeping under a treated net. For example, in the Gambia, where the programme has had a longer and more aggressive promotion, 49 % of children under-five were estimated to be sleeping under an ITN in 2006, whereas in nearby Senegal, the figure is only 16 %, and in Nigeria only 1 %.[36]

The relatively high cost is a factor. A treated net can cost anywhere from £3 to £7, and promoters have realised that can be prohibitively high for many families. For this reason, a wide variety of distribution strategies are now being used, with a combination of free distribution, subsidies and 'social marketing' campaigns being taken up depending on the needs and preferences of the target population. For example, the 'Social Marketing of ITNs (SMARTNET)' programme in Tanzania, funded by DFID and the Royal Netherlands Embassy since 2002, is now providing LLINs free of charge to mothers of children under five, and for a reduced price of 500 Tanzanian shillings (about £0.20) for others.

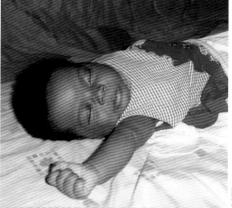

Figure 1.16 – A baby sleeping under an Insecticide Treated Net

They are also using social marketing to lobby for transport subsidies, run press and media campaigns and organise displays at markets and in rural areas. Some three million nets a year are now being sold in Tanzania, double the annual sales at the beginning of the initiative.[37]

The Global Malaria Programme's goal is for 80% of people in Africa, at risk of malaria, to be using ITNs by 2010,[35] which, while ambitious, is now being backed by more funding and political support than ever before.

Common elements of success

These two examples of successful science for development share several features common to the model of Global Innovation Systems described in Figure 1.4. Firstly,

© Jo Lines – LSHTM

Figure 1.17 – Independent sellers of locally made ITNs in Lagos, Nigeria

fundamental developments in science and technology triggered the innovations: tissue culture for the NERICAs and the development of pyrethroid insecticides for ITNs. Both of these inventions arose in the developed world and had been applied there for decades before they found these specific applications in Africa.

Both developments began in advanced research institutions, the Africa Rice Center (WARDA), and ORSTOM/LSHTM, respectively. While they were led and inspired by first class innovators, they were products of multidisciplinary teams linked into larger networks of scientists in both the developed and developing countries with whom they exchanged ideas and techniques. This international dimension was crucial. The Chinese helped with appropriate tissue culture for the NERICAs in West Africa, while the long-lasting mosquito nets made in Tanzania at the A to Z plastics factory, use resin from ExxonMobil in Saudi Arabia and Japanese insecticide technology from Sumitomo Chemicals.[38]

For both success stories, a range of donors were involved, including the World Bank, UNDP, the Gatsby Charitable Trust, Rockefeller Foundation, and the governments of Japan, Netherlands and the UK. The UK contribution, for example, was both specific and general: DFID supported the SMARTNET programme in Tanzania, and provided general support to WARDA laboratories and research through its contribution to the CGIAR[†].

These examples focus on technologies that were successfully adapted to new contexts, and so far this is how most successes have been achieved. As the global scientific environment changes, however, with new players emerging and many more slowly strengthening their capacity and joining the network, it is feasible that more innovative technologies will be developed with poor countries' needs in mind from the start.

† CGIAR is the Consultative Group on International Agricultural Research and is explained more fully in Chapters 2 and 3.

5. Conclusion – Improving science for development

The examples of NERICA rice and long-lasting insecticide-treated mosquito nets show how scientists in developed and developing countries can together address and solve problems, bringing us closer to the achievement of the Millennium Development Goals (MDGs). They illustrate the value of global science innovation systems and the collaboration they foster in improving science for development.

In conclusion, improving science for development will involve two main activities:

- First, the creation of effective global science innovation systems which engage scientists in developing and developed countries in addressing developing country science needs. These systems will be able to address major opportunities for achieving the MDGs as illustrated in Chapters 5 to 7 to follow.

- Second, strengthening the science and technology capacity of developing countries in key, relevant areas, including development of national institutions and innovation systems, enables them to address local scientific challenges with local knowledge and resources, and to participate more effectively and influentially in global science innovation systems.

- In the following two chapters we explore the sources of scientific innovation for development, and then discuss the kinds of partnerships in science innovation systems that may be involved. This is followed in the second part of this book with a detailed discussion of a set of MDGs – reducing hunger, improving health and conserving the environment, where we show how science innovation has the potential to contribute to these important challenges. In the third part we focus on the scientific and technological challenges in adapting to climate change.

Chapter 1 references and further reading

1   Vermeulen, S. & Bass, S., (2005) *Science and Development*. [Internal Scoping Paper]. IIED, London.

2   Office of Health Economics. (2007) *Life Expectancy in England and Wales*. Available at: www.ohe.org/page/knowledge/schools/appendix/life_expectancy.cfm [Accessed 08 Oct 2009].

3   Wagner, C., (2008) *The New Invisible College, Science for Development*. Brookings Institution Press, Washington DC.

4   UN. (2009) *The Millennium Development Goals Report*, 2009, UN, New York.

5   Juma, C., (2006) Redesigning African Economies – The Role of Engineering in International Development. *The 2006 Hinton Lecture*. Royal Academy of Engineering, London.

6   Serageldin, I., (2008) Joining the Fast Lane. *Nature*, **456**, TWAS Supplement. 18-20.

7   Annan, K., (2004) Science for All Nations. *Science Magazine*, **303**, 925.

8   NASAC. (2006) Joint Statement to African Science Ministers and Heads of States and Governments by NASAC – *Building science, technology and innovative capacities in Africa*.

9   NEPAD. (2007) *Governing Science, Technology and Innovation in Africa, Building National and Regional Capacities to Develop and Implement Strategies and Policies*. NEPAD Available at: www.nepadst.org/doclibrary/pdfs/gstia_june2007.pdf [Accessed 08 Oct 2009].

10 ASADI. (2009) African Science Academy Development Initiative. Available at: www.nationalacademies.org/asadi/ [Accessed 08 Oct 2009].

11 ASADI. (2008) [London conference brochures].

12 Thorton, I., (2009) [Email] (Pers. Comm. 29 April 2009).

13 Easterly, W., (2001) *The Elusive Quest for Growth: Economists' Adventures and Misadventures in the Tropics*. The MIT Press, Cambridge.

14 Lall, S., (2000) Technological Change and Industrialization in the Asian Newly Industrializing Economies: Achievements and Challenges. In: Kim, L. & Nelson, R., (eds). *Technology, Learning & Innovation*. Cambridge University Press, Cambridge.

15 Hassan, M., (2008) Worlds Apart Together *Nature*, **456**, TWAS Supplement. 6-8.

16 *The Lessons of the Loess Plateau* (2008) [Video] Environmental Education Media Project. Available at: www.earthshope.org [Accessed 08 Oct 2009].

17 World Bank. (2003) *Implementation Completion Report, China Loess Plateau Watershed Rehabilitation Project*. World Bank Report No: 25701.

18 World Bank. (2008) *Restoring China's Loess Plateau*. Available at: go.worldbank.org/RGXNXF4A00 [Accessed 08 Oct 2009].

19 Chen, S. & Ravaliion, M., (2008) *The developing world is poorer than we thought, but no less successful in the fight against poverty*. Development Research Group, World Bank, Washington DC.

20 Statistics from: UNESCO Institute of Statistics. (2008) *Statistics on Research and Development. Science and Technology database*. Available at: www.uis.unesco.org/ev.php?URL_ID=3755&URL_DO=DO_TOPIC&URL_SECTION=201 [Accessed 08 Oct 2009].

21 Wagner, C. et al., (2001) *Science and Technology collaboration: Building capacity in developing countries?* RAND Science and Technology, Santa Monica, CA.

22 Kim, L. & Nelson, R., (eds) (2008) *Technology, Learning & Innovation*. Cambridge University Press, Cambridge.

23 UNESCO. (2005) *UNESCO Science Report 2005*. UNESCO Publishing, Paris.

24 UN Millennium Project. (2005) *Innovation: Applying Knowledge in Development*. Task Force on Science, Technology and Innovation.

25 UNCTAD. (2007) *The Least Developed Countries Report 2007: Knowledge, Technological Learning and Innovation for Development*. United Nations Publications, Geneva.

26 CSTD. (2008) *Science, Technology and Engineering for Innovation and Capacity-Building in Education and Research.* Paper from the 2008 Inter-sessional Panel in Santiago, Chile. UN Commission on Science and Technology for Development (CSTD).

27 Juma, C., (2008) Learn to Earn. *Nature,* **456**, TWAS supplement, 15-17.

28 Watson, R. Crawford, M. & Farley, S., (2003) *Strategic approaches to science and technology in development.* World Bank Policy Research Working Paper 3026.

29 R4D. (2007) *UK project boosts Rwandan science.* DFID Research for Development Research News Available at: www.research4development.info/news.asp?ArticleID=50120 [Accessed 29 Nov 2009].

30 Hassan, M., (2008) Worlds Apart Together *Nature,* **456**, TWAS Supplement, 6-8.

31 Sawahel, W., (2007). *Malaysia to lead south-south collaboration.* SciDev.net. [Internet] Available at: www.scidev.net/en/news/malaysia-to-lead-southsouth-collaboration.html [Accessed 08 Oct 2009].

32 García, L., (2009) *Latin American S&T investment shows major growth.* SciDev.net. [Internet] Available at: www.scidev.net/en/news/latin-american-s-t-investment-shows-major-growth.html [Accessed 08 Oct 2009]

33 Malakata, M., (2007) *Nigeria initiates Africa's institute of science.* SciDev.net. [Internet] Available at: www.scidev.net/en/news/nigeria-initiates-africas-institute-of-science.html [Accessed 08 Oct 2009].

34 Somado, E. Guei, R. & Keya, S., (eds). (2008) *NERICA, the New Rice for Africa, a Compendium.* WARDA, Cotonou.

35 MRC. (2006) *Improving health, improving lives, MRC-funded research in Africa.* MRC, London.

36 WHO. (2008) *World Malaria Report.* WHO, Geneva.

37 DFID. (2008) *Smart protection against malaria in Tanzania.* 22 April. Available at: www.dfid.gov.uk/casestudies/files/africa/tanzania-malaria-nets.asp [Accessed 08 Oct 2009].

38 Snow, J., (2006) The main obstacle to the eradication of malaria lies within Africa itself. *The Guardian.* 3 January. Available at: www.guardian.co.uk/world/2006/jan/03/g8.internationalaidanddevelopment [Accessed 08 Oct 2009].

Appropriate Innovation

Researchers at the Kenya Medical Research Institute (KEMRI) © Rebecca Nduku – Commonwealth Secretariat

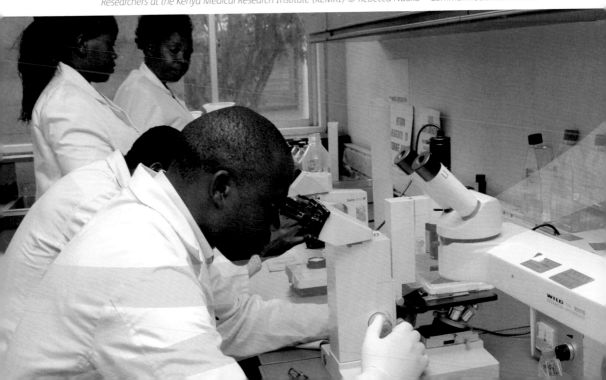

Science for development is undergoing rapid change. Traditional perspectives about the source of science ideas for development and how research should be done are being replaced by a new, broader perspective. This embraces ideas as diverse as traditional local practices and the most recent cutting-edge international science, and engages players ranging from farmer-innovators to multinational corporations. The result will be a science innovation system with enormous new potential to address international development challenges.

1. Where does science and innovation for development come from?

In the 20th century, there was a widespread view that most of the technological needs of the developing world could be addressed by extending to it technologies from developed, industrialised countries, most of which have been produced over the past 150 years through application of modern physical, chemical and biological knowledge. These "conventional technologies" typically deliver desired products in a ready-to-use 'packaged' form, e.g. a seed of a new crop variety, a bag of fertiliser, a medicine, computer or tractor. Such packages are often global or at least regional in their appropriateness and are easy to market.

While it is true that conventional technologies have provided a crucial stimulus to national growth in emerging economies, their benefit to the poorest communities has often been limited. In some cases, these products are of direct value to the poor, but unaffordable, or requiring delivery systems, maintenance or training to which they do not have adequate access. The technologies may also have environmental side effects which are more severe or less manageable in developing countries than in the industrialised communities for which they were developed.

In other cases, conventional technologies may be valuable to potentially poor people, but most existing products do not address their specific needs. For instance, a number of crop and livestock varieties, important to the poor, have not benefited from conventional breeding technology. Similarly, many diseases common in developing countries have not benefited from conventional pharmaceutical technologies, earning them the title of "neglected diseases". Market failure has been largely responsible for this, and in Chapter 3 we will see how the problem can be addressed through partnerships in science innovation.

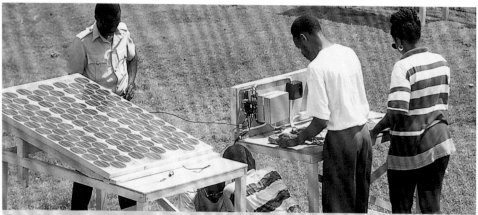

Figure 2.1 – Learning how to construct solar electric systems in Africa

© Commonwealth Secretariat

Efforts to apply products from conventional technologies in developing countries have sometimes proven highly unsuccessful. Projects delivering machinery without training or maintenance, or crop or animal varieties unsuitable to the local conditions of poor communities, highlighted the need for appropriate application of science and technology. These errors have also stimulated greater interest in the "traditional technologies" of local communities, the understanding and support of which has often been overlooked in the rush to apply imported technologies from industrialised countries. In some cases, as we shall see, these traditional technologies can be integrated with conventional technologies to make "intermediate technologies" whose products are both appropriate and superior to those presently available.

Whatever the source and wherever the application, the important feature of technologies is that they are locally appropriate. For a technology to be appropriate in a developing country, as anywhere, it has to:

- Be readily accessible and affordable;

- Be easy-to-use and maintain;

- Serve a real need;

- Be effective.

In this chapter we will first discuss innovation in the more selective and appropriate use of conventional technologies and then look at the role of local traditional technologies, as well as how these have been combined with conventional ideas to produce intermediate technologies. We will conclude with a discussion of the promise for emerging new platform technologies and the way in which these, if developed in an appropriate manner, can be of critical value to international development. We will base our discussion on the following definitions:

Box 2.1   Sources of technology

Conventional: Technologies from industrialised countries developed through the application of modern physical, chemical and biological knowledge, and delivered as products in a packaged form for a regional or global market. *e.g. Fertilisers, conventional water treatment plants.*

Traditional: Technologies which have been developed, usually over an extended period of time, by communities in developing countries to meet local needs. *e.g. Natural medicines, rainwater harvesting techniques.*

Intermediate: Traditional technologies which have been improved in appropriate respects by their integration with modern conventional technologies. e.g. *Traditional treadle pump improved by engineers, soil bricks used for housing improved by incorporating new materials.*[1]

New Platform: New scientific "platforms" for innovation, based on advanced sciences which have the potential to be developed simultaneously for the needs of the industrialised and the developing world. *e.g. New forms of water treatment developed using nanotechnology; genetically modified, drought or pest resistant crop varieties.*

---

2. Selective use of conventional technologies

Most conventional technologies were developed in the 19th and 20th centuries, as products of large scale industrial processes often reliant on petrochemicals. The development of cement and concrete in the 19th century made large scale dams and irrigation systems possible. Widespread use of synthetic fertilisers was the result of the innovative production of ammonia from atmospheric nitrogen by Fritz Haber and Carl Bosch at the beginning of the 20th century. Both synthetic pesticides and modern antibiotics had their origins in the large scale chemical processes developed during the Second World War.

Such technologies continue to be highly effective and relatively inexpensive in developed countries where they are widely used. However, as we argued earlier, they may not result in products appropriate to developing countries. For instance, products are often costly in terms of energy and petrochemical inputs. Even where they can be produced cheaply on a large scale, transport costs make them expensive in developing countries, particularly in inland sub-Saharan Africa (Box 2.2).

Box 2.2 The high cost of fertilisers in inland Sub-Saharan Africa (2002 figures)[2]	
Cost of a tonne of urea – FOB (free on board)	
Europe	$90
The coastal cities of Mombasa, Kenya or Beira, Mozambique	$400
Western Kenya	$500
Landlocked Malawi	$770

They may also have deleterious local environmental effects. Large scale dam construction and impoundment can displace communities and destroy biodiversity, while synthetic fertilisers, if used to excess, can pollute water sources. Synthetic pesticides can be very destructive to wildlife and harmful to humans if they are not applied correctly. In each instance, the poor tend to suffer disproportionately from these unintended effects. Protective regulations are often lacking in poor areas and, if present, are rarely effectively enforced. The rich and powerful usually have the means, often corrupt, of avoiding compliance. The poor, by contrast, are usually the major victims and have little recourse to redress.

Unintentional poisoning by pesticides kills thousands per year in developing countries, where safe equipment, expert advice and training are often lacking.[3] Many farmers overuse pesticides and do not take proper precautions. Pesticides banned or restricted in industrialised countries are widely available in the developing countries.[4]

Both pesticides and modern pharmaceuticals are also prone to the evolution of resistance. In the case of drug resistance the poor have very limited access to the intensive health care systems that can provide appropriate treatment and monitoring.

Precision in application

For these various reasons there has been a move, since the 1960s, to find ways of using such technologies in a more sparing and selective manner. The high cost of fertilisers has resulted in a move to more precise applications in the developed countries, using controlled-release fertilisers, fine grained soil analyses and variable application on individual fields employing tractors fitted with Geographic Information Systems (GIS) devices.[5,6] This is not likely to be appropriate for smaller-scale farmers in developing countries until the prices come down, but farmers can substitute more selective placement of fertilisers instead of the widespread practice of broadcasting them. For example, urea super granules (USG) inserted in the middle of every four rice plants in Bangladeshi paddy fields (Figures 2.2 and 2.3), results in an extra tonne of paddy with a reduction of fertiliser by over a third.[7]

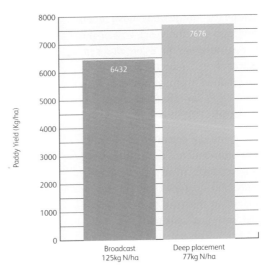

Figure 2.2 – Improvement in yield with reduction in fertiliser due to deep placement technique[7]

Countering resistance

Pesticides can also be applied more selectively, partly to reduce cost, partly to encourage natural enemies to control the pests and partly to counter resistance (see examples in Chapter 5). A notorious example of rapidly evolving resistance is of *Anopheline* mosquitoes to insecticides of all kinds. DDT became largely ineffective in the 1960s because of this. The new insecticides such as the pyrethroids worked well for a while but resistance is now spreading very rapidly in Africa (Box 2.3).

Box 2.3 Mitigating the risk of mosquito resistance to insecticides

Insecticide resistance in mosquitoes is a classic example of natural selection. Resistance occurs as a result of natural mutation or genetic recombination in the absence of the insecticide, but usually at a very low level because it is generally disadvantageous in other respects. However, it rapidly spreads through the mosquito population from generation to generation in response to the pressure of insecticide use. Survivors tend to be resistant and pass on the resistance through their genes to their offspring.

It is almost impossible to prevent this from occurring but the risk can be minimised in a number of ways:

- Using insecticides which are slow to elicit a resistance response;

- Using different insecticides in rotation from year to year or as mosaics (i.e. different compounds for different houses in a village);

- Avoiding opportunities for cross-resistance by knowing the resistance status of local mosquito populations to different pesticides (e.g. mosquitoes resistant to DDT may also be resistant to pyrethroids);

- Reducing agricultural use of the same pesticides (against crop pests) which are used locally against mosquitoes.

Malaria control is also affected by evolving resistance by the parasite *Plasmodium* to the various therapeutic drugs that have been developed over the years. Part of the answer here lies in using drugs in combination (see Chapter 6). Combination therapy has also long been used in the treatment of tuberculosis (TB) (Box 2.4).

Thus there are a number of ways to make conventional technologies and their products more appropriate to developing countries, by limiting or integrating their use so as to reduce their cost and maintain their value. Still, many conventional technologies remain inappropriate for a range of reasons. In some cases it makes more sense to make use of traditional technologies which are adapted to the local environment from the outset.

Figure 2.3 – A farmer in Bangladesh places USG granules in the centre of each of four rice plants

© IFDC

Box 2.4   Strategies to reduce drug resistance in TB[8]

The available conventional drugs to cure patients of TB require relatively long periods of treatment to be effective. Missed doses rapidly result in the build-up of resistance. Part of the answer lies in using a combination of compounds.

The World Health Organisation (WHO) recommends a drug regime consisting of two phases:

1. An initial intensive phase of four drugs – rifampicin, isoniazid, pyrazinamide and ethambutol – administered for two months;

2. A continuation phase of two drugs – rifampicin and isoniazid – for four months.

The drugs have to be administered daily in the initial phase and daily or at least three times a week in the continuation phase. But success depends on ensuring this regime is strictly adhered to and directly observed. The person ensuring the drugs are taken need not be a health worker; a community worker, neighbour or family member can be effective in this role.

When done according to these guidelines the treatment can be over 95 % effective. But when lack of supervision or drug availability results in missed doses it is not only ineffective but stimulates the spread of multiple drug resistance.

One answer to the problem is to develop new chemotherapy regimens which can be effective in a matter of a few weeks or even a few days so minimising the likelihood of missed doses.

3. The use of traditional technologies

One aspect of science and technology for development which is often overlooked is the important contribution that the knowledge and experience of communities in developing countries can make to technology development and adaptation. There is, however, a long history of appropriate technology for development having a strong element of local input, often referred to as Indigenous Technical Knowledge.

Traditional technologies are approaches to problems that have been used by people for hundreds, if not thousands, of years. They can be thought of as having 'stood the test of time.' Some have clearly worked and still work today; for others there is no scientific evidence that they are effective.

Herbal medicines

The use of plants for healing purposes pre-dates human history and forms the origin of much modern medicine. Many conventional drugs originate from plant sources: aspirin (from willow bark), digoxin (from foxglove), quinine (from cinchona bark) and morphine (from the opium poppy).[9]

Traditional healers who rely on herbal medicines are an important source of health care in developing countries. WHO estimates that 80 % of the African population makes use of traditional medicine.[10] In Uganda the ratio of traditional medicine practitioners to the population is between 1:200 and 1:400 while that of allopathic ('western') practitioners is typically 1:20,000.[11] For many rural people, traditional healers are the only source of health care within reach.

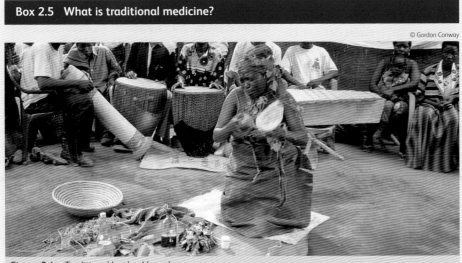

Box 2.5 What is traditional medicine?

© Gordon Conway

Figure 2.4 – Traditional healer, Uganda

WHO defines traditional medicine as *'diverse health practices, approaches, knowledge and beliefs incorporating plant, animal, and/or mineral based medicines, spiritual therapies, manual techniques and exercises applied singularly or in combination to maintain well-being, as well as to treat, diagnose or prevent illness.'*[11]

While many false claims have been made for the treatment of HIV/AIDS, there is evidence that herbal medicines can successfully treat some of the opportunistic infections that accompany AIDS such as *Herpes zoster*.[12]

The most important herbal-derived medicine in use today is artemisinin (Box 2.6). In combination with other drugs it is now recommended by WHO as the first line of attack against malaria where there is resistance to other drugs.

Box 2.6 Artemisinin – a frontline drug against malaria

Artemisinin is derived from *Artemisia annua*, known as sweet wormwood or qínghǎo by the Chinese. It has fern-like leaves and bright yellow flowers. For over 2,000 years it has been used as an anti-malarial by the Chinese in the form of tea. In the 1970s Chinese scientists isolated the active ingredient artemisinin.

Artemisinin or its derivatives, such as artesunate and artemether, are now commonly used in combination with other anti-malarial drugs as Artemisinin-based Combination Therapies (ACT) (see also Chapter 6).

© Kristian Peters – Wikimedia Commons

Figure 2.5 – Sweet Wormwood, *Artemisia annua*

In several settings there are current attempts to integrate, semi-formally, the traditional healer network with the allopathic system. The ubiquity of traditional healers means they can be a valuable resource in the frontline against various diseases, not least HIV/AIDS. Organisations such as Traditional and Modern Health Practitioners Together against AIDS (THETA) in Uganda, have shown that with appropriate training, traditional healers have performed as well as, if not better than, community health workers in educating communities, promoting and distributing condoms, and counselling, treating and referring the sick.[13]

Agricultural systems

Traditional systems of small-scale agriculture and gardening such as shifting cultivation and home gardens are examples of fundamental organic systems that, until recently, have relied exclusively on recycling of nutrients, biological forms of pest and disease control and household labour. Modern organic agriculture makes use of similar principles. In developing countries if there is sufficient organic matter and enough labour, organic cultivation can also provide profitable niche exports of vegetables, fruits and commodities such as coffee and tea to developed countries.

The home garden is a traditional agricultural system that has provided rural households with food and fibre on a sustainable basis for several thousand years (Box 2.7).

Box 2.7 Home gardens as a valuable resource[14]

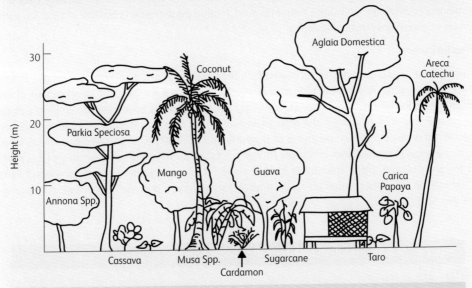

Figure 2.6 – The diversity in a Javanese home garden[15]

Home gardens are one of the oldest forms of farming system and may have been the first agricultural system to emerge in hunter gatherer societies. Today, home or kitchen gardens are particularly well developed on the island of Java in Indonesia, where they are called *pekarangan*.

The immediately noticeable characteristic is their great diversity relative to their size: they usually take up little more than half a hectare around the farmer's house. Yet, in one Javanese home garden 56 different species of useful plants were found, some for food, others for condiments and spices, some for medicine and others for feed for livestock. A cow, a goat, chickens and ducks were also present, as well as fish in the garden pond. Most of the garden products are used for household consumption, but some are bartered with neighbours or sold.

The plants are grown in intricate relationships with one another: close to the ground are vegetables, cassava, taro and spices; in the next layer are bananas, papayas and other fruits; a couple of metres above are soursop *Annona spp*, guava and mango, while emerging through the canopy are coconuts, timber trees and fruit trees. The planting is so dense that to a casual observer the garden seems like a miniature forest.

Figure 2.7 – Javanese home garden

4. The development of intermediate technologies

Intermediate technologies have been defined in a number of ways, but fundamentally they are traditional technologies that have been improved in appropriate respects by their integration with modern conventional technologies.

Treadle pumps

There are numerous examples of such intermediate technologies in action. Some are simple, others more sophisticated. A good example of a relatively simple technology is the development of an affordable and reliable treadle pump. For many years, engineers have been developing pumps which allow farmers to replace the arduous task of lifting irrigation water from shallow wells by bucket. Oil driven pumps are expensive to purchase and to run. The modern treadle pump is ideal in many respects – it is efficient and easy for farmers to use and maintain and is virtually fool-proof. It relies on human rather than oil or electric power. It is also relatively cheap, as a result of a combination of public subsidies with private manufacture and servicing, and community involvement (Box 2.8).

Box 2.8   Making irrigation possible with treadle pumps

First innovated by local people in Bangladesh in the early 1980s, the treadle pump is a simple machine which a farmer can stand on and pump with his or her feet to irrigate a field. The pump produces the suction or pressure needed to pump water from a natural source or dug well to be sprayed on the crops. The technology has been improved upon by a number of enterprising engineers, producing a variety of effective and easy-to-maintain designs which can be used to irrigate up to two acres of land without any motor or fuel.

International Development Enterprises (IDE) began in 1984 by refining the pump design they encountered in Bangladesh. After successfully creating a market and supply-chain for the product there, they have since expanded the approach to countries across Africa and Asia.[16]

The Non-Governmental Organisation (NGO) *KickStart* responded to farmers in Kenya who needed a device which would pump water uphill, useful when water sources are at the bottom of a hilly plot or for filling overhead tanks.

© Bimala Colavito – IDE

Figure 2.8 – Using an IDE treadle pump this Bangledeshi woman can now support her family and run a small shop

They developed the 'Super-Money Maker' pump in 1998, which as of 2009 has been sold to over 129,000 farmers in Kenya, Tanzania and Mali.[17]

Pumps like these help farmers by extending the traditional growing season and expanding the number of crops that they can cultivate.

For example, Nazrul Islam, a farmer in Bangladesh, applied for a micro-loan of about US$20 to cover the costs of digging a well and buying a treadle pump. He was able to repay the loan and buy additional land and livestock within the first year of use.[18]

© Al Doerksen – IDE

Figure 2.9 – An IDE treadle pump dealer works on a pump in Zambia

Chinese technologies

The Loess Plateau project, discussed in Chapter 1, also provides examples of intermediate technologies (Box 2.9). In order to effectively and sustainably rehabilitate this very degraded area, project planners combined large-scale engineering technology in the use of bulldozers for shaping terraces and dams, with local knowledge of past efforts, in erosion control and of the needs and priorities of the communities, to formulate a set of appropriate solutions.

While traditional and intermediate technologies offer a great deal to science innovation, in practice they may require considerable skill and experience; they can be labour intensive and time consuming; and they are often difficult to transfer to other areas. It is for this reason that we urgently need new technologies, derived from cutting edge science, that from the outset are designed for developing country conditions.

Box 2.9 Intermediate technologies on the Loess Plateau, China

- Construction of **modern terraces** using local bulldozer operators with additional manual labour for shaping – creating terraces that are broader, horizontal and sloping inwards. These terraces have converted sloping land to level fields, virtually eliminating erosion and helping to maintain moisture in the soils, allowing higher crop yields and more diversified cropping patterns.[19]

© Environmental Education Media Project for China, 2005

Figure 2.10 – Terraces on the Loess Plateau

© Gordon Conway

Figure 2.11 – Wheat growing on the Loess plateau through plastic covering to retain soil and moisture

- Construction of **sediment traps and dams** in the uninhabited gully areas to intercept sediment at its source. By using a combination of key, warping and check dams, the project was able to reduce sediment loads to the river by around 50 %, provide a new water supply, and greatly increase the arable land available for farming. All dams were constructed with earthfill, and can be easily maintained and modified as required.[19]

- **Improved transplantation methods** for planting trees on the upper slopes. Previous methods had been disrupting the rhizosphere, the important region of soil near the roots of a tree. Chinese scientists devised a method of wrapping the root ball of the trees in grass mats, rope or removable plastic, thus keeping existing soil intact.[20]

- Use of **plastic** to conserve water and for livestock housing. Modern plastics provide a cheap and efficient way of both protecting the soil and reducing water loss. They can also be used to trap heat – especially in the winter – providing warm housing for livestock and the temperatures to raise cut flowers, tomatoes and other horticultural crops for local and distant markets. Chinese researchers are currently working on the production of biodegradable plastics.

© Gordon Conway

Figure 2.12 – Plastic covered 'greenhouses' raising cut flowers for market, Loess Plateau (note combination with traditional mud and straw construction)

5. The promise of new platform technologies

In the past, most application of scientific innovation from industrialised countries has involved a process of adaptation to developing country conditions, in the ways described above. This two-step process of innovation and adaptation inevitably slows science innovation for development, that is why we have argued in Chapter 1 for the involvement of developing country scientists and perspectives in global science innovation systems. In this way developing country needs can be included from the outset in the interaction of basic, translational and applied science.

The increasingly global nature of science innovation, the "internationalisation" of universities and the engagement of new players in development research, including government institutions, industry and civil society is making this ambition all the more feasible. In the next chapter we will examine how these different players may be engaged in accelerating science innovation for development. Here we highlight three key areas of scientific advance – new scientific "platforms" for innovation – that have the potential to be developed simultaneously for the needs of the industrialised and the developing world. These new platform technologies are:

- Information and communication technology for development;
- Nanotechnology;
- Biotechnology.

While these research platforms have, not surprisingly, begun in industrialised research institutions, considerable effort is now underway to bring development agendas into the innovation process. Further, there is now a growing convergence and integration of application between all these technologies.

Information and Communication Technology (ICT) for development

Traditionally, ICT in developing countries has been based on indigenous forms of storytelling, song and theatre, the print media and radio. Modern ICT, based on electronic communications and the internet, has enormous but still largely unrealised potential for improving the lives of poor people. The challenge for science innovation here is to improve and encourage the effective use of existing technologies by the poor, while at the same time creating collaborations between developed and developing country scientists and engineers that will result in new communication technologies that are more appropriate to the environment and users in developing countries.

Improved ICT can benefit international development in many diverse ways, not the least of which is the improvement of science innovation itself through the engagement of developing country scientists in global innovation systems that require a capacity for rapid communication and transfer of scientific data.

Mobile phones

ICT development has already had demonstrable development value in the widespread use of mobile phones. This is a good example of an imported technology that has been widely and successfully adopted by developing countries. It was not specifically designed for, or with the involvement of, poor people and in many cases its primary advantage to poor people is unrelated to the key purpose for which it was designed, namely, mobility.

Furthermore, its success has not depended on a specific policy initiative on the part of donors or developing country governments to promote uptake of the technology. Nevertheless, the use of mobile phones has exploded in recent years, across Asia and Latin America, and especially in Africa. In 1995 there were 650,000 mobile phone subscribers in Africa; by 2003 there were nearly 52 million. Over the past five years the continent's mobile phone usage has increased at an annual rate of 65%, twice the rate of Asia, and by 2008 there were over 250 million subscribers.[21,22]

Not surprisingly, new users are putting mobile phones to use in all kinds of situations, making things like banking, disease surveillance and election monitoring faster and easier. (Box 2.10)

Box 2.10 Putting mobile phones to use

Mobile phones can be used by everyone, including those who are poor, remote and/or illiterate. They can be shared between individuals and households, and made public at booths as a pay-service. Their use has not only dramatically improved communication and the flow of information in developing countries, but it has spurred a variety of completely new ways of doing things, in the areas of business, health and even social advocacy.

First and foremost, mobile phone use has given previously disconnected communities a means of communicating with family and friends, connecting with markets and facilitating the flow of remittances from abroad. Mobiles can serve to provide households with an increased sense of

© Gordon Conway

Figure 2.13 – Mobile phone booth in a Nairobi slum

security, especially in health and other emergencies. The mobile market has also provided employment for countless individuals selling phones, cards and services.[23-25]

A huge number of innovators in developing countries have taken advantage of the flexibility and power of mobile phone technology, and used it to transform various aspects of local life. The examples below illustrate a few of these beneficial applications:

Mobiles for farming – Expanding mobile phone use has begun to remove many long-standing obstacles for farmers in developing countries. Mobiles can be used to find out the location and prices of inputs and crop market rates, with the cost of a phone call being a mere fraction of that previously spent on transport. New services such as *AppLab*, run by the Grameen Foundation in partnership with Google and the provider MTN Uganda, are allowing farmers to get tailored, speedy answers to their questions. The initiative includes platforms such as *Farmer's Friend*, a searchable database of agricultural information, *Google SMS*, a question and answer texting service and *Google Trader*, a SMS-based "marketplace" application that helps buyers and sellers find each other.[26-28]

M-Health – Mobile phones are increasingly being used in new ways to improve health systems, resulting in Mobile or M-Health, or 'telemedicine.' They can be used to improve communication between health officials and patients, for example, by sending SMS reminders of treatment or vaccination dates. Public health officials have also begun taking advantage of the technology for disease surveillance and response, by interfacing GIS and mobile technology on smart phones to provide real-time information on both diseases and medication supply.[29] The organisation Voxiva has designed

© Ken Banks – kiwanja.net

Figure 2.14 – Mobile phone use is spreading quickly in the developing world

integrated 'mobile-centric' programmes for such projects as, reducing maternal mortality in Peru, while the group Cell-Life has done so for HIV treatment in South Africa, using the phone as a tool for education, action and social networking.[30,31]

M-Banking – Mobile banking systems are revolutionising the banking industry by allowing users to convert cash in and out of 'stored value' accounts linked to their mobile phone, use the stored value to pay for goods, and even transfer stored value between their own and other people's accounts. This gives customers a simple and secure service, and allows them to avoid the expense and time of travelling to and waiting in a bank, and the risk of theft. A variety of successful initiatives are now running in South Africa, Kenya and the Philippines.[32]

Mobiles for advocacy – Mobile phones can be used by citizens as a tool for fostering improved governance and equality, by aiding in monitoring and mobilisation. Organisations such as Tactical Technology in the UK have worked with local NGOs in developing countries to use mobile phone technology to report problems such as corruption, violence and environmental degradation, as well as monitor elections. They have also helped groups use mobiles to improve their social advocacy campaigns, by using SMS messages, ringtones and mobile news updates to mobilise, inform and even fundraise for causes such as workers' and women's rights.[33]

The internet

Internet access in the developing countries is growing fast – with usage increasing between 2000 and 2008 by over 1,000 % in Africa, 800 % in Latin America and 400 % in Asia,[34] and the use of computers for education, communication and information processing is steadily expanding. This will be further helped by improvements in infrastructure, such as the new 17,000km long underwater fibre optic cable installed by the African-owned company Seacom along the eastern coast of Africa. The cable, which went live in July 2009, creates a much needed digital link between Eastern Africa, South Asia and Europe, and will bring higher-speed, lower-cost broadband to millions of users.[35]

The internet is a powerful communication tool for connecting people and groups, accessing up-to-date information from around the world, and as a medium for posting news, business information and even campaign or advocacy messages. Use in internet cafés, schools and businesses has taken off, and there are many less traditional ways in which the internet is being used (Box 2.11).

Box 2.11 The internet as a development tool

Broadcasting information

© HiWEL

In the town of Veerampattinam in India, the M.S. Swaminathan Research Foundation has put up loudspeakers to broadcast information such as weather and ocean-wave forecasts, agricultural and fishing techniques, market prices, government programmes, and local bus schedules. This allows citizens to access accurate information without even touching a computer or phone, thus adapting internet technology for the specific local context.[36]

Figure 2.15 – Children crowding around a HiWEL learning station in India

Revamping education

In 1999 in New Delhi, India, local physicist Dr Sugata Mitra cemented a computer with a high-speed internet connection into a wall adjacent to a rubbish dump used by the poor – and just left it there. He monitored the use of the machine using a remote computer and a hidden camera. The results were surprising. Local children quickly began experimenting with the machine in groups, and within days had acquired basic computer literacy – able to use the mouse to point, drag, drop, copy, and to browse the internet. They came up with names for the objects such as *sui* (needle) for the mouse pointer and *damru* (Shiva's drum) for the hourglass.

This phenomenon has since been termed the "hole in the wall" project, and after a few more similar successes, the idea proved worth pursuing. In 2001 the Hole-in-the-Wall Education Ltd. (HiWEL) partnership was formed between Dr Mitra's computer software and training company NIIT and the International Finance Corporation. The group has since worked to expand the number of learning stations across India and other countries. By 2009 there were more than 400 in place across India, as well as some in Cambodia and seven African countries.[37] The HiWEL stations are cheap and easy to set-up and, due to their explorative nature, research has shown the programme benefits across gender as well as socio-economic groups equally.[38] Students who have had access to a HiWEL learning station are performing better in subjects such as mathematics and science, with the benefits multiplying as children form groups and share information.[39,40]

Improving NGO networking

The organisation *Rede de Informações para o Terceiro Setor* (RITS) in Brazil works to help local NGOs use the internet as a tool for accessing and communicating information, thus enabling them to better serve those they are trying to help. RITS hosts a virtual research centre on Brazilian civil society, publishes a weekly e-magazine of NGO news, and also provides web site hosting, email access, and Intranet services for hundreds of NGOs.[41]

Improving access

The key challenge now is to improve both mobile telephony and internet access in developing countries and particularly in rural areas. Access is frequently limited by policies and regulation which make the uptake of the technology more difficult for the poor. For example, in Ethiopia, where the government regulates the mobile phone industry very tightly, the average annual cost of using a mobile is one tenth of a person's average annual income, whereas it is only 1/150th in the freer South African market.[42]

On top of this, the way in which existing technologies are designed and applied can prevent expansion to the full-range of possible users. Current efforts are focusing on new and innovative solutions to bring the benefits of telephone and internet technology to more people, for less money.

For instance, standardised hardware and software designed for students and professionals in developed countries are often challenging for the partly illiterate, or those who are not comfortable in a main language available on the keyboard, computer programmes, or internet. Most common operating systems today are not always the easiest to learn, or indeed the cheapest to install.[42] In addition, standardised set-ups for phone and computer networks often require users to either purchase their own device, or pay an unaffordable fee for use.

A number of designers have been working to address these issues. The One Laptop per Child (OLPC) group has sparked innovation in laptop design for education in developing countries, while the non-profit Movirtu has devised a way for the poorest to have a telephone number without buying a phone, and computer rooms are being redesigned so that many users can work off a single processor (Box 2.12).

Box 2.12 ICT for all

Laptops for education

© OLPC

Released in 2005, the OLPC XO laptop is small, rugged and energy-efficient. It can withstand high heat and humidity and has a screen readable in bright sunlight. Even more novel, however, is the open-source Linux-based software created by the team, called 'Sugar.' It reinvents the traditional user interface allowing children to 'learn by doing,' with 'objects' and a 'daily journal' rather than a file and folder system, and has the ability to create easy working connections with other students and teachers.[43]

Figure 2.16 – The XO-1 Laptop

The XO laptop has been a hit with many students in countries where it has been piloted, however its integration into school systems and as a viable business model have been harder to achieve. More teacher training and more educational content have been highlighted as areas which could improve its usefulness in schools.[44]

Regardless, it has helped to spur a wave of innovations in laptop hardware and software technology for more diverse users including the rise of 'netbooks', or smaller, cheaper and simpler laptops. While the OLPC project had an original target price of US$100, researchers at the Indian Institute of Science and the Indian Institute of Technology are developing a cheaper machine, called 'Sakshat' meaning 'before your eyes,' which can store learning materials for students.[45,46]

A phone number without a phone

Currently, those who cannot afford to buy a mobile handset must either share a phone with others or pay to use a public one. While making calls this way is workable, if a bit inconvenient, it does not allow the person to have a phone number, or 'identity' so that they can receive calls, voice and text messages, or remittances. The non-profit enterprise Movirtu has designed a platform called 'MXShare', which can be installed in the core of a mobile network, and allows the operator to provide a service which they have named 'M-KADI.' Through this service paper cards with individual fully functioning mobile numbers can be sold or given away, working much like a 'SIM-only' option but without the need to hold onto or transfer a SIM card between phones. This new model has the potential to allow millions of new users into the mobile network.[47,48]

Affordable computing

Another innovation involves changing the way in which computers are connected in internet cafés, school computer rooms or offices. 'Thin client' systems use very cheap 'dummy terminals' with only a keyboard, mouse, screen and remote desktop software. These are connected to a more powerful server which does all of the processing. This type of system is not only cheaper, but more energy efficient and less likely to break down.[42]

Combining technologies

Currently, user interfaces for communication such as radios, telephones and computers remain quite separate. The recent trend in integration of these technologies in developed countries has not, by and large, reached developing country markets.[41] However, as access expands and new technologies are created, a huge number of possibilities exist. Radio stations can use mobile phones and the internet to improve listener interaction and the quality of information available for broadcasts. Devices based on the technology used in *Blackberries*, or other smartphones, may be able to combine mobile phone, internet, radio

Figure 2.17 – Women refugees from Ghana speaking at a local radio station in Cote D'Ivoire

© Ami Vitale – World Bank

and television interfaces to improve rural access to information. Some exciting new ideas have already emerged, such as software which allows users to surf the internet using voice commands on a mobile phone or another which enables messages to be sent via a mobile phone network on a computer without the use of the internet (Box 2.13).

Box 2.13 Creating ICT hybrids

'An entirely new kind of web'

A team from the IBM India Research Laboratory in New Delhi is now testing a completely new way of connecting to the internet – using voice commands spoken into mobile phones. They have created new software called *VoiceGen*, which allows users to create *VoiceSites* rather than websites, where they can enter information about their business or organisation through a series of prompts in the local language.

© Ken Banks – kiwanja.net

Figure 2.18 – Men texting in Kenya

For example, a seller of agricultural products could create a *VoiceSite* which is then assigned a phone number, which acts as its URL. It can be accessed by customers using a voice controlled browser, which allows them to go back, forward and even to bookmark pages for later use. To make this possible, IBM developed a new type of transfer protocol, called hyperspeech transfer protocol (HSTP), to replace the text-version HTTP. This type of service will allow business owners who do not have the money for a storefront or advertising to get their information out to customers, and enable anyone to access information without needing to read or have access to a computer.[49]

Texting power

While the expansion of the mobile network and greater access to computers have been helpful to NGOs in developing countries, the non-profit kiwanja.net has gone a step further and designed a software package which allows users to combine the benefits of both. After downloading the free software, called *Frontline SMS*, a user can plug any mobile phone, or phones into the computer and send, receive and store text messages using the mobile networks to and from individuals or large groups.

This gives users great flexibility, enabling them to send messages where there is no internet, even while on the road using a laptop. It also avoids the use of outside servers, useful in places with strict internet controls. The software can be used to set up automatic replies to messages with keywords, such as the time of a scheduled vaccination clinic. NGO managers, doctors and researchers around the world have enthusiastically picked up this technology and used it to solve their communication challenges – from election monitoring, to communicating health and agricultural updates, to conducting surveys, to fundraising – the list is endless.[50]

The potential of nanotechnology

Nanotechnology involves the manipulation of matter at atomic and molecular levels, i.e. at a scale of a billionth of a metre, to produce a great variety of materials and devices. At this scale materials often have unique characteristics.

While the US is currently leading the way in nanoscience research, many emerging countries have also established strong programmes.

China currently ranks second to the US in the number of articles published on the subject in international peer-reviewed journals. Indian scientists are also big contributors, with India recently launching a five year, US \$220 million national strategy for advancing nanoscience.[51]

Applications of nanotechnology may include: energy storage, production and conversion, disease diagnosis, drug delivery systems, air and water pollution detection and remediation, and food processing and storage. Most of these applications are being developed for wealthy countries, but many of them have applications in developing countries as well.

Water purification

One of the most promising applications for nanoscience is in the use of nanomembranes, nanosensors, and magnetic nanoparticles for water purification – allowing for desalination, detoxification, remediation and detection of contaminants and pathogens. Research is in the early stages and many of the products thus far are still too expensive for developing country applications, but the ability to

Figure 2.19 – Children using the Seldon WaterBox in Rwanda

immediately treat even very contaminated water to a high quality, at the source, without the use of electricity, heavy chemical dosages or high pressure makes it an area worth pursuing.[52]

Scientists at Seldon Laboratories in the US have used carbon nanotubes to create a patented nanomesh™ material. The material works by attracting contaminants to its surface, and can be used to remove bacteria, viruses and pathogens as well as reduce lead, arsenic and uranium to US drinking water quality standards.

They currently have two products using this technology. The WaterBox (US\$5,000) (Figure 2.19) is a durable and portable treatment system which can be either plugged in or used with a foot-pump, and is able to produce clean water at an average of about two litres per minute. For smaller-scale, individual treatment, the WaterStick (US\$95), (Figure 2.20) can filter contaminated water as the user drinks, at a flow rate of up to 200 mls per minute. These products have already been used by aid workers in Uganda and Rwanda.[53]

Also working with carbon nanotubes, scientists at Banaras Hindu University, India, in a partnership with the Rensselaer Nanotechnology Center (US), have discovered how to create strong, reusable and heat resistant carbon nanotube filters by *spraying* the nanotube structure directly onto the carbon cylinders. The filters can be used to remove contaminants such as polio viruses and *E.coli* from water.[52-54]

Figure 2.20 – The Seldon WaterStick

Disease diagnostics

The diagnosis of disease can be a time-consuming process, often involving analysis of samples in a laboratory and the culturing of micro-organisms suspected of causing the disease. Advances in nano-science are making possible diagnosis of diseases at the point of care, without the need for laboratory analysis, thereby speeding up the time it takes to make a diagnosis and reducing costs. Rapid, inexpensive, point of care diagnosis is particularly important for new and emerging human, animal and plant diseases that pose risks of epidemics, and for reaching poor communities remote from medical and agricultural services and associated laboratories.

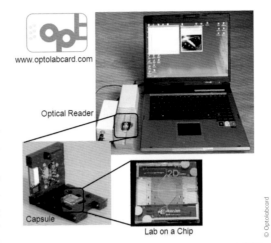

Figure 2.21 – The Optolab Card setup

Recent breakthroughs in diagnostics have been based on using biomarkers of disease-causing organisms. These may be characteristic chemicals produced by the pathogen, or its own DNA. Nano-surfaces are created with sensors that react with biomarker molecules and in so doing generate an electrical or visual signal that can be measured. These "labs on a chip" can be incorporated into handheld devices which can deliver a diagnosis in minutes after application of a sample such as saliva, blood or plant sap.[55,56]

For instance, the EU funded Optolab Card project is developing and mass producing a miniaturised optical laboratory on a card, allowing bacterially infectious diseases, such as *Salmonella*, to be diagnosed in just 15 minutes as opposed to the six to 48 hours for conventional tests.[57] And, the Central Scientific Instruments Organisation (CSIO) in Chandigarh, India is working to develop a nanotech based TB diagnostic kit which would measure only 1cm^3 and can work more quickly, cost less (around rupees 30 per kit) and use less blood.[58]

Pharmaceutical efficiency

Nanotechnology can be used to improve the usability, effectiveness or efficiency of drugs. One example comes from the area of tuberculosis (TB) medication, where the current treatments are lengthy and difficult to remember – patients need to take their drugs every day for six to nine months. This is challenging even for those with good access to medical care, and failure to complete this full regimen can lead to complications and the emergence of drug-resistant strains (Box 2.4 and Chapter 6).

Dr Tumi Semete, a researcher at the Council for Scientific and Industrial Research (CSIR), in Cape Town, South Africa, has developed an idea which could greatly improve this situation. With funding from the Bill and Melinda Gates Foundation, she plans to use nano-size sticky 'balls' of conventional TB drugs, which have already been developed by scientists at CSIR, to improve the efficiency of treatment. Currently only about 20% of the medicine taken gets to the infected tissue, while up to 80% of it is excreted. With these nanoparticles, Dr Semete believes she can get the medicine to stick directly to infected cells, increasing efficiency to close to 100%. The drug can also be released slowly, so that patients may not have to remember to take their pills daily.[59]

The utility of biotechnology

Biotechnology is defined as any technological application that uses biological systems, living organisms, or derivatives thereof, to make or modify products or processes for specific use.[60] Traditionally biotechnology has been associated with the centuries' old practice of fermentation, used in the making of bread, beer and spirits. Today's biotechnology is based on the revolution in cellular and molecular biology that occurred in the second half of the 20th century.[61] In particular, it exploits advances in understanding the DNA and RNA of an organism and their functions in order to identify and manipulate the genes that produce particular traits in animals and plants. Biotechnology has found applications across a range of fields (Box 2.14).

Biotechnology in agriculture

Modern plant breeding, derived from the discovery by Gregor Mendel of the particulate nature of inheritance, and developed over much of the last century, has transformed agricultural production. It was at the core of the Green Revolution (see Chapter 5). However, such plant breeding is often an uncertain and lengthy process: discovery of mutations with desirable properties is serendipitous, and incorporating only those traits into the crops we presently use involves many crop generations and hence years of careful breeding, often with limited success. A recent example of successful, conventional breeding is the development of "quality protein maize". A discovery in the 1960s of maize mutants with high levels of desirable amino acids started a breeding programme which, after several decades, has successfully incorporated these desirable traits into better maize varieties for developing countries.[63]

Biotechnology makes this process of incorporating beneficial traits more effective and rapid, through three practical techniques:

> **Box 2.14 Biotechnologies that can help developing countries meet the MDGs[62]**
>
> **Hunger**
> - High yield crops
> - Drought and disease resistant crops
> - More nutritious crop and animal products
>
> **Health**
> - Microbicides against sexually transmitted diseases
> - Recombinant vaccines
> - Combinatorial chemistry for new medications
> - Molecular diagnostics
> - Pathogen genome sequencing
> - Bioinformatics for identification of drug targets
> - Improved drug delivery
> - Vitamin enriched crops
>
> **Environment**
> - Bioremediation for organic waste and heavy metal treatment

- *Tissue culture* – which permits the growth of whole plants from a single cell or clump of cells in an artificial medium;

- *Marker-aided selection* – based on the ability to detect the presence of particular DNA sequences at specific locations in an organism and link these to the presence of genes responsible for particular traits;

- *Recombinant DNA* or genetic engineering technology – which enables the direct transfer of genes from one organism to another.

The first two technologies, in the hands of international and national agricultural research centres are already delivering improved staple crops to poor farmers.

Tissue culture

Tissue culture has produced new rices for Africa (discussed in Chapter 1) and has also produced new pest and disease free bananas in East Africa that can yield up to 50 tonnes/ha (Box 2.15). One of its desirable features is its ability to generate rapidly many copies of a plant with desirable traits, a kind of cloning. Another feature is the ability, through this process, of generating planting materials that are known to be free of disease.

Box 2.15 Healthy bananas through tissue culture

© Jean Marc Fleury – IDRC/CRDI

Bananas are a major source of food and income throughout the tropics, and especially in East Africa. Ugandans, for example, are the largest consumers of bananas in the world, eating on average nearly 1kg/person/day.[64] The banana tree is, however, very susceptible to disease, as new plants are grown directly from cuttings from a 'mother plant,' thus transferring any disease present, even if it is not visible.[65]

The Black Sigatoka fungus, a leaf spot disease, has been particularly devastating to banana crops worldwide since its first outbreak in Fiji in 1963. It arrived in East Africa in the 1970s, delivering a major blow to farmers' yields, decreasing productivity by as much as 40%. The fungus can be controlled with fungicides. However the disease has developed increasing resistance over the years, making this option both expensive and damaging to the environment.

Figure 2.22 – Black Sigatoka disease on banana tree

Farmers needed a way to break the chain of disease. Kenyan agricultural scientist Florence Wambugu, having studied plant pathology and biotechnology in both the US and the UK, made a move to bring the benefits of tissue culture to the problem. With tissue culture, a banana shoot is dissected into tiny pieces and placed in a sterile container, quickly generating healthy new plants which can be planted in the field.[66]

© Gordon Conway

Figure 2.23 – Tissue cultured bananas in a village nursery, Uganda

After the end of apartheid in South Africa, Wambugu made a visit to the country to observe the previously closely guarded work on tissue culture bananas. She was enthused, and quickly pitched the idea to the Kenyan Agricultural Research Institute (KARI), where trials began on local varieties in the mid-1990s. The work was successful, and with funding from the Rockefeller Foundation, Wambugu moved to expand the programme, offering training and credit to farmers to get started.[67]

The results have been remarkable. Yields have increased from averages of ten tonnes/ha to 30-50 tonnes/ha, and the national banana production has more than doubled since 1995, from approximately 400,000 tonnes to over one million tonnes in 2004.[66]

Wambugu has since founded the group Africa Harvest to spread this technology and others to farmers in Kenya. They are now working on increasing the benefits to small-holder farmers through support and training in post-harvest handling, marketing and sales.[68]

Marker-aided selection

With marker-aided selection (MAS) it is possible to identify segments of the plant genome that are closely linked to the desired genes, so the presence of the trait can be determined at the seedling or even the seed stage. This makes it possible to achieve a new variety in four to six generations instead of ten (Box 2.16).

Box 2.16 Marker-aided selection delivers resistance to Maize Streak Virus

Maize streak virus (MSV) is the most serious disease of maize in Africa, affecting 60% of the planted area and causing an estimated 37% yield loss, or roughly 5.5 million tonnes/year losses in production.[69]

Excellent genetic resistance to MSV has been known for over 20 years, but it has not been widely deployed in local maize varieties because few national breeding programmes can afford to maintain the insect colonies and other infrastructure necessary to measure for resistance against insect-vectored viral diseases.

© AGRA
Figure 2.24 – A plant with Maize streak virus

Now, using genetic markers on the molecular map of maize, it is possible to identify the precise location of the resistance gene, and using the DNA markers flanking the gene, to backcross it into numerous well-adapted local varieties without expensive disease screening.

MAS is being used to introduce quality-protein genes into maizes already grown in Africa. It is also particularly useful for breeding drought-tolerance, which typically occurs as the result of a number of different traits – deeper roots, early flowering, water diffusion properties – working together. Breeding for drought-tolerance is a difficult and slow process using conventional techniques, but markers are now permitting combinations of these traits to be accumulated in new varieties.

Recombinant DNA

Recombinant DNA crops, otherwise known as Genetically Modified (GM) crops are produced by first isolating and culturing a gene of potential usefulness. This is then inserted into the cell of a crop plant by a process of transformation (Box 2.17).

Box 2.17 Transforming a crop[65]

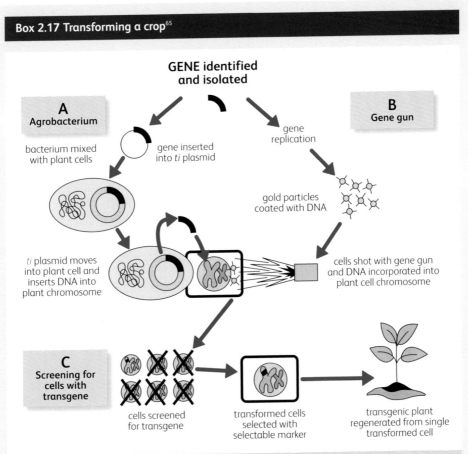

GENE identified and isolated

A
Agrobacterium

bacterium mixed with plant cells

gene inserted into *ti* plasmid

gene replication

B
Gene gun

gold particles coated with DNA

ti plasmid moves into plant cell and inserts DNA into plant chromosome

cells shot with gene gun and DNA incorporated into plant cell chromosome

C
Screening for cells with transgene

cells screened for transgene

transformed cells selected with selectable marker

transgenic plant regenerated from single transformed cell

Figure 2.25 – Two processes of transformation in producing GM crops[70]

Once a crop cell has been produced by tissue culture it is transformed in one of two ways (Figure 2.25):

The first uses a naturally occurring bacterium *Agrobacterium tumefaciens* that infects some plants, causing Crown Gall disease for instance. It contains a small circular piece of DNA called a plasmid into which the cultured gene is inserted. The plasmid will then infect cells of certain plants transferring the gene to the DNA of the crop's cell.

The second involves coating gold particles with the gene of interest. The gold particles are then shot into single crop plant cells with a gene gun and in this way incorporated into the cell's DNA. It is not particularly efficient but can be used on crops that *Agrobacterium* cannot affect.

The transformed cells are then cultured and grown into whole plants which are tested in the greenhouse to ensure that the transferred gene, the transgene, functions properly. Not all transgenic plants will express the trait or gene product well. But once the trait is stable it can be bred using conventional plant breeding methods into cultivars with adaptation to the environmental conditions where the crop is produced.

Figure 2.26 – The Rapid Growth of GM crops *(note: a trait hectare is an area multiplied by the number of GM traits (stacked traits) present[71]*

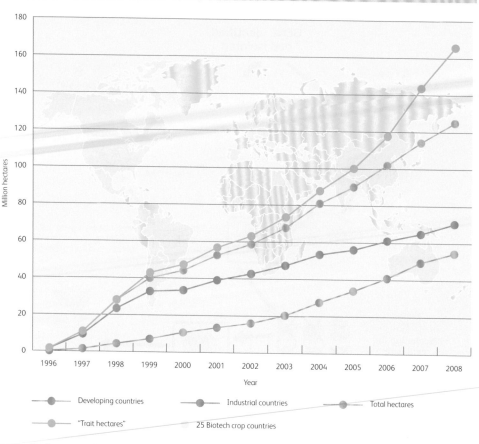

Developing countries   Industrial countries   Total hectares

"Trait hectares"   25 Biotech crop countries

An "apparent" increase of 9.4% or 10.7 million hectares (ha) between 2007 and 2008, equivalent to a "real" increase of 15% or 22 million "trait hectares"

GM crops are spreading rapidly in developing countries. About a third (some 34 million ha) of the total global GM hectarage is in developing countries, with some 7.7 million farmers putting the new technology to use (see Figure 2.26). China is a major investor in the science of GM. Several other countries, including some in Africa, are following suit.

The benefits of GM technology in developing countries so far have come principally from engineering several crops to express a bacterial gene which controls certain insect pests, thereby reducing the need for chemical pesticides, and from engineering herbicide-resistance into other crops to allow reduced, targeted use of safer herbicides. The total economic benefits for developing country farmers were estimated at US$22 billion between 1996 and 2007.[71] Bt cotton, in particular, has proved to be beneficial in a number of countries (Box 2.18).

What is now needed are crops that benefit a wider range of farmers, as well as consumers, in developing countries. We explore this topic further in Chapter 5.

Box 2.18 The benefits of Bt cotton for developing countries

Cotton is a crop that suffers heavily from insect pest attack. Various species of bollworms, boll weevils, flies and mites cause significant damage to the crop, reducing yields and the quality of the cotton. As a consequence, cotton was until the early 1990s the target of 25 % of all the insecticides applied in the world.[72]

A gene contained in the naturally occurring bacterium *Bacillus thuringiensis* (Bt) codes for a toxin that is lethal to plant feeding bollworms (use of the bacterium is approved for organic farmers for pest control).

© ISAAA

Figure 2.27 – Bt Cotton growing in a field

It has proven very effective against such pests when transferred to a variety of crops through recombinant DNA engineering. Bt cotton was first developed in the US and introduced in 1996. It now accounts for 87 % of the crop there (28 % of world-wide production).[73]

It has been rapidly taken up in China, South Africa and most recently India and Burkina Faso. Over 12 million farmers, mostly in China and India, planted Bt cotton on 3.8 million and 7.6 million ha, respectively, in 2008.[71] China's adoption was driven by low seed cost, largely due to publicly developed Bt cotton varieties, and decentralised breeding that enabled the transfer of the Bt trait into locally adapted varieties. The dramatic take-off in India, from an initial 500,000 ha in 2004[71,74] has brought many farmers significant yield increases. Over 80 % of India's cotton is Bt and the country is now the world's second largest producer and exporter.

Although the benefits vary across years, institutional settings and agro-ecological zones, farm-level studies largely confirm higher profits from adoption of Bt cotton, and also document substantial environmental and health benefits through lower pesticide use,[75,76] with worldwide use of insecticides for cotton now down to about 18 %.[77] Table 2.1 below shows the benefits for a range of countries.

	Argentina	China	India	Mexico	South Africa
Added yield (%)	33	19	26	11	65
Added profit (%)	31	340	47	12	198
Reduced chemical sprays (number)	2.4	–	2.7	2.2	–
Reduced pest management costs (%)	47	67	73	77	58

Table 2.1 – The economic and environmental benefits of Bt cotton in developing countries[78]

Biotechnology in human and animal health

While much progress has been made in reducing the burden of disease through conventional technologies such as oral-rehydration therapy, improved water supply and traditional vaccines, there still remain many challenges. There are no conventional treatments that will cure AIDS patients, current TB regimens are lengthy and expensive, and resistance to malaria drugs is rising. The place to look for these new breakthroughs is biotechnology.[79]

Biotechnology for health, as for agriculture, takes a number of forms. For example, tissue culture has been instrumental in developing a vaccine against the cattle disease, Rinderpest, discussed in Chapter 5. Scientists can also use biotechnology to target critical molecular processes, thus making drug production more efficient and effective. The highly active anti-retroviral drugs used in treating HIV/AIDS are examples. Hundreds of new and improved medical diagnostic tests would not be possible without modern molecular biology.[80]

To date, however, the most striking successes in health biotechnology have been the development of pharmaceuticals through recombinant DNA (rDNA) technology. This technology allows scientists to isolate a gene of interest, incorporate it into a host cell such as *E.coli*, and replicate it to produce a large, reliable, pure source of new DNA. The first application of this technology was the production of recombinant insulin in 1982, which gave diabetic patients an alternative to insulin from animal sources (Box 2.19). Since then there has been a steady stream of products, and there are now over 200 in common use, and more than 400 in clinical trials.[80] The vaccines for hepatitis A and B are among the most important.

The industry has grown considerably over the last few decades, with US revenues alone rising from US$8 billion in 1992 to $58.8 billion in 2006.[80] But despite the enormous opportunity inherent in the technology for better, faster and cheaper drugs and vaccines, only a tiny proportion of the efforts in health biotechnology have focused on the specific diseases of the poor in the developing countries. This is slowly changing however, and as discussed further in Chapter 3, creative financing mechanisms, such as public-private partnerships like the Global Alliance for Vaccines and Immunization (GAVI), are drawing more resources to products for developing world diseases.

Current research is focused on new Highly Active Anti-Retroviral Therapies (HAARTs), microbicides and vaccines to combat HIV AIDS, as well as vaccines against malaria, TB and influenza, the details of which are explored further in Chapter 6.

Figure 2.28 – Biotechnology laboratory in Vietnam

© Gordon Conway

Box 2.19 Making recombinant DNA insulin[81]

The production of rDNA insulin paved the way for recombinant DNA technology in the health arena, showing that genetically modified products could be made and used safely. It makes it possible to produce human insulin quickly and comparatively cheaply from bacteria in an industrial fermentation unit. The procedure is illustrated in figure 2.29.

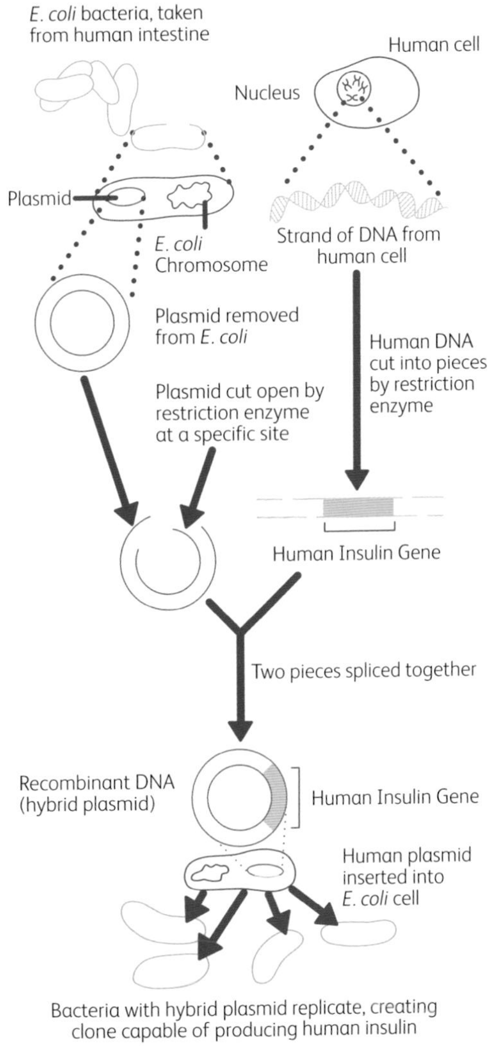

Here we describe the basic process by which the human insulin gene is inserted into a bacterium. It is a relatively complicated process similar in some respects to the recombinant DNA process used in producing GM crops.

First, an insulin gene is identified and cultured. As in the GM process the piece of DNA (in this case human DNA) is cut out using a special bacterial enzyme known as a restriction endonuclease. Each restriction enzyme recognises and cuts at a different nucleotide sequence, so it is possible to be very precise about DNA cutting by selecting one of several hundred of these enzymes that cuts at the desired sequence.

Next, the human insulin gene is spliced into a plasmid, a circle of bacterial DNA in this case contained in an *E.coli* bacterium. This plasmid

E. coli bacteria, taken from human intestine

Human cell

Nucleus

Plasmid

E. coli Chromosome

Strand of DNA from human cell

Plasmid removed from *E. coli*

Human DNA cut into pieces by restriction enzyme

Plasmid cut open by restriction enzyme at a specific site

Human Insulin Gene

Two pieces spliced together

Recombinant DNA (hybrid plasmid)

Human Insulin Gene

Human plasmid inserted into *E. coli* cell

Bacteria with hybrid plasmid replicate, creating clone capable of producing human insulin

Figure 2.29 – Production of insulin by recombinant DNA[81]

has been opened with another restriction enzyme. Attaching the cut ends together is done with a third enzyme (obtained from a virus), called DNA ligase. The result is a cut-and-pasted mixture of human and bacterial DNA.

The last step involves putting the new, hybrid plasmid containing the recombinant DNA back into the bacterium *E.coli*. Once cultured the bacterium is capable of expressing the human insulin gene and hence producing suitable insulin for the treatment of diabetes.

Risk and uncertainty with new platform technologies

By their very nature, the indirect effects of applying new platform technologies will often be unknown. Product registration and regulatory systems help to ensure that potential, unanticipated environmental and health risks associated with new technologies are identified and addressed before any technologies are licensed and deployed. However, countries may differ in their regulatory requirements and interpretation of risk, hence the difference between the US and European countries in regulation and decisions regarding the use of GM crops.

In developing countries, risks and uncertainties associated with new technologies will often be different than in industrialised countries where new platform technologies will probably be registered first. There may be a difference in the conditions under which the new technology may be deployed, for example, the efficacy and safety of a new medicine for a particular disease may be affected by local background levels of other diseases and treatments. There may also be differences in local capacity to address potential hazards. New technologies may require training or monitoring capacity which may not be locally available, and this could increase risks associated with the technology's use. This has been the case, for instance, in many parts of the developing world with the application of new chemical pesticides developed originally for industrialised countries, where lack of training in safe and appropriate use has, in some cases, led to local food contamination, poisonings and pesticide resistance.

National regulatory systems in developing countries are frequently under-resourced and challenged by the process of registering new platform technologies. Very often, they can make use of data from the registration of products in industrialised countries, but there always needs to be a capacity to relate this to local conditions, and this may require additional resources and expertise. Sometimes countries do not have the basic registration systems for new technologies. For instance, traditional pesticide regulatory systems in developing countries have had difficulty in evaluating and approving new, biological pesticides which have many local advantages. This is due to a lack of regulatory protocols for such products, in contrast to industrialised countries. As a result, in Africa, the donor agencies which funded the development of new biological pesticides to replace harmful chemicals for locust control, have also supported national regulatory programmes to develop new and regionally harmonised systems for biological pesticide registration.[82] Regional harmonisation of regulatory and registration systems may also help to accelerate registration and use of other new platform technologies, including new medicines.[83] Box 2.20 looks at the particular challenges in the nanotechnology field in gaining harmonised understanding of its risks and formulating regulation.

Box 2.20 Issues in regulating nanoparticles

Nanoparticles, or three dimensional materials in the range of one to 100 nanometres, occur naturally in the environment, yet it is only with recent technological advances that we have gained the ability to manipulate materials at this scale. With this has come a surge in research and development of new products, with applications ranging from improving solar panels to creating new types of antiperspirant.

However, as with any new technology, standardised safety testing and regulations are not yet in place, and policy makers are struggling to keep up with the pace of discovery.

While frameworks exist to evaluate novel materials, nano-materials are stretching these boundaries for a number of reasons. Particles at the nano-scale actually behave quite differently from those at a conventional or bulk scale, exhibiting properties that have not previously been observed in traditional chemistry or materials science.

One reason for this is that nanoparticles are more reactive due to their *higher surface area to volume ratio*. This leads to changes in surface reactivity and charge, making the quantum (atomic and subatomic) level behaviour of the particles significant, and many argue that new safety protocols are quite essential.

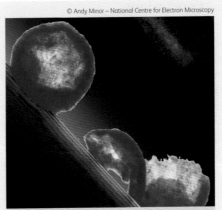

© Andy Minor – National Centre for Electron Microscopy

Figure 2.30 – Cadmium sulfide nanospheres during an experiment to test resistance to stress[84]

In addition, nanoparticles which exist in nature tend to clump together, and thus the behaviour of particles designed in the laboratory specifically to stay apart is largely unknown. And, while particles can be tested in the laboratory for safety, once released into the environment unpredictable, self-assembly of new structures could lead to unforeseen effects.

Therefore, while there is no evidence yet of harm, there is reason to be cautious. Studies have begun in both Europe and the US,[85-88] looking into the potential effects on human and animal health, and the environment. Many questions remain to be answered, including the persistence of particles in the environment, their behaviour when airborne or in the ground, or how they may behave inside the body.

Reports have called for greater coordination and a real need for vigilance, but most stress a flexible and adaptive governance regime which can be developed along with production, rather than halting innovation in this otherwise promising field.

Potential concerns regarding new platform technologies in development extend beyond technical issues of risk and the capacity to evaluate and regulate it. Inevitably, new technologies have the potential to create inequity and to disadvantage parts of society, particularly the poor. New information technologies may reduce or widen the digital divide, disadvantaging rural populations whose access to the internet may be less than city dwellers, and new agricultural and health nano- and bio-technologies will inevitably be more available and affordable to more wealthy parts of society. Therefore, use of these technologies in a development context must always consider how best to ensure that they benefit the poor and reduce, rather than increase, inequities.

In the future, development of new platform technologies should consider these developing country opportunities and issues from the outset, not as an afterthought. An example of such proactive effort has been the development in 2005 of a "Global Dialogue on Nanotechnology and the Poor: Opportunities and Risks" by the Meridian Institute, with support from DFID, the Rockefeller Foundation and IDRC. This has generated a rich dialogue in the international scientific community on the implications of nanotechnology for the poor and how these technologies can play an appropriate role in the development process.[89-91]

6. Conclusions

Science and technology for development today enjoys a broad range of sources of ideas, by virtue of the increasingly global nature of science innovation systems. But there remain enormous challenges in accessing these and integrating them into appropriate technologies. What unites the various examples in this chapter is that the source of a technology is not important as long as that technology is *appropriate*. Ultimately, the appropriateness of a technology in a developing country is demonstrated by how it is used, not by the intentions or the assertions of those who design and market it.

We also believe that in the rush to apply cutting edge science to development problems, we must avoid the tendency to ignore indigenous and local knowledge and innovation, and to use this to develop intermediate technologies. Secondly, in developing new platform technologies, we must move beyond the traditional model where initial applications are focused on wealthy countries and international development applications are a much-delayed afterthought. Developing country needs and opportunities must be incorporated from the outset in the development of new platform technologies, through involving developing country scientists and interests in global science innovation systems. Development agencies have played, and will continue to play, a crucial role in achieving this engagement.

Chapter 2 references and further reading

1   Practical Action. (2008) *Stabilised Soil Blocks*. Practical Action website. Available at: practicalaction.org/?id=stabilised_soil_blocks [Accessed 22 Oct 2009].

2   Sanchez, P., (2002) Soil Fertility and Hunger in Africa. *Science*, **295**, 2019-2020.

3   Thundiyil, J. et al., (2008) Acute pesticide poisoning: a proposed classification tool. *Bulletin of the World Health Organisation*, **86**, 205–209.

4   Goldman, L. & Tran, N., (2002) *Toxics and Poverty: The Impact of Toxic Substances on the Poor in Developing Countries*. World Bank, Washington, DC.

5   Blaylock, A., (2007) *The Future of Controlled-Release Fertilisers*. Agrium Advanced Technologies presentation at the International Nitrogen Conference. Oct 1-5 2007. Costa do Sauipe, Brazil.

6   Fairchild, D. & Malzer, G., (2008) *The Future of Spatial N Management*. The Mosaic Company. Presentation. Jan 1 2008.

7   Roy, A., (2008) *Managing access to farm inputs*. Presented at the World Bank Symposium, Cultivating Innovation: A Response to the Food Price Crisis. IFDC, Washington, DC.

8   WHO. (2008) *Implementing the STOP TB strategy: A handbook of national tuberculosis control programmes*. WHO, Geneva.

9   Vickers, A. & Zollman, C. (1999) ABC of complementary medicines: Herbal Medicine. *BMJ*, **319**, 1050-1053.

10 WHO. (2008) *Traditional medicine*. Available at: www.who.int/mediacentre/factsheets/fs134/en/ [Accessed 29 November, 2009].

11 WHO. (2002) *WHO Traditional Medicine Strategy 2002-2005*. WHO, Geneva.

12 Homsy, J. et al., (1999) Evaluating herbal medicine for the management of Herpes zoster in human immunodeficiency virus-infected patients in Kampala, Uganda. *J. Altern. Complement Med:* **5**, 553-565.

13 Homsy, J. et al., (2004) Traditional health practitioners are key to scaling up comprehensive care for HIV/AIDS in sub-Saharan Africa. *AIDS*, **18**, 1723-5.

14 Soemarwoto, O. & Conway, G., (1991) The Javanese Homegarden. *Journal for Farming Systems Research and Extension*, **2**, 95-118.

15 FAO. (1989) Schematic representation of the structural composition of a Javanese homegarden. In: *Forestry and food security*. FAO, Rome. Available at: www.fao.org/docrep/T0178E/T0178E05.htma.

16 IDE. (2006) *Bangladesh*. International Development Enterprises. Available at: www.ideorg.org/OurStory/History.aspx [Accessed 23 Oct 2009].

17 KickStart. (2009) *Our Impact*. KickStart. Available at: www.kickstart.org/what-we-do/impact [Accessed 22 Oct 2009].

18 IDE. (2006) *I Am Not Worried About My Children's Future Any More – An IDE Success Story from Bangladesh*. International Development Enterprises.

19 World Bank. (2003) Implementation Completion Report, China Loess Plateau Watershed Rehabilitation Project. World Bank Report No: 25701.

20 Liu, J., (2008) [Email] (Pers. Comm. 05 Dec 2008).

21 MIT. (2009) *Why Africa?* Entrepreneurial Programming and Research on Mobiles. Available at: eprom.mit.edu [Accessed 22 Oct 2009].

22 Mugira, F., (2008) Africa leads in mobile phone subscription. *AfricaNews*. 28 September. Available at: www.africanews.com/site/list_messages/20730 3/10/08 [Accessed 22 Oct 2009].

23 Vodaphone. (2005) *Africa: The Impact of Mobile Phones*. The Vodafone Policy Paper Series, Number 2, March 2005.

24 Souter, D. et al., (2005) *The Economic Impact of Telecommunications on Rural Livelihoods and Poverty Reduction: a study of rural communities in India (Gujarat), Mozambique and Tanzania*. Report of DFID KaR Project 8347. Commonwealth Telecommunications Organisation, London.

25 Heeks, R. & Jagun, A., (2007) Editorial in: Mobile Phones and Development. *id21 Insights*. September 2007. Institute of Development Studies (IDS), Brighton.

26 Kasozi, E., (2009) *Uganda: Using a Mobile Phone to Reduce Farming Cost*. The Monitor. 8 July. Available at: www.allafrica.com/stories/200907081084.html [Accessed 22 Oct 2009].

27 Ron, L. & Katragadda, L., (2009) *Taking Africa's Data to the Next Level*. Google Africa Blog. 19 August. Available at: www.google-africa.blogspot.com/2009/06/google-sms-to-serve-needs-of-poor-in.html [Accessed 22 Oct 2009].

28 Grameen Foundation. (2009) *Uganda Projects: AppLab Uganda*. Available at: www.grameenfoundation.applab.org/section/applab-initiatives [Accessed 22 Oct 2009].

29 Iluyemi, A., (2007) *Mobile eHealth for health workers in developing countries: impact on organisational process and users' behaviour: Research in progress*. Conference presentation at 'Mobiles and Development: infrastructure, poverty, enterprise and social development'. 16 May 2007. University of Manchester.

30 Voxiva website. Available at: www.voxiva.com. [Accessed 22 Oct 2009].

31 Cell-Life website. Available at: www.cell-life.org. [Accessed 22 Oct 2009].

32 Donner, J., (2007) Micro-enterprise and the 'mobile divide', New benefits and old inequalities in Nigeria's informal sector. In: Mobile Phones and Development. *id21 Insights*. September 2007. Institute of Development Studies (IDS), Brighton.

33 Tactical Technology website. Available at: www.tacticaltech.org [Accessed 22 Oct 2009].

34 Internet World Stats. (2009) World Internet Usage and Population Statistics. 31 March. Available at: www.internetworldstats.com/stats.htm [Accessed 22 Oct 2009].

35 BBC News. (2009) *East Africa gets high-speed web*. 23 July. Available at: news.bbc.co.uk/1/hi/world/africa/8165077.stm [Accessed 22 Oct 2009].

36 Shore, K., (2005) *Work in Progress – Rural Pondicherry's Wireless Internet*. The International Development Research Centre. Available at: www.idrc.ca/en/ev-47023-201-1-DO_TOPIC.html [Accessed 22 Oct 2009].

37 Gupta, A., (2009) [Email] (Pers. Comm. 3 August 2009).

38 NITT Ltd. (2009) *Hole in the Wall – lighting the spark of learning*. Hole-in-the-Wall Education Ltd.

39 Frontline World. (2002) *India – Hole in the Wall. The Story*. October 2002. Available at: www.pbs.org/frontlineworld/stories/india/thestory.html [Accessed 22 Oct 2009].

40 HiWEL Website Available at: www.hole-in-the-wall.com/index.html [Accessed 22 Oct 2009].

41 Srivastava, C., (2005) *A Robin Hood for the Digital Age*. The International Development Research Centre. Available at: www.idrc.ca/en/ev-47029-201-1-DO_TOPIC.html [Accessed 22 Oct 2009].

42 Unwin, T., (2009) Chapter 3 – Information and Communication for Development. In: Unwin, T (ed.) *ICT4D*. Cambridge University Press, Cambridge.

43 OLPC website. Available at: www.laptop.org [Accessed 22 Oct 2009].

44 Hollow, D., (2009) *The $100 Laptop in Ethiopia – A Case Study*. Presentation at Africa Gathering. 25 April 2009. London.

45 Emigh, J., (2008) *India wants to develop a $10 laptop for students*. Betanews. 29 July. Available at: www.betanews.com/article/India-wants-to-develop-a-10-laptop-for-students/1217365236 [Accessed 22 Oct 2009].

46 TelecomTV. (2009) *Indian Government to orchestrate $20 netbook*. TelecomTV One News. 4 February. Available at: www.telecomtv.com/comspace_newsDetail.aspx?n=44492&id=e9381817-0593-417a-8639-c4c53e2a2a10# [Accessed 22 Oct 2009].

47 Waller, N., (2009) *How we're creating access to basic phone services for more than a billion people earning less than two dollars a day*. Presentation at Africa Gathering. 25 April. London.

48 Movirtu website. Available at: www.movirtu.com [Accessed 22 Oct 2009].

49 Ananthaswamy, A., (2008) Cellphones could be used to build 'audio internet'. *New Scientist*, **2659**, 22-23.

50   Frontline SMS website. Available at: www.frontlinesms.com [Accessed 22 Oct 2009].

51   Chunli, B., (2008) Nano Rising. *Nature*, **456**, TWAS Supplement. 36-37.

52   Meridian Institute. (2005) *Nanotechnology and the Poor – Opportunities and Risks*. Meridian Institute.

53   Seldon website. Available at: www.seldontechnologies.com [Accessed 22 Oct 2009].

54   Physorg.com. (2004) *Efficient Filters Produced from Carbon Nanotubes*. Physorg.com Nanotechnology News. 12 April. Available at: www.physorg.com/news803.html [Accessed 22 Oct 2009].

55   Cass, T. & Toumazou, C., (2006) State of Science Review: Biosensors and Biomarkers. In: *Foresight. Infectious Diseases: Preparing for the Future*. Office of Science and Innovation, London. Available at: www.foresight.gov.uk/Infectious%20Diseases/s7.pdf [Accessed 22 Oct 2009].

56   Yager, P. et al., (2006) Microfluidic diagnostic technologies for global public health. *Nature*, **442**, 412-418.

57   Optolabcard website. Available at: www.optolabcard.com [Accessed 22 Oct 2009].

58   The Times of India. (2004) *CSIO develops nanotechnology for TB diagnostic kit*. 3 January. Available at: timesofindia.indiatimes.com/articleshow/401636.cms [Accessed 22 Oct 2009].

59   Philp, R., (2009) *SA achievers score with Bill Gates*. The Times, 24 May. Available at: www.thetimes.co.za/PrintEdition/Article.aspx?id=1005591 [Accessed 22 Oct 2009].

60   UN. (1992) *The Convention on Biological Diversity, Article 2 – Use of Terms*. United Nations – Treaty Series.

61   Conway, G., (2003) Biotechnology and the War on Poverty. In: Serageldin, I. & Persley, G J., *Biotechnology and Sustainable Development: Voices of the South and North*, Proceedings of a Conference at the Bibliotheca Alexandrina, Alexandria, Egypt, March 16-20, 2002, CABI Publishing, Wallingford, Oxford.

62   UN Millennium Project. (2005) *Innovation: Applying Knowledge for Development*. Task Force on Science, Technology and Innovation. p. 60.

63   Bjarnason, M. & Vasal, S., (1992) Breeding of quality protein maize (QPM). *Plant Breeding Reviews*, **9**. 181-216.

64   Bhandari N., (2008) *Going bananas: fighting hunger with Africa Harvest*. 20 Nov. Available at: www.peopleandplanet.net/doc.php?id=3434 [Accessed 22 Oct 2009].

65   Taylor D., (2009) *Disease Threatens African Banana Industry – Part 2 of 5*. VOA News. Washington. 19 January 2009. Available at: www.voanews.com/english/Africa/Disease-Threatens-African-Banana-Industry-PART-2-of-5.cfm [Accessed 22 Oct 2009].

66   Mbogo, S., (2008) Farmers turn to new banana variety. *Business Daily*. Nairobi.12 May.

67   Riungu, C., (2008) Banana research earns Dr. Wambugu world fame. *The EastAfrican*. Nairobi. 29 September – 5 October 2008.

68   Africa Harvest website. Available at: africaharvest.org [Accessed 22 Oct 2009].

69   Jeffers, D., (2001) *Maize Pathology Research: Increasing Maize Productivity and Sustainability in Biologically Stressed Environments*, International Maize and Wheat Improvement Centre, Mexico.

70   Peel, M., (2001) *A Basic Primer on Biotechnology*. NDSU Extension Service. Available at: www.ag.ndsu.edu/pubs/plantsci/crops/a1219w.htm [Accessed 22 Oct 2009].

71   James, C., (2008) Global Status of Commercialized Biotech/GM Crops 2008. *ISAAA Brief*, No. 39. ISAAA, Ithaca, NY.

72   Bryant, R., (2009) [Email] (Pers. Comm. 5 June 2009).

73   Lackman, M. & Lackman, S., (2008) *The New Cotton Debate: What is sustainable cotton?* 21 April. Available at: organicclothing.blogs.com/my_weblog/2008/04/the-new-cotton.html [Accessed 22 Oct 2009].

74   Gruere, G. Bhatt-Mehta, P. & Sengupta, D., (2008) *Bt Cotton and Farmer Suicides in India – Reviewing the Evidence*. IFPRI Discussion Paper 00808.

75   FAO. (2004) *The State of Food and Agriculture 2003-2004: Agricultural Biotechnology – Meeting the Needs of the Poor?* Food and Agricultural Organisation, Rome.

76   Smale, M. et al., (2006) *Parables: Applied Economics Literature about the Impact of Genetically Engineered Crop Varieties in Developing Economies.* Environment and Production Technology Division Discussion Paper 159. International Food Policy Research Institute, Washington, DC.

77   Agranova. (2009) *Agrochemicals – Executive Review (20th edition).* Agranova, Kent.

78   World Bank. (2007) *Agriculture for Development,* World Bank, Washington DC.

79   Singer, P. & Daar, A., (2001) Harnessing Genomics and Biotechnology to Improve Global Health Equity. *Science,* **294**. 87-89.

80   Biotechnology Industry Organisation. (2007) *Guide to Biotechnology.* Available at: bio.org/speeches/pubs/er/statistics.asp. [Accessed 22 Oct 2009].

81   NIGMS. (2006) *The New Genetics.* National Institute of General Medical Sciences, Bethesda, MD. Available at: publications.nigms.nih.gov/thenewgenetics/thenewgenetics.pdf [Accessed 22 Oct 2009].

82   Cherry, A. & Gwynn, R., (2007) Perspectives on the development of biological control agents in Africa. *Biocontrol Science and Technology,* **17**. 665-676.

83   Moran, M. et al., (2005) *The New Landscape of Neglected Disease Drug Development.* Wellcome Trust, London.

84   Andy Minor, National Centre for Electron Microscopy, Lawrence Berkeley National Laboratory.

85   Defra. (2007) *Characterising the Potential Risks Posed by Engineered Nanoparticles. A Second UK Government Research Report.* Defra, London.

86   RCEP. (2008) *Novel Materials in the Environment: The case of nanotechnology.* Royal Commission on Environmental Pollution, London.

87   UK Government. (2009) *UK Government Response to the RCEP Report.* TSO, London.

88   The Project on Emerging Nanotechnologies. Available at: www.nanotechproject.org [Accessed 22 Oct 2009].

89   Meridian Institute. (2005) *Nanotechnology and the Poor – Opportunities and Risks.* Meridian Institute.

90   Salamanca-Buentello F. et al., (2005) Nanotechnology and the Developing World. *PLoS Med,* **2(5)**, e97.

91   Foladori, G. & Invernizzi, N., (2005) Nanotechnology for the Poor? *PLoS Med,* **2(8)**, e280.

Building Partnerships
for Innovation

Villagers discussing a watershed plan with a state official in Haryana, India. © Gordon Conway

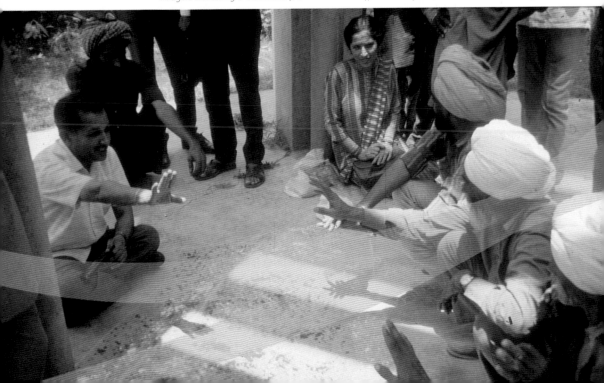

Producing successful science and technology for development involves creating science innovation systems in developing countries and building partnerships between developing and developed country scientists. In this way appropriate technologies can be generated that will address local challenges and opportunities while drawing on global sources of innovation.

The process requires that scientists interact with a wide range of partners. These range from local communities in developing countries with their traditional knowledge and understanding of the local context, to multinational corporations that have substantial investment in relevant R&D.

This chapter begins with a discussion on building national innovation systems and of the partnerships that are created between scientists in both national and international public research institutions. It then describes efforts to utilise indigenous knowledge and skills in the research and development process. Finally attention is drawn to the need to engage industry, especially in respect of innovative new platform technologies. In all these instances we illustrate the way in which national innovation processes are becoming more closely linked, in productive ways, with global systems.

1. Building national innovation systems

In Chapter 1 the benefits of building national science and technology capacity for developing countries were discussed. Now we describe the ways in which this can be achieved.

Innovation networks and clusters

National innovation systems are defined in many ways.[1] In the simplest terms they are *'networks of institutions in the public and private sectors whose activities and interactions initiate, import, modify and diffuse new technologies.'*[2] The networks involve: universities and research institutes; small and large companies; financial and legal institutions; industrial associations; government ministries; NGOs of various kinds and individuals as both stakeholders and innovators in their own right.

It is generally agreed that such networks generate seven key functions:[3]

- Knowledge generation including R&D;
- Competence building;
- Financial support;
- Provision of regulatory frameworks and measures;
- Facilitation of information exchange;
- Stimulation of demand and creation of markets;
- Reduction of uncertainties and resolution of conflicts.

Experience suggests that successful innovation networks also depend on the creation of clusters of competing and complementary companies and research institutions. A key component is the existence of a vibrant small and medium-sized enterprise (SME) community with access to venture capital, either indigenous or foreign. Banks and other financial institutions are critical as are supportive economic incentives. Governments are also important, providing funding for technology incubators, export processing zones and production networks, as well as helping with skills training.[4]

Allied to SMEs is the need for a group of entrepreneurs. These may be scientists or engineers with strong experience of the practicalities of applying inventions to real life problems. But frequently, they are individuals with a business background, an appreciation of the market opportunities and a capacity to understand the essentials of the technologies on offer. In other words, they have a certain flair for spotting winners and seeing the process through from the embryonic stage to production and sale. These entrepreneurs can range from small farmers to senior scientists or engineers in companies or universities.

Often some of the most energetic national entrepreneurs are working abroad in industrialised countries. For example, India has made significant efforts to lure entrepreneurs back, at least on a part-time basis. The Rwandan diaspora have also developed contacts and skills, making them well placed to access global innovation systems and business networks. This has helped to generate income and bring capital funds into the country. Projects there have included the production and export of high-value coffee exports based on coffee-washing machines and the export of hand-woven baskets and bowls, which command high prices in up-market western retail outlets (Figure 3.1).[5,6]

Generally, the technologies are imported but there are significant local variations, which add greatly to the value of the processes. Two aspects are key to success. One is quality control, itself a technology, and the other is access to international markets.

(Left and centre) © Gordon Conway
(Right) © Joy Ndungutse / Gahaya Links

Figure 3.1 – A Rwandan basket making enterprise, Gahaya Links, started by sisters Janet Nkubana and Joy Ndungutse. Joy used the connections, market knowledge and capital she acquired while living in the US after moving there at the time of the 1994 genocide.

The national context

The goal of innovation policy is to embed education, training and R&D initiatives in a broader policy of competitiveness, linkages, cluster formation and entrepreneurship.[7,8] Innovation also depends on a wider supportive environment including customers who know what they want or can seize on the potential of new products and apply them to good purpose. In developing countries such customers are often government agencies. This requires a level of relatively sophisticated understanding, not only of the problems a country and its inhabitants are facing, but also of the potentials and pitfalls of new technologies and how they can be best adapted to local circumstances.

Innovation, in the developing country context, implies a strategic vision for national economic development and an integration of innovation networks within such a strategy. It is seen as a way to increase domestic productivity and international competitiveness. Also implied is the necessity to 'catch-up' with more technologically advanced countries. To begin with, innovation processes usually involve the acquisition and adaptation of existing technologies which have been successful elsewhere or, in the case of the new platform technologies, undergoing R&D elsewhere. In more sophisticated settings, particularly in the emerging economies, it may involve the development of quite new and 'surprising' technologies.

Experience suggests this is an evolutionary process that takes time and involves cumulative learning in which earlier, simpler capabilities and activities become more advanced. An important lesson to be learned is that development policies should adopt a calculated approach to technological catch-up. They need to choose key areas in which to build a critical mass of knowledge and skills, work along with the growth of business capabilities and domestic knowledge systems and keep in line with changes in the structure of the national economy.[9]

Capacity strengthening and education

Strengthening scientific capacity building is crucial and, among other tasks, this means investing in education at all levels. Recently emphasis has been placed on MDG targets of increasing enrolment in primary education. Many countries will achieve the 2015 target of MDG 2 to provide 100% primary enrolment.[10] But this focus on primary education has created expectation and demand for secondary and tertiary education. Although less than 55% of eligible children in developing countries currently enrol in secondary school, demand for higher education is growing rapidly. In Sub-Saharan Africa, for instance, enrolment in higher education has increased from 660,000 in 1985 to over 3.4 million in 2005.[11] Demand for places greatly exceeds supply, despite a rapid growth in provision, particularly by private universities. Many successful students are therefore entering universities that are under-staffed, under-resourced and poorly regulated.

© Sara Delaney

Figure 3.2 – Students at a village primary school in Mali

One recently launched African-led initiative has set out to address the problem. Organised by the African Development Bank the initiative aims to improve the training of highly skilled scientists and engineers in West Africa (Box 3.1).

The curriculum at universities in developing countries is often based on outdated models adopted from former colonial systems. There is a need to focus the curricula more on subjects which have local relevance and fit in with national capacity-building plans. Also programmes need to be revamped and be more creative in order to give talented students the tools they need to become entrepreneurs in their communities.[12]

Box 3.1   African Development Bank supports science and technology institutions[13,14]

The African Development Bank recently approved a US $17.6 million-equivalent grant beginning in 2010, to fund the 'Network of African Institutions of Science and Technology Project' in West Africa. The bank, recognising that *'higher education and skills development are central to economic growth and sustainable development,'* will be providing funds to improve education, training and networking opportunities for science and engineering students and professionals in the region.

The grant will start by targeting two key institutions, the African University of Science and Technology (AUST) based in Abuja, Nigeria, and the International Institute for Water and Environmental Engineering (2iE) in Ouagadougou in Burkina Faso. Through these two schools the project will host faculty exchanges and conferences as well as facilitate collaboration between the universities and local industry.

Concentrating efforts in this area should give a much-needed boost to the recruitment and training of skilled professionals in science and technology who can use their skills and knowledge to solve challenges specific to the West Africa region. To promote links with regional innovation, the bank will also train over 600 students from local petroleum companies who can bring their skills back into the private sector.

Under-resourced and poorly targeted higher education systems bring dissatisfaction amongst both students and trained scientists. For this reason, bright students and researchers leave to study and pursue careers in developed countries. This "brain drain" denies national science innovation systems some of their most skilled and motivated individuals. One way of addressing the "brain drain" is through new programmes, such as those coordinated by the Science Innovation Group, which supports MSc and PhD training for scientists and engineers in Africa. The group, through the Regional Initiative in Science and Education (RISE) programme, has set-up networks across a number of African universities, so that resources can be pooled in key subject areas, such as biochemistry and marine science. This support, along with links to experts abroad, helps encourage students to stay, and to prepare new, highly qualified teachers for the region.[15]

There is also enormous potential to make better use of the academic diaspora and their valuable education, experience and social networking resources in order to link developing countries into global research networks.[11,12,16]

2. Partnerships between scientists in public institutions

As described above, modern national innovation systems are highly developed partnerships involving scientists in a wide range of institutions. But to function effectively in today's world, developing country systems need to encourage their scientists to interact with scientists in other institutions and, in particular, with institutions in the advanced industrialised countries. Today such partnerships are most often formed between public sector institutions, such as universities and government research institutes.

These public sector partnerships will become increasingly important, as national innovation systems in developing countries build scientific capacity and become linked to global innovation systems. They should also become more equitable. Historically, where research has been funded by development donors, experts have commonly been drawn from developed country institutions and given management responsibility for the project funds. As a result, northern partners have usually dominated the research agenda. This means that, in the worst cases, they have approached science and technology challenges in developing countries with little appreciation of local context or existing knowledge or research, and left developing country partners with only token roles. Without their own resources or comparable specialised expertise, developing country partners have been compelled to let northern partners lead.

Developing equitable partnerships

The path to building national scientific capacity will often involve a shift from a dependence on short-term externally funded projects, to a position where core funding supports a scientific programme which can engage partners in a more equitable way. Figure 3.3 illustrates a concept developed by the Wellcome Trust for how this might happen for health research in Africa, where an initial research collaboration, wholly dependent on northern partners/funders can evolve into a local research centre.

Figure 3.3 – The development of locally-led health research centres[17]

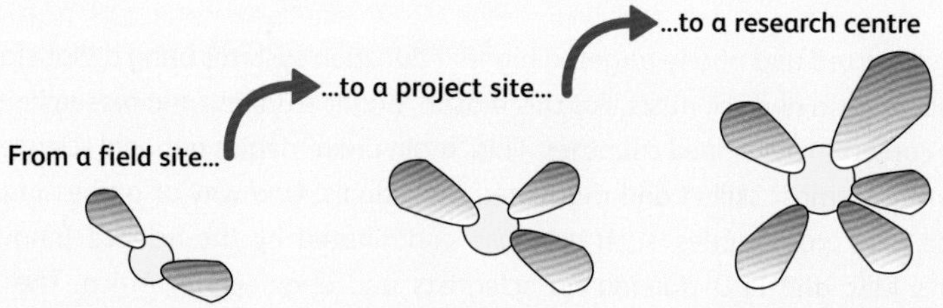

	From a field site...	...to a project site...	...to a research centre
What is the core?	Informal alliance of projects and trials at a site	Established infrastructure to projects and trials	Fully established entity that provides all science infrastructure
Core funding	Resources from projects fund the core	Small amount of core-funding and resources	Funding for core established and projects contribute to core
Portfolio	Small number of projects that drive the core	Small number of projects, but able to add different diseases or interventions	Different interventions or different diseases
Time focus	Short term	Mid term 3–5 years	Long term > 10 years
Infrastructure	Very basic and dependent on project funding	Established basics that survive individual trial and project	Full infrastructure maintained over time with projects paying share

The yellow circle indicates the core and the purple petals indicate the projects

Governments play a key role in this process by investing in infrastructure and core funding of scientific facilities. Recently, donors have supported the transition from project-dependent to institutional research in a number of ways. They have provided core research funding directly to national and regional scientific organisations in developing countries, the intention being that these institutions will set their own research priorities and provide funding competitively to local or international scientists in order to address these priorities. In African agricultural research, for instance, DFID, the EU and other donors provide funding to institutions such as the Forum for Agricultural Research for Africa (FARA) and regional research bodies like the Association for Strengthening Agricultural Research in Eastern and Central Africa (ASARECA) and West and Central African Council for Agricultural Research and Development (CORAF) which then develop and fund regional research initiatives.

Early career schemes can provide individual scientists with resources and opportunities to work internationally, while support to senior research leaders and their groups can help to develop career structures for young scientists. National recognition of the value of supporting and retaining scientists is critical. The establishment of scientific academies and national competitive grant schemes can also play a role in encouraging this political commitment. The Wellcome Trust has recently launched an African Institutions Initiative which gives five to ten years support to networked African universities and institutes, including funding for postdoctoral researchers to develop their careers, and for developing local postgraduate degree programmes.[17]

The Consultative Group on International Agricultural Research (CGIAR)

Over the years, a number of international research institutions have been set up to deal specifically with development research problems, and to bring together scientists and expertise from both the North and South for this purpose. The most unique and longstanding of these is the CGIAR.

The CGIAR was created in 1971 as an informal association of donors to provide financial support to four international agricultural research centres that the Ford and Rockefeller Foundations had established over the previous decade. They focused on rice, wheat and maize crops and had already produced dramatic results. Cereal yields, total cereal production and total food production in the developing countries more than doubled between 1960 and 1985. Over the same period their population grew by about 75%. As a result, the average daily calorie supply in the developing countries increased by a quarter, from under 2,000 calories per person in the early 1960s to about 2,500 in the mid-80s, of which 1,500 was provided by cereals.[18]

The so-called "Green Revolution" has proved most effective where there are well-resourced, national research and extension systems to distribute and support the new varieties, as well as good access to inputs, such as fertilisers and pesticides. This has been achieved in Asia, but only to a limited degree in Africa. Nonetheless, on a global scale, the uptake of crop varieties developed at the CGIAR Centres has been impressive: 65% of the global area under improved varieties of the ten most important food crops is planted with varieties derived from the CGIAR-funded research. Without the CGIAR contribution, it is estimated that world food production today would be 4-5% lower and in developing countries 7-8%.[19]

Figure 3.4 – IRRI researchers examine a wild rice variety in the Philippines

In the 1980s and 1990s, new Centres joined the CGIAR, enjoying the benefits of core research funding provided by the donor group (Figure 3.5). These extended the research activity of the CGIAR beyond food crops to include: livestock; living aquatic resources; forestry and agroforestry; water resources; agriculture capacity building and policy. The focus of the CGIAR on crop genetic improvement has also been expanded to include natural resource management and policy research, which has emerged as important to realizing the benefits of crop improvement and sustainable agricultural growth.

Figure 3.5 – The world-wide spread of the CGIAR centres[†]

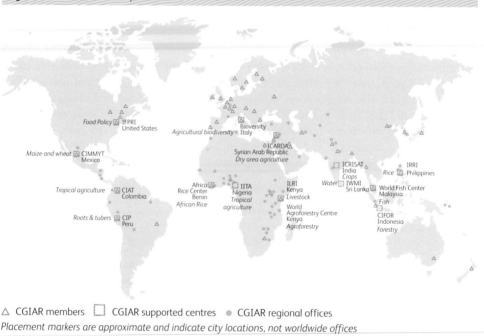

△ CGIAR members   ☐ CGIAR supported centres   ● CGIAR regional offices

Placement markers are approximate and indicate city locations, not worldwide offices

Since their establishment in the 1960s up until 2001, the Centres, supported by the CGIAR, have spent about US$7 billion (in 1990 US$). Cost benefit studies indicate that, by conservative criterian, overall economic benefits attributable to CGIAR research have been at least double the cost of research costs. This only includes a very limited set of directly attributable impacts. If expanded to include all of the known 'significantly demonstrated' and 'plausible' impacts, the benefits through to 2001 are estimated to be about nine times greater than research costs. If this is then extrapolated through to 2011, it is as much as 17 times greater.[20,21]

Fundamental to the success of the CGIAR centres has been the development of partnerships with national scientific centres. Box 3.2 describes the way in which the International Maize and Wheat Improvement Center (CIMMYT) has partnered with the Kenya Agricultural Research Institute (KARI).

The CGIAR has not been without its challenges. The critical core funding from donors has declined over time and Centres have operated independently, missing opportunities for synergy.

---

† The CGIAR centres include: Africa Rice Center (WARDA); Bioversity International, CIAT – Centro Internacional de Agricultura Tropical; CIFOR – Center for International Forestry Research; CIMMYT – Centro Internacional de Mejoramiento de Maíz y Trigo; CIP – Centro Internacional de la Papa; ICARDA – International Center for Agricultural Research in the Dry Areas; ICRISAT – International Crops Research Institute for the Semi-Arid Tropics; IFPRI – International Food Policy Research Institute; IITA – International Institute of Tropical Agriculture; ILRI – International Livestock Research Institute; IRRI – International Rice Research Institute; IWMI – International Water Management Institute; World Agroforestry Centre (ICRAF); WorldFish Center.

Box 3.2   A complementary partnership between CIMMYT and KARI[22-24]

CIMMYT was one of the first CGIAR centres. Founded in 1966 in Mexico, it is a large-scale international research and training consortium with offices in Asia, Africa and Latin America and over 600 staff. CIMMYT has built-up considerable expertise on maize crops. Maize varieties, developed by CIMMYT and its partners, are now planted on nearly half of the area sown to improved varieties in non-temperate areas of the developing world. CIMMYT's gene bank holds 25,000 unique collections of native maize races.

To effectively bring this high-level knowledge to the national and local levels in Kenya, CIMMYT has been working with KARI. Established in 1979 by the Kenyan government, KARI brings together national research and dissemination efforts in food crops, livestock management, land and water use.

Since the early 1990s, CIMMYT has worked with KARI on various projects, including developing maize varieties that are resistant to streak virus, stem borers, the weed Striga and drought. For example, to help tackle the destruction caused by stem borers, CIMMYT researchers found strains resistant to the borer in the centre's gene bank, in maize seed originally from the Caribbean.

KARI provides the crucial next steps in the innovation chain. Working with Kenyan farmers, the scientists used conventional plant breeding techniques to cross the introduced varieties with maize varieties already adapted to the conditions found in eastern Africa, selecting for traits which the farmers valued. KARI then facilitated the testing of the new strains through the Kenya Plant Health Inspectorate Services and helped to create a dissemination process involving local seed distributors and extension agents. When this is fully complete the new varieties will be available not only to farmers in Kenya, but will be given back to CIMMYT to be used in future research.

More importantly, investment in the CGIAR Centres has not been matched by investment in national research capacity in many regions, particularly Africa. This has led in some cases to research resources flowing disproportionately to CGIAR Centres, as well as a brain drain from national programmes into better supported Centre jobs, undermining the partnerships between Centres and national scientific research systems.

All of these problems are the target of an ambitious plan, launched in 2008, to reform the CGIAR system, bringing Centres and partner institutions together around a single strategic results framework with more sustainable funding.[25]

3. Participatory research and innovation

In addition to the conventional partnerships between scientists in Northern and Southern public sector institutions, science innovation systems for development are now building quite different kinds of research partnerships. Here we explore one – participatory research which involves local communities as research partners.

It is hard today to conceive that one might develop appropriate technologies in developing countries without the participation of the people they are meant to benefit. And yet the concept of the participation of users and beneficiaries in the development of new technologies is relatively young. This is sometimes true even in developed countries. However, developed countries have strong, well resourced innovation systems in which potential users participate and articulate demand which guides basic and translational research. In developing countries technology users, and in particular the poor, are rarely included in innovation systems.

The scientific community in both the developed and developing world is now recognizing the value of extending partnerships in research beyond scientists to user communities, so ensuring technologies are appropriate and, therefore, adopted. This has often meant that user communities, which were originally engaged only at the point of testing new technologies and their local adaptation, are now becoming engaged much earlier in the process. They help to identify objectives for research and development and participate pro-actively in the research.

The techniques of participation

As a result of a long-term accumulation of work undertaken in the 1970s and 80s, we now have effective techniques to make local participation in research and project design a reality. Under the headings of Participatory Rural Appraisal (PRA) and Participatory Learning and Action (PLA) there is a formidable array of methods which allow communities to analyse their own situations and, importantly, to engage in productive dialogue with research scientists and extension workers (Box 3.3).[26-29]

Box 3.3   Participatory learning, analysis and action

Participatory Rural Appraisal (PRA) methods, which help farmers to collect, analyse and present their own information, began in the late 1980s. They developed out of earlier participatory approaches of combining semi-structured interviewing with diagram making, drawn from the classical tools of ecology. The term Participatory Learning and Action (PLA) followed on from the success of PRA, as practitioners realised that the tools could be applied to many challenges beyond the rural and agricultural.

These approaches have enabled local people to take the lead, producing their own diagrams, undertaking their own analyses, developing solutions to problems and providing recommendations for change and innovation. For example, maps are readily created by providing villagers with chalk and coloured powder and giving them no further

© Robert Chambers – IIED

Figure 3.6 – Farmer constructing a calendar to describe the seasonal sequences in the farming year. The stones mark the months of the year and the seeds indicate the amount of activity, such as days of weeding

instruction other than the request to produce a map of the village, a watershed or a farm. People who are illiterate and barely numerate can construct seasonal calendars using pebbles or seeds.

Such diagrams not only reveal existing patterns but highlight problems and opportunities and are seized on by people to make their needs felt.

Participatory methods have now spread to most countries of the developing world, and have been adopted by government agencies, research centres and university workers as well as by NGOs. In many ways it has been a revolution, a set of methodologies, an attitude and a way of working, which has finally challenged the traditional top-down process that has characterised so much development work. In every exercise the traditional position of rural people being passive recipients of knowledge and instruction has been replaced by the creation of productive dialogues.

In one of the villages participating in the DFID funded Western Orissa Rural Livelihoods Programme in India, for example, the villagers produced a portfolio of maps and analyses of their local area. This included maps of landforms, bodies of water, holdings and crops, an analysis of households, including their income status, and a list of project priorities that they formulated and requested funding for.[30,31] In some ways this is the ultimate example of demand-led development.

Institutionalized participatory research

While the benefits of using participatory methods for village or regional-level data gathering, discovery or analysis have become increasingly clear, involving local communities in scientific research on a wider scale is more challenging. Research scientists, policy makers and product developers are frequently far removed in location, language, priorities and methods, from the community members who are meant to benefit from the process. However, a number of groups have indeed had success, with positive results.

Developing new crop varieties and production methods

One area where a participatory approach has been widely adopted is in development of new crop varieties, for very specific reasons. The first Green Revolution targeted some of the best favoured lands in the developing countries. The land holdings were reasonably large, flat and well watered. In these situations it was relatively easy for agricultural extension workers to promote a simple, uniform package of seeds, fertilisers and pesticides, a model for crop production typical of that in industrialised countries.

The targets now are very different – millions of small farmers inhabiting an extraordinary diversity of land, soil and climatic types – and thus a new 'Doubly Green Revolution'[†] is required which is both productive and environmentally sensitive. There are no simple technology packages or messages. Indeed every farm requires its own special set of recommendations. In this context, the traditional top-down approach will not work and the only way forward is to involve farmers in the analysis, design and experimentation processes.

Figure 3.7 – Small farmers face a wide range of different situations

† A Doubly Green Revolution is one which *'repeats the success of the Green Revolution on a global scale in many diverse localities and is equitable, sustainable and environmentally friendly.'*

It is common now for breeders to involve farmers in the selection of new varieties, Participatory Varietal Selection (PVS), and in the breeding process itself, Participatory Plant Breeding (PPB) (Box 3.4). In PVS researchers choose a set of varieties which they think farmers may prefer to the one currently being grown. Farmers then test these side-by-side in community fields and individually in their own fields (see also Box 9.14). They can then select varieties which meet their priorities – often bringing up valued traits which the researchers had not thought of, such as ease of threshing or aroma.[32]

Box 3.4 Farmers call the crosses[32]

In PPB scientists start with a set of varieties which are not completely desirable in themselves, but which contain traits selected for by farmers. They then cross these varieties to produce a diverse segregating population. Selections are then made from this population grown under farm management by researchers and farmers. Subsequent generations are grown by farmers, with the most desirable varieties being selected from each cycle.[33]

© Katherine Steele, University of Wales: Bangor

Figure 3.8 – Farmers selecting among the crosses

This process has been improved with the aid of molecular biology and marker-aided selection (MAS). The characteristics being sought by farmers are often difficult for them to detect or select for when testing, such as a good rooting system. Researchers can also use genetic markers to help prioritise farmers' choices in the breeding programme.

For example, rice breeders from the DFID Plant Sciences Research Programme in eastern India started with a very broad cross between Kalinga III – a popular variety but prone to breakage of stems (causing "lodging" and loss of yield) and to early season drought – and IR64, a high-yielding variety bred by IRRI with good disease, pest and lodging resistance. The farmers selected 20 varieties from this cross and grew them in diverse ecological settings in India and Nepal.

The breeders then tested 28 markers on the genome and found that the farmers were selecting for specific genomic regions from Kalinga III for the uplands, and from IR64 for the lowlands. With this information, new varieties can be designed which contain the desired 'bits' of the genome for each different growing condition.

The process has continued and just recently an upland rice variety 'Birsa Vikas Dhan III' (Pyramid 84) was released in Jharkhand state, India, that was developed through the combined use of PPB as well as MAS.[34,35]

Participatory research may extend beyond the breeding of varieties, to the development of new production methods. An example of this is work done in Syria to improve olive tree cultivation methods, described in Box 3.5.

Box 3.5 Participatory olive tree cultivation research in Syria[36-38]

Beginning in the 1990s, farmers in the arid Khanasser Valley in northern Syria started planting olive trees to supplement their incomes – hoping to turn marginal lands into profitable resources. The number of olive trees grew by 50 % in a decade, up to around 11,000 by 2003, with an average household cultivating around 100-150 trees. The farmers, however, did not have a long history of olive cultivation to draw knowledge from, and with little water available for irrigation and poor soil quality, yields were far from ideal.

The International Center for Agricultural Research in the Dry Areas (ICARDA) came to the area in 2003 to work with the farmers. Rather than attempt to find solutions on their own, researchers formed a committee of farmers and local extension workers to begin a process of participatory research, evaluation and innovation. Meetings were held to identify the most pressing problems the farmers were facing, which included limited water supply and how to cope with droughts.

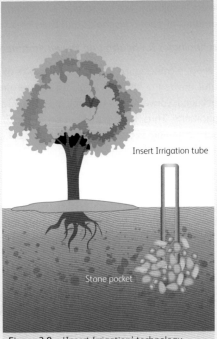

Insert Irrigation tube

Stone pocket

Figure 3.9 – 'Insert Irrigation' technology brought from Tunisia to Syria[36]

Experiments were designed and implemented by the farmers and scientists together, with regular meetings held to evaluate progress. At the end of the trial period a number of new technologies were identified, and are now being adopted by some of the farmers in the area. These include:

- *Water Harvesting* – the construction of V or fishbone-shaped, stony-earth bunds around each of the trees to create micro-catchments which can contain water around the tree and control soil erosion.

- *Stone Mulching* – covering the soil around the tree trunk with stones to reduce evaporation losses from the soil surface. Project experiments showed that basalt stone worked better than the chalky limestone the farmers had previously been using.

- *Sub-surface Insert Irrigation* – One of the farmers in the valley suggested an irrigation method he had seen being used in Tunisia. A stone pocket or gravel layer is constructed underground around the root zone of each tree. A PVC tube is then inserted vertically into the pocket and water is applied through the tube, so that it goes directly to the deeper roots.

So far these innovations are working reasonably well. But they do have problems, for example increased weed growth in the water harvesting basins. However, such issues can now be addressed by the group, leading to further research and collaboration, rather than ending in a failed research and extension project.

These examples illustrate the challenges of the new Doubly Green Revolution. Instead of starting with the biological problems inherent in producing new high yielding food crops or improved farming practices and then determining how the benefits can reach the poor, this new Doubly Green Revolution has to reverse the chain of logic.[18] It has to start with the socio-economic demands of poor households and then seek to identify the appropriate research priorities.

Technologies for health and the environment

It is not a coincidence that these examples of participation relate to rural land use and agriculture. Rural environments and local, traditional practices are highly variable, and the application of packaged, conventional technologies often fail to be universally appropriate over such a range of conditions. Thus, local participation and experimentation are particularly important in ensuring that technologies are well adapted to local environments and land management practices, and therefore of value to the poor.

However, local participation can also be important in the uptake of other, less location-sensitive technologies, such as those associated with engineering or healthcare, particularly where human behaviour is involved, as will be discussed in Chapter 6. Technologies for sanitation are one example where the input of local people is highly important in determining acceptance and use. Box 3.6 below considers one initiative that aims to involve communities in the design, construction and continued improvement of household latrines.

Box 3.6 Community-Led Total Sanitation[39-41]

Community-Led Total Sanitation (CLTS) is an approach that was pioneered in Bangladesh in 2000 by an independent consultant from India, Kamal Kar, who was working with WaterAid, Bangladesh and its local partner Village Education Resource Center (VERC). He realised that the programme being used at the time, which concentrated on the construction of highly subsidised household toilets, was not working. While the number of toilets was increasing, people continued to defecate in the open, and so the desired health benefits were not being realised.

© Petra Bongartz

The basic principle of CLTS is "the empowerment of local communities to do their own analysis and take their own action to become open defecation free."[39] A facilitator, who can be either a trained local person or an NGO or local government worker, helps the community to analyse their sanitation practices, through a variety of activities, many based on PRA techniques. They

Figure 3.10 – A proposed latrine design drawn by a group during CLTS activities in Zambia

include mapping the community and its defecation areas, 'transect walks' to see where people defecate, calculating the amount of faeces produced each year, as well as the medical expenses for treatment of diarrhoeal diseases. Other exercises illustrate the faecal-oral contamination route. Feelings of shame and disgust often arise and the realisation that

© Kamal Kar

Figure 3.11 – A man in West Bengal showing the latrine he built after CLTS activities

everyone is literally 'eating each others' shit (the crude word is always used), usually triggers the desire for change. This is called the ignition moment and spurs discussion as to what can be done.

The facilitator is not there to teach or tell the community what to do. Instead he or she allows the community to discuss its options and often natural leaders emerge and take charge of the process. If the community insists that building latrines is too expensive, the facilitator, upon request, may share low cost latrine designs that other poor communities have developed. The community often decides to take immediate collective action to end open defecation and become Open Defecation Free (ODF). Communities across Bangladesh, and in more than 20 countries in Asia, Africa, Latin America and elsewhere, have designed and constructed thousands of pit latrines as a result of this initiative.

Designs range from close replications of others that have been seen nearby, to creative and original ideas based on available materials and space – and the desires of the household. The big change here from other sanitation programmes is that the construction is motivated by real demand from community members and is therefore more sustainable. As households discover the benefits of sanitation, they may decide to move up the sanitation 'ladder', improving on the initial simple pit latrines over time. Plan International, UNICEF, WaterAid and the Water and Sanitation Programme (WSP) of the World Bank have been leaders in spreading CLTS and many NGOs and governments are now using this approach.

4. Engaging with industry in research for development

In the past, the development of most new technology for the poor in developing countries was supported from public funds. For example, the semi-dwarf wheat and rice varieties that were at the core of the Green Revolution's success were produced by the publicly funded CGIAR centres such as the International Rice Research Institute (IRRI) and CIMMYT.

International spending on research as a whole however, has come predominately from the private sector and has been directed at profitable markets in developed countries. Consequently, the range of products for use in developing countries remains small with major constraints on their access by poor people.

The cause of the failure of the market in developing countries is the actual or perceived lack of profitability of producing goods for poor people. Although the size of the market, in terms of need, is enormous, it is small in terms of market demand. For example, the average national expenditure on health care in most of the countries of Sub-Saharan Africa is less than US$10 per person per year. By contrast, per capita expenditure in developed countries is in the thousands of US dollars.[42]

Box 3.7 Quotation from Jean-Pierre Garnier, former CEO of GlaxoSmithKline

"The pharmaceutical industry must continue to invest in innovation to seek better solutions for tackling these killers. However, there is a dilemma. While we feel a moral duty and a fundamental desire to conduct research and development into vaccines and medicines for the diseases that blight the developing world, the harsh truth is that there is limited profit to be made from them. Yet to survive pharmaceutical companies must be profitable to deliver shareholder value."[43]

The market in the developed countries, targeted on the diseases of the rich – cancers, heart and circulatory failure and the diseases of ageing – is very profitable, giving a high return on the research and development investment. Development costs for vaccines, however, range from US$250 million up to US$1 billion[44], largely due to the costs involved in undertaking clinical trials. The pay-off is relatively low compared to more profitable pharmaceuticals. The annual global market for vaccines was US$20 billion in 2008, compared to US$770 billion for pharmaceuticals.[45,46]

The economics of commercial drug development do not favour products for the poor, where inexpensive vaccines and medicines are needed for diseases such as HIV/AIDS, TB and malaria. Until recently, these three diseases alone were estimated to account for 90 % of the global disease burden but only attract 10 % of international research – the so-called 90:10 gap. They carry – with a wide range of other largely tropical diseases – the title of "neglected diseases" which have a disproportionate impact in developing countries. Not surprisingly there is a lack of effective products and no commercial market to attract R&D from the private sector. However, with growing attention being paid to these diseases, largely through the public-private partnerships discussed below, this ratio is gradually changing.[47]

In 2007, about US$2.5 billion was spent on R&D in the area of neglected diseases, almost 80 % of it directed to the three diseases just mentioned. Other groups of important neglected diseases, like diarrhoeal diseases, received less than 5 % of the total funding. Most of the funding for this research – about 70 % – comes from public sector institutions, with philanthropic organisations contributing about 21 % and the private sector only about 9 %.[48]

In agriculture, the situation is similar. There is considerable demand in the developed countries for improved seed for highly subsidised farms. While there are important public sector crop improvement programmes, much of the research funding for this is provided by the private sector and goes towards key food crops like maize and wheat. But in developing countries the private sector is largely concentrating on cash crops such as cotton, where farmers can afford to buy seed, rather than staple crops. Developing countries share a number of staple crops with developed countries, but the varieties grown are different. Many staple crops for the poor are largely tropical, including rice, sorghum, millet and a range of root crops and pulses. These crops of the developing world have been relatively neglected with respect to modern plant breeding. Public sector funding for crop breeding in the developing world has been limited and the private sector even more so. These crops do not offer markets which are attractive to the kind of private sector agricultural R&D investment enjoyed in developed countries.

For example, the combined annual funding of the CGIAR consortium, which comes from governments and philanthropical organisations, is about US$500 million.[49] By contrast, the fifteen leading agricultural research multinationals – which include Bayer, Dow Agro, DuPont, Monsanto and Syngenta – spent about US$5 billion on agricultural research in 2008, but this is largely to produce technologies for subsidised, commercial agricultural producers in developed countries.[50]

Public Private Partnerships (PPPs)

In some situations, public sector research generates important technologies for the poor which would not otherwise exist. But, it is also critical to attracting private sector investment in the development and marketing of new technologies of all kinds. Such investment may come from local small and medium-sized enterprises or from multinational corporations. Both can benefit from the capacity of public sector research to:

* Provide access to up-to-date information on new technologies;

* Leverage private sector investment by taking technologies "near market";

* "Backstop" and "trouble-shoot" the commercial launch of new technologies and their uptake;

* Create an appropriate enabling and regulatory environment.

One particularly effective approach to accessing private sector research in support of development goals is through the creation of PPPs. These may invovle a wide range of participants: public sector; government or university research institutions; private industry; NGOs and Foundations. But the principle underlying PPPs is that they bring together quite different players to share resources and complementary skills. The key benefits of PPPs include:

* Combining private sector skills in specification, innovation and product development with public sector knowledge of the social, political and economic dimensions of the problem at hand;

* Bringing private sector infrastructure and manpower into partnership with public sector institutions that have insufficient capacity to develop products efficiently;

* Permitting access to proprietary know-how and technology to address problems of the poor.

Health PPPs

Significant progress has been made by PPPs that address neglected diseases of humans and animals. Box 3.8 illustrates a number of these. Some disease-related PPPs are aimed at the development of a single drug or vaccine, or a range of products against a single disease. Others are directed at improving access to treatment. Still others provide a global coordination mechanism for funding research on different targets, e.g. the Global Fund to Fight Aids, Tuberculosis and Malaria. Such funds "leverage" private sector funding by guaranteeing to purchase the products of research, up to a certain value, if they meet agreed standards.[51]

Box 3.8   Examples of PPPs for health and veterinary products funded by DFID

- Global Alliance for TB Drug Development (TB Alliance)
- International AIDS Vaccine Initiative (IAVI)
- International Partnership for Microbicides (IPM)
- Microbicides Development Programme (MDP)
- Medicines for Malaria Venture (MMV)
- Global Alliance for Vaccines and Immunizations (GAVI)
- Drugs for Neglected Diseases Initiative (DNDi)
- Alliance for Livestock Veterinary Medicines (GALVmed)

In 2004 an analysis of drug development projects for neglected diseases revealed that about 75% of projects involved PPPs. Indeed the development of PPPs was a major contributor to the increase in such projects over the previous decade.[51] Further, PPPs, while still largely funded through public sector investment, proved more efficient than wholly private or wholly public ventures on a number of criteria. One of these was the speed of new product development. Figure 3.13 compares the trajectories of development of some selected for neglected diseases under these different mechanisms. The charts show that PPP ventures have timelines of progression through the different stages of drug development and trialling as short or shorter than wholly private ventures and considerably shorter than wholly public ones.

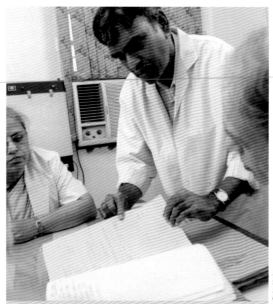

© Atul Loke

Figure 3.12 – Local researchers in Chennai, India consult with senior TB Alliance executives to further work to better treat and control TB

Figure 3.13 – Comparing drug development speeds through different mechanisms. The y-axis indicates the stages of drug development, with each line representing a different product. It illustrates the time it took to move from a particular stage to a later one. Colours indicate different types of development projects. The green area indicates industry standard development rates for all drugs, not just those for neglected diseases[52]

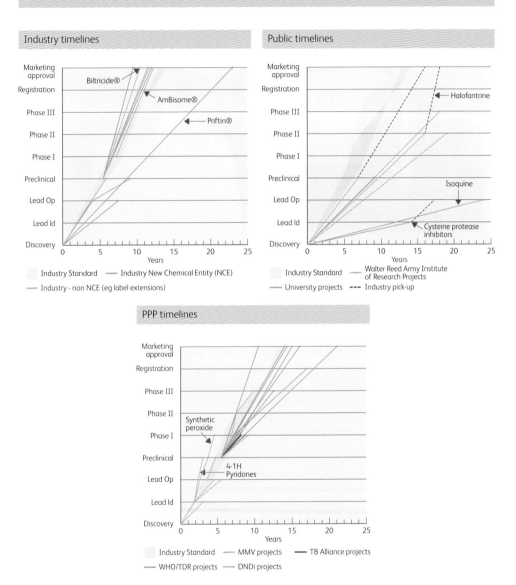

In drug development PPPs funds are seen more as investments than grants, with projects managed as they would be in an industrial portfolio. Recipients are expected to meet defined benchmarks and pass research results on to the next phase of product development. In exchange for delivering products to developing countries at a reasonable price, the private sector partners can use patents, derived from collaboration, to develop products for more profitable markets in industrialised countries.

An example of one of the first PPPs for neglected diseases is the International AIDS Vaccine Initiative (Box 3.9).

Box 3.9 The International AIDS Vaccine Initiative (IAVI)[53,54]

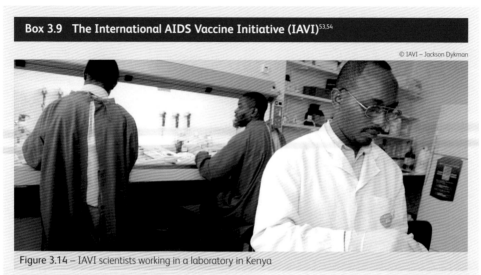

Figure 3.14 – IAVI scientists working in a laboratory in Kenya

With concerns over the growing HIV pandemic in developing countries, the Rockefeller Foundation convened a conference in Bellagio, Italy in 1994 to address the roadblocks in the development of a vaccine. Participants noted that private pharmaceutical firms had little financial incentive to devote resources to the task, and those that did were targeted at HIV variants present in developed countries.

From these discussions, one of the first PPPs in drug development was formed, bringing together private sector expertise with public sector funding. IAVI, launched in 1996, began by working to generate support for the cause in the international arena. Then, with the help of a wide variety of donors, from governments, to charitable foundations and private companies, the group established a central laboratory in London to coordinate efforts, and set up a network of clinical trial centres in developing countries.

Over the last 13 years, IAVI has worked in partnership with over 40 research, technology, pharmaceutical and government organisations. At first it concentrated on helping with the clinical assessment of vaccine candidates developed by others. IAVI is now looking to improve vaccine design approaches from the start, and has recently opened new laboratories in New York and California. Simultaneously, IAVI is working on building capacity in developing countries to deliver AIDS vaccines once they have proven to be effective and have been approved. With offices in New York, Amsterdam, New Delhi, Nairobi, and Johannesburg, IAVI collaborates with local groups to support AIDS education, engage communities in the vaccine trial process and improve medical infrastructure.

Agricultural PPPs

A small number of agricultural PPPs are also being developed. The African Agricultural Technology Foundation (AATF), a group which works to facilitate the transfer of crop technologies developed by large international organisations to users in Africa, is a particularly successful example (Box 3.10).

Box 3.10 The African Agricultural Technology Foundation (AATF)[55]

© CIMMYT

Figure 3.15 – Researchers observe local maize taken over by Striga, alongside the healthy new imazapyr-resistant variety

AATF is an African-based and African-led institution established in 2004. It negotiates royalty-free licenses for new proprietary agricultural technologies from corporations and other research organisations. Then, while assuring appropriate stewardship of the technologies, the AATF sub-licenses their use in specific projects by national and international research and development organisations in Africa. So far, five major crop-biotechnology corporations and the USDA have agreed to share their technologies with Africa through the AATF.

Two current projects are:

Striga control: A major pest of staple crops is the parasitic weed *Striga (Striga hermonthica)*, which sucks nutrients from the roots of maize, sorghum and other host crops and transfers toxins to them. The weed is readily controlled by an herbicide, imazapyr, but this kills the crops. Recently, a mutant gene in maize was discovered that confers resistance to the imazapyr herbicide and this is being bred into local maize varieties.[56] The maize seed can then be coated with the herbicide before being planted. In response to germination stimulants from the host plant, the parasitic weed seeds germinate and attach to the maize roots to suck nutrients, including the systemic herbicide from the maize. In the process, the herbicide kills the weed seedling in the ground, allowing maize to grow with little or no impact from the herbicide.

The AATF is facilitating the release of these new maize seeds through public-private partnerships with local and international partners including a number of CGIAR centres, BASF – a private chemical company, the Weizmann Institute of Science in Israel, and local public and private partners in Kenya, Uganda, Tanzania and Malawi. On-farm trials have shown increases in yield from a mean of half a tonne per hectare to over three tonnes.[57]

Cowpea pests and diseases: Cowpea is one of the most important legumes grown throughout the semi-arid tropics of Sub-Saharan Africa. The crop can withstand the hot and dry conditions of the savannah, and is both rich in protein and high in energy, making it an extremely valuable food resource. Unfortunately it is susceptible to a wide-range of pests and diseases which can significantly reduce yields. A variety of insect pests attack the plant at every stage of its life cycle, and a number of fungal, bacterial and viral diseases can add to the damage. The *Maruca* pod borer is particularly problematic, attacking at flowering and pod formation and at its worst reducing yields by 70-80%.

Researchers at Australia's Commonwealth Scientific and Industrial Research Organisation (CSIRO) have recently isolated a gene from *Bacillus thuringiensis (Bt), cry1Ab*, and successfully introduced the gene into elite varieties to protect cowpea against the pod borer. This should lead to higher yields and less insecticide use. AATF is providing assistance with licensing, regulation and product stewardship to the partner organisations, which include the CSIRO, International Institute of Tropical Agriculture (IITA), Monsanto, and national research centres across West Africa.[58] One confined field trial has been carried out in Puerto Rico, USA, with indications of successful *Maruca* resistance. The first trials in Africa are planned to take place in Nigeria in 2009.

New platform PPPs

Some partnerships are now being formed to share advances in new platform technologies, such as renewable energy, to communities in the developing world. One such example is the PPP between the German energy company, Energiebau, and a German non-profit capacity building organisation, *InWEnt*, which has been working to install decentralised power systems in rural areas. (Box 3.11)

> **Box 3.11 German partnership brings the power of 'micro-grids' to rural communities[59-62]**
>
> Most rural communities in the developing world are not connected to the electricity grid. They must get their energy from gathering wood or from expensive gasoline powered generators. As expanding the grid in most of these large, relatively sparsely settled areas is not practical or economically feasible, the private German energy company, *Energiebau Solarstromsysteme GmbH*, has worked to design a system of 'micro-grids' which can sustainably supply entire villages, schools or other organisations with electricity.
>
> These innovative micro-grids combine photovoltaic technology with jatropha oil powered generators, thus creating a cost-effective and self-sustaining local system. First, single-axis sun-tracking solar power systems are set up on site, which capture the sun, converting it to electricity. This can then be used, or stored in batteries. Second, jatropha plants, grown locally, are pressed for their oil and used to power retrofitted generators which are used as auxiliary power sources during peak loads or when there is insufficient sunlight.
>
> Jatropha is an inedible plant which can grow in dry soils and therefore does not have to compete with food production. It is high in oil, and provides an alternative to diesel oil which must be transported long distances.

In addition, the plants help to prevent erosion, and are climate neutral, giving as much energy as they take to produce.

One hectare of jatropha can produce one to two tonnes of nuts per year, which when pressed yield around 300 litres of oil, or 600 kilowatt hours.

Energiebau has teamed up with the non-profit, *InWEnt*, also based in Germany, to help deliver the systems to communities and organisations. InWEnt has helped to establish local partners, train groups in the system's installation, operation and maintenance, and worked closely with each community to design the best framework for ownership. So far, the German team has established successful operations in Tanzania, Ghana, Mali, and Indonesia.

© Energiebau Solarstromsysteme GmbH

Figure 3.16 – A staff member from InWEnt works with the Sisters in Tanzania

In Mbinga, Tanzania, for example, they have set up micro-grids for the Vincentian Sisters, who run schools, health centres and training workshops through their convent. As a result it has allowed them to produce power independently and expand their operations. The same system has also benefitted the local carpenter in Mbinga, who has been able to set up machines to do the work his team had previously done by hand.

5. Conclusion

We tend to think of science and technology for development as a public sector activity, practised largely by developed country scientists working on developing country problems. This model is changing rapidly. Public sector research will continue to play a key role, through new, international science innovation systems and continuing international research institutes. However, the important role of the private sector is emerging through our understanding of how innovation works. New models for PPPs are developing which, in a supportive regulatory climate, allows industry to invest in science for development, even in situations of market failure.

The "northern-driven" nature of this science also needs to change. It must involve local scientists more in innovation systems. This requires a very substantial investment in scientific capacity building to create an equitable research environment, supported by development assistance initiatives that put more research funding under the management of developing country partners.

Finally, research programmes themselves need to be developed more closely with intended beneficiaries, through application of participatory approaches with local, civil society organisations. This will draw local, as well as internationally-gained, knowledge into innovation systems.

Chapter 3 references and further reading

1   Nelson, R. & Rosenberg, N., (1993) "Technical innovation and national systems." In: R. Nelson. (Ed.) (1993) *National Systems of Innovation: a Comparative Study*. Oxford University Press, Oxford.

2   Freeman, C., (1995) The National System of Innovation in historical perspective, *Cambridge Journal of Economics* 1995, **19**, 5-24.

3   Oyelaran-Oyeyinka. Systems of Innovation and Underdevelopment: An Institutional Perspective. *Science Technology Society*. (2006) **11**, 239-269. Modified from Edquist, C. (2004) Systems of innovation – Perspectives and challenges.' In: J. Fagerburg, D.C. Mowery. & R. Nelson (eds), *The Oxford Handbook of Innovation*, Oxford University Press, Oxford.

4   Lalkala, R., (2003) Business incubators in developing countries: characteristics and performance.' *International Journal of Entrepreneurship and Innovation Management*, **3**, 31-55.

5   van Gardingen, P., (Pers. Comm. 8 September 2009).

6   Doing Business Project. (2009) *Weaving peace in Rwanda*. Available at: www.doingbusiness.org/documents/Women_in_Africa-JanetNkubana.pdf [Accessed 03 Nov 2009].

7   World Bank. (2009) Science, Technology, and Innovation – *Key Issues, Innovation vs. Everything Else*. Available at: go.worldbank.org/1BJKXUTHE0 [Accessed 03 Nov 2009].

8   Furman, J. Porter, M. & Stern, S., (2002) The determinants of national innovative capacity. *Research Policy*, **31** 899-933.

9   UNCTAD. (2007) *The Least Developed Countries Report 2007: Knowledge, Technological Learning and Innovation for Development*. United Nations Publications, Geneva.

10 UN. (2008) *The Millennium Development Goals Report 2008*. United Nations Department of Economic and Social Affairs, New York.

11 Griffiths, P., (2008) Losing Faculties *Nature*, **456**, no.4, 9-11.

12 Juma, C., (2008) Learn to Earn. *Nature*, **456**, no.4, 15-17.

13 University World News, Africa Edition. (2009) *West Africa: Bank grant for network of S&T institutions*. 22 March 2009. Issue: 0025. Available at: www.universityworldnews.com/article.php?story=20090320110603944 [Accessed 03 Nov 2009].

14 AfDb (2009) *Support to Network of Regional African Institutions of Science and Technology (AUST & 2IE) project*. Available at: www.afdb.org/en/projects-operations/project-portfolio/project/support-to-network-of-regional-african-institutions-of-science-and-technology-aust-2ie-project-835 [Accessed 03 Nov 2009].

15 Science Initiative Group website. Available at: sites.ias.edu/sig [Accessed 03 Nov 2009].

16 Wagner, C., (2008) *The New Invisible College, Science for Development*. Brookings Institution Press, Washington.

17 Whitworth, J. et al., (2008) Strengthening capacity for health research in Africa. *Lancet*, **372**, 1590–93.

18 Conway, G., (1999) *Doubly Green Revolution – Food for All in the 21st Century*. Cornell, Ithaca.

19 Evenson, R. & D. Gollin., (eds.), *Crop Variety Improvement and its Effect on Productivity: The Impact of International Agricultural Research*. CABI Publishing, Wallingford.

20 Raitzer, D., (2003) *Benefit-Cost Meta-Analysis of Investment in the International Agricultural Research Centres of the CGIAR*. Consultative Group on International Agricultural Research Science Council. Prepared on Behalf of the CGIAR Standing Panel on Impact Assessment. FAO, Rome.

21 Raitzer, D. & Kelley, T., (2008) Benefit-Cost Meta-Analysis of Investment in the International Agricultural Research Centres of the CGIAR. *Agricultural Systems*, **96**, Issues 1-3, 108-123.

22 CIMMYT. (2001) *Are Researchers Giving up on Africa?* Available at: www.cimmyt.org/whatiscimmyt/AR00_2001/africa/researchers/researchers.htm [Accessed 03 Nov 2009].

23 CIMMYT. (2007) *Body blow to grain borer*. CIMMYT E-News, vol 4 no. 9, September. Available at: www.cimmyt.org/english/wps/news/2007/sep/borers.htm [Accessed 03 Nov 2009].

24 Ininda, J. et. al., (2006) 'Performance of Three-Way Cross Hybrids for Agronomic Traits and Resistance to Maize Streak Virus Disease in Kenya.' *African Crop Science Journal*, Vol **14**. No.4 287-296.

25 CGIAR (2009) *Change Management*. Available at: www.cgiar.org/changemanagement/index.html [Accessed 03 Nov 2009].

26 Chambers, R., (1997) *Whose Reality Counts?: Putting the First Last*. Intermediate Technology Publications, London.

27 Chambers, R., (2005) *Ideas for Development*. Earthscan, Brighton.

28 Scoones, I. & Thompson J., (1994) *Beyond Farmer First: rural people's knowledge, agricultural research and extension practice*. Intermediate Technology Development Group, London.

29 Scoones, I. & Thompson, J., (2009) *Farmer First Revisited, Innovation for Agricultural Research and Development*. ITDG Publishing, Oxford.

30 Western Orissa Livelihoods Porject. Available at: www.worlp.com [Accessed 03 Nov 2009].

31 DFID. (nd) *Transforming Rural Livelihoods in India*. Write-Arm, Bangalore. Available at: www.dfid.gov.uk/Documents/publications/transforming-rural-livelihoods-india.pdf [Accessed 03 Nov 2009].

32 Stirling, C. & Witcombe, J., (2004) *Farmers and Plant Breeders in Partnership*. 2nd Edn. Centre for Arid Zone Studies. University of Wales, Bangor.

33 Witcombe, J. et al., (2006) Participatory Plant breeding is better described as Highly Client-Oriented Plant Breeding. II. Optional Farmer Collaboration in the Segregating Generations. *Expl. Agric*, **42**, 79-90.

34 Virk, D. Steele, K. & Witcombe, J., (2007) Mass and line selection can produce equally uniform rice varieties. Field Crops Research. *Field Crops Research*, 100, 341-347.

35 Steele, K. et al., (2006) Marker-assisted selection to introgress of rice QTLs controlling root traits and aroma into an Indian upland rice variety. Theoretical and *Applied Genetics*, **112**, 208-221.

36 Tubeileh, A. et al., (2007) Olives – The Fruits of Partnership. *ICARDA Caravan*, **24**. [www.icarda.org/Publications/Caravan/Caravan24/Focus_9.htm].

37 Thomas, R., (2004) *Progress Report 2004: Khanasser Valley Integrated Research Site*, Syria. ICARDA.

38 ICARDA. (n.d.) Participatory Research: CASE 9: *Water and Soil Management in Olive Orchards in the Khanasser valley*. Available at: www.icarda.cgiar.org/Participatory_Research/Olive.htm [Accessed 03 Nov 2009].

39 Kar, K. & Chambers, R., (2008) *Handbook on Community-Led Total Sanitation*. London, Plan UK.

40 CLTS writeshop at IDS. 19-23 May 2008. Notes, interviews and papers.

41 CLTS website. Available at: www.communityledtotalsanitation.org [Accessed 03 Oct 2009].

42 UNDP. (2007) *Human Development Report 2007/2008*. UNDP, New York.

43 Garnier, J., (2005) A prescription for combating global diseases. *Financial Times*. London, 30 May.

44 Graham, B. Ledgerwood, J. & Nabel G., (2009) Vaccine Development in the Twenty-First Century: Changing Paradigms for Elusive Viruses. *Clinical Pharmacology & Therapeutics*, **86**, 3, 234–236.

45 RNCOS. (2009) *Global Vaccine Market Forecast to 2012*. RNCOS. Available at: www.emailwire.com/release/24452-Vaccine-Market-to-Drive-Future-Pharmaceutical-Growth.html [Accessed 03 Nov 2009].

46 Global Pharmaceutical Market Review and World Top Ten/Twenty Drugs (2008) Available at: knol.google.com/k/krishan-maggon/global-pharmaceutical-market-review/3fy5eowy8suq3/6# [Accessed 03 Nov 2009].

47 Javier G., The George Institute for Public Health. [Email] (Pers. comm. 4 September 2009).

48 Moran, M. et al., (2009) *Neglected Disease Research & Development: How much are we really spending?* The George Institute for International Health, Sydney, Australia.

49 CGIAR. (2008) *Financial Report 2008*. Consultative Group on International Agricultural Research, Washington D.C.

50   CropLife. (2009) Facts and Figures, *The Status of Global Agriculture*. CropLife International, Brussels.

51   Global Fund to Fight AIDS, Tuberculosis and Malaria website. Available at: www.theglobalfund.org [Accessed 03 Nov 2009].

52   Moran, M. et al., (2005) *The New Landscape of Neglected Disease Drug Development*. Wellcome Trust, London.

53   IAVI website. Available at: www.iavi.org. [Accessed 03 Nov 2009].

54   Dykman, J., (2009) [Email] (Pers. Comm. 14 August 2009).

55   Muchiri, N., (2009) AATF Communications and Partnerships Manager. [Email] (Pers. comm. 11 August 2009).

56   AATF. (2005) *A New Bridge to Sustainable Agricultural Development in Africa: Inaugural Report, May 2002 – December 2004*, African Agricultural Technology Foundation, Nairobi.

57   AATF. (2008) *Striga control in maize*. Available at: www.aatf africa.org/aatf_projects.php? sublevelone=9&subcat=5 [Accessed 03 Nov 2009].

58   AATF. (2008) *Cowpea productivity improvement*. Available at: www.aatf-africa.org/aatf_projects.php? sublevelone=10&subcat=5 [Accessed 03 Nov 2009].

59   Funcke-Bartz, M, & Wolf, B., (2007) *Role of Hybrid-Systems in Rural Electrification – Experiences from pilot projects in Africa*. Presentation at the Eastern and Southern Africa Workshop on Bio-Fuels. 28 June, Nairobi. InWEnt and Energiebau. Available at: www.unep.org/urban_environment/PDFs/funcke_wolff.pdf [Accessed 03 Nov 2009].

60   D+C., (2007) Energy for Rural Africa. *Development & Cooperation*, No. 3, Vol **48**. Available at: www.inwent.org/ez/articles/056720/index.en.shtml [Accessed 03 Nov 2009].

61   Hug, R., (2008) *Solar Energy System of the Month*. The SolarServer, Forum for Solar Energy. 29 January 2008. Available at: www.solarserver.de/solarmagazin/anlage_0207_e.html [Accessed 03 Nov 2009].

62   Daniela A., Energiebau. [Email] (Pers. Comm. 4 September 2009).

Part 2

Science and the Millennium Development Goals

Progress towards the Millennium Development Goals

Women and children carrying water in India. © Ray Witlin – World Bank

In this chapter we focus on how on track we are to achieving the Millennium Development Goals (MDGs). The short answer is that progress is mixed. At the global level there have been significant achievements, but at regional and country level, especially in Sub-Saharan Africa and South Asia progress is disappointing. The reasons are complex, involving many factors, some generic, most very specific to particular countries. We believe that science and innovation will play an important part in accelerating progress towards the MDGs.

1. How did the MDGs originate?

The MDGs represent an extraordinary consensus by the international community on the nature of development and on a set of potentially achievable targets. In one sense they were not new. They had antecedents in the Universal Declaration of Human Rights, the Development Decade of the 1960s and the many United Nations (UN) summits in the second half of the 20th century that set goals for reducing hunger, improving health, eradicating diseases and educating children.[1] Unfortunately, few of these goals went beyond rhetoric. This began to change in 1990 with the recognition, by both the World Bank and the United Nations Development Programme (UNDP), of the need for economic reform to be accompanied by social policies.[2,3] The UNDP went so far as to argue that human beings are the ends, as well as the means, of development, challenging the focus of many economists and policymakers on per capita economic growth. It encouraged a focus on the poor and poorest and the prioritisation of capability enhancing services (such as food security, education and health).[1,4,5,6]

1990 was also the year of the World Summit for Children in New York, which was highly effective in mobilising public support and political commitment and in setting concrete targets which were then successfully implemented. This was followed by a number of other target setting summits and a series of meetings under the Organisation for Economic Cooperation and Development's (OECD) Development Assistance Committee which, in 2000, resulted in a joint OECD UN, World Bank and International Monetary Fund (IMF) report called 'A Better World for All', that drew up seven 'International Development Goals' (IDGs). These included halving the number of people living in extreme poverty by 2015 and targets related to infant, child and maternal mortality, access to safe and reliable family planning methods and universal primary education.[7]

The IDGs received a mixed reception, not least in the developing countries where they were seen as another imposition by the rich nations. However, they began to gain acceptance, in part, through the efforts of Clare Short, then Secretary of State for the UK's Department for International Development (DFID). She, and other world development leaders, were successful in gaining support from developing country leaders.

In 1999 preparations began among senior UN staff for the Millennium Assembly of the United Nations, to be held in New York in September 2000. The UN's new Secretary-General, Kofi Annan, was keen to make global poverty reduction central to the UN agenda. This resulted in April 2000 with the launch of 'We the Peoples: the Role of the United Nations in the 21st Century.' In some respects it was different from A Better World for All. It was longer and covered a much wider range of topics. But it also lacked the clear targets approach of the IDGs.

'We the Peoples' formed the basis for the Millennium Declaration of 8 September 2000 and for the subsequent intense negotiations between the various multilateral and bilateral agencies which led to the final, 'Road map towards the implementation of the United Nations Millennium Declaration', published by the UN in 2001. This set out, for the first time, the MDGs.[8]

2. What are the goals?

The final set of goals, combine the aspirations in *'We the Peoples'* with their roots in the concept of human development and the measurable targets approach of the IDGs. The targets reflect an attempt to incorporate a results-based management approach taking the goals beyond rhetoric, to outputs and outcomes, for which the international community has to be accountable.[9]

Although approved by the UN General Assembly in 2000, the baseline for the targets is 1990. The end date is 2015. In summary they are to:

- Halve poverty and hunger;
- Achieve universal primary education;
- Eliminate gender disparity in education;
- Reduce by two thirds the under-five mortality rate;
- Reduce by three quarters the maternal mortality ratio;
- Halt and reverse the HIV/AIDS epidemic and the incidence of malaria and other major diseases;
- Ensure environmental sustainability, including halving the proportion of the population without sustainable access to safe drinking water and basic sanitation, and achieve a significant improvement in the lives of a 100 million slum dwellers;
- Develop a global partnership for development.

The UN in its 2009 report records significant measurable progress:[10]

- 'Those living in extreme poverty in the developing regions accounted for slightly more than a quarter of the developing world's population in 2005, compared to almost half in 1990;
- Major accomplishments were also made in education. In the developing world as a whole, enrolment in primary education reached 88 % in 2007, up from 83 % in 2000;
- Deaths of children under five declined steadily worldwide – to around nine million in 2007, down from 12.6 million in 1990 – despite population growth. Although child mortality rates remain highest in Sub-Saharan Africa, recent survey data shows remarkable improvements in key interventions that could yield major breakthroughs for children in that region in the years ahead. Among these interventions are the distribution of insecticide-treated mosquito nets to reduce the toll of malaria – a major killer of children. As a result of 'second chance' immunizations, dramatic progress is also being made in the fight against measles.'

But on balance, as the World Bank notes, the record is mixed. *'Progress is uneven across MDGs, with goals related to human development (primary school completion, child and maternal mortality) recording slower progress than those more immediately influenced by economic growth or the expansion of infrastructure networks (income poverty, gender parity at school, access to water and sanitation); mixed because progress differs significantly across countries, regions, income groups, or institutional status – with fragile and conflict-affected states lagging behind on all counts.'*[11] (Figure 4.2 – page 92)

Figure 4.1 – Children in a makeshift school room after a cyclone destroyed their school in Mozambique

© Moira Hart

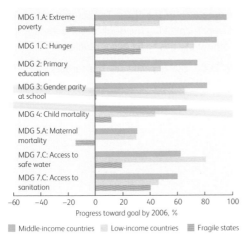

Figure 4.2 – Progress towards the MDGs is least in the fragile states[11]

MDG 1.A: Extreme poverty
MDG 1.C: Hunger
MDG 2: Primary education
MDG 3: Gender parity at school
MDG 4: Child mortality
MDG 5.A: Maternal mortality
MDG 7.C: Access to safe water
MDG 7.C: Access to sanitation

-60   -40   -20   0   20   40   60   80   100
Progress toward goal by 2006, %

■ Middle-income countries   Low-income countries   ▨ Fragile states

It is evident that formidable challenges remain. As was clear from the beginning, the targets are very ambitious. Moreover, it is important to remember that the MDGs were established as global goals. Indeed, some of them were determined by simply extending recorded global trends in improvement in education and health to the year 2015, and calculating from this the percentage improvement that would be required, relative to 1990 levels. As global targets, success would be achieved by a combination of countries moving at different rates towards 2015, some much more rapidly than others, reflecting both their starting point and their effort. However, MDGs have been consistently interpreted as national targets, not global ones. While this provides extra impetus to national efforts to achieve MDGs, it runs the risk of mis-representing some countries as successes and others as failures.

As a region, Africa has often been portrayed as "failing" on the MDGs, which is neither an entirely fair, nor a helpful perspective. It ignores significant achievements that can be built upon and provide a basis for optimism.

African countries such as Ghana, Mozambique, Rwanda, Tanzania and Uganda, which together account for a third of the region's population, have been growing at 5-6 % in economic terms in recent years. They, and other countries, have impressive development records, for example:

- Ghana, Mozambique, Tanzania and Uganda in accelerating growth and reducing poverty;
- Malawi in achieving particular success in boosting agricultural productivity;
- Ghana, Kenya, Tanzania and Uganda in increasing primary school enrolment;
- Niger, Togo and Zambia in combating malaria;
- Senegal and Uganda in increasing access to water and sanitation;
- Niger in promoting reforestation;
- Rwanda in achieving an impressive recovery from conflict.[11]

They demonstrate that rapid and large-scale progress is possible. The necessary conditions are strong government leadership and policies and strategies that effectively target the needs of the poor, combined with adequate financial and technical support from the international community.

Nevertheless, as is clear from Figure 4.3, of most concern is Sub-Saharan Africa. The challenges ahead are large and in Africa and elsewhere, progress is likely to be severely set back by the recent financial market turbulence and the resulting global economic slowdown.[11]

In the following sections, we look at progress on each of several MDGs where science and innovation play an important role – the goals for reducing hunger, improving health and achieving environmental sustainability.

Figure 4.3 – Sub-Saharan Africa's progress towards some of the MDGs. Dotted lines show the necessary trajectory to meet the goal, while solid lines show actual progress[11]

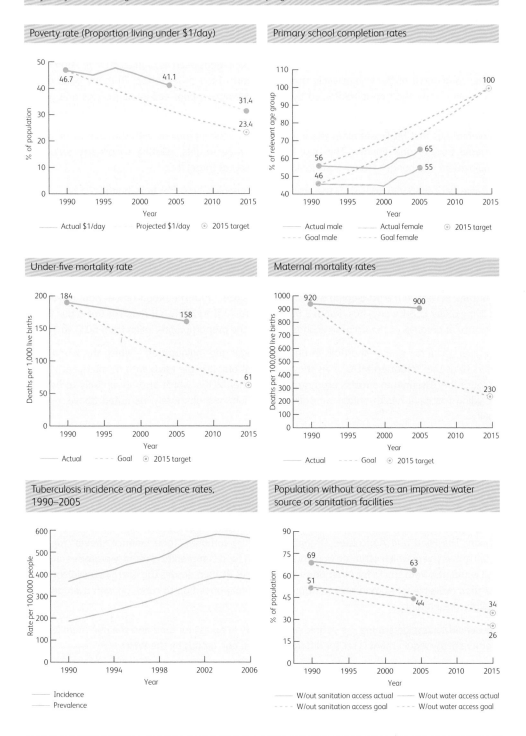

3. Reducing hunger

Hunger is caused by many, often interacting, factors of which poverty is the key. Poverty drives hunger, but lack of adequate nutrition reduces the ability to work productively thus resulting in lower incomes and less food production, so further increasing hunger. The urban poor can spend over 60 % of their incomes on food but for the rural poor it has been as high as 80 % in 2009.[12] This is one component of the vicious circle that forms part of the poverty trap. In many parts of the developing world the trap is reinforced by weak governance, poor economic policies and armed conflict.[13]

Therefore, the first MDG addresses this large and overarching problem, with the goal to: eradicate extreme poverty and hunger. The goal contains three targets, relating to poverty reduction, employment and hunger. Here we will look more closely at target 1.C:

- Halve, between 1990 and 2015, the proportion of people who suffer from hunger.

Which is measured using two indicators:

- Proportion of the population below the minimum level of dietary energy consumption;

- Prevalence of underweight children under-five years of age.

First, it is interesting to note that the poverty goal target of this MDG may be met for the developing countries. Poverty in the developing world has fallen since 1990. The proportion of poor (measured as living under US$1 a day) has dropped from 46 % to 27 % in 2005, but much of this is due to the spectacular progress of the Chinese economy where the proportion has fallen from 60 % to 16 %.[14]

However, there are serious shortfalls in fighting hunger and malnutrition – which the World Bank refers to as the "forgotten MDG".[11] As they also point out, it is the MDG with a "multiplier" effect, because it is essential to success on a number of other MDGs, which also are unlikely to be met, including maternal health, infant mortality, education, and ultimately, as noted above, poverty itself.

Measures of hunger

The first indicator for the hunger target, the proportion of the population below the minimum level of dietary energy consumption, is essentially a measure of food deprivation. As it is not possible to monitor how much food each person in the world consumes, the measurement is based on the average amount of food available for human consumption per person in each country, the level of inequality in access to that food and the minimum number of calories required for an average person. The Food and Agriculture Organisation (FAO) compiles "food balance sheets" for each country every year which estimate how much of each food commodity a country produces, imports and withdraws from stocks for other non-food purposes. It then divides the energy equivalent of all the food available for human consumption by the total population to come up with average daily energy consumption.

Household surveys determine the degree of inequality in access for food and the minimum level of dietary energy requirement is set for different sex and age groups by the WHO.

The second indicator, the prevalence of underweight children under-five is not only a measure of food deprivation, but also of other factors such as infections, adverse environmental conditions and inadequate care.

From 1990, in the developing regions, the proportion of the population undernourished has fallen from 20 % to 17 % in 2008 (Figure 4.4). Much of this is due to the fall in China from 15 % to 9 % in 2004. South East Asia has also done very well. For the developing regions as a whole the proportion of children under-five who are underweight still remains high, having fallen from 31 % to 26 % by 2007, but again there has been a dramatic fall in China, from 19 % to only 7 % in 2005.[15]

In Sub-Saharan Africa, Ghana is the only country that is going to meet the MDG, indeed it has already done so. Its proportion of undernourished has fallen from 34 % to a mere 9 %, although the drop in under-five underweight has fallen less, from 27 % to 18 % by 2006, but still on track.

Figure 4.4 – Declines in the proportion of undernourished people and % underweight children under-five.[10]
(Note the percentage undernourished in developing countries rose from 16 % to 17 % in 2008 largely as a result of the food price spike, which is discussed in the next chapter)

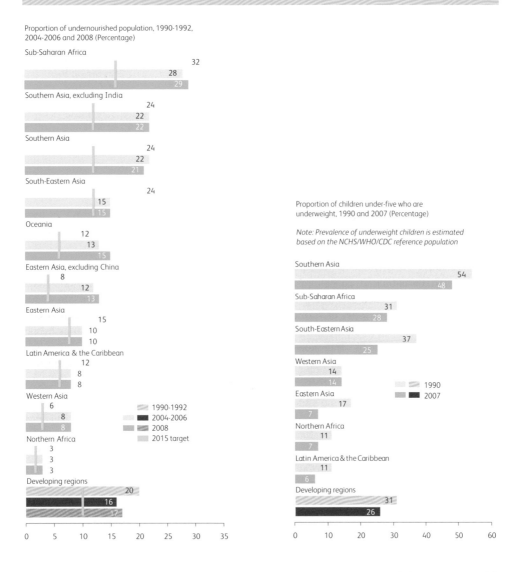

Proportion of undernourished population, 1990-1992, 2004-2006 and 2008 (Percentage)

Proportion of children under-five who are underweight, 1990 and 2007 (Percentage)

Note: Prevalence of underweight children is estimated based on the NCHS/WHO/CDC reference population

Figure 4.5 – Most of Sub-Saharan Africa and South Asia is not on track for the hunger MDG[16]

Progress towards the MDG target, with countries classified according to the following thresholds:

- **On track:** Average annual rate of reduction (AARR) in underweight prevalence (1990-2006) is greater than or equal to 2.6%, or latest available estimate of underweight prevalence is less than or equal to 5%, regardless of AARR

- **Insufficient progress:** AARR is between 0.6% and 2.5%
- **No progress:** AARR is less than or equal to 0.5%
- Data not available

Progress in China and Ghana

China's progress is largely due to the agricultural reforms that occurred between 1978 and 1989 bringing in a decentralised agricultural production system and liberal markets. Agricultural production growth increased as a result, from 2.6% to 7.1% a year. It fell back in the late 1980s but increased again as a result of further reforms in the 1990s. The reforms provided strong incentives for investment in infrastructure, irrigation systems, new crop varieties (such as hybrid rices) and cropping systems. The growing prosperity in agriculture in turn stimulated the development of rural non-farm activities which, by providing additional sources of income beyond farming, were one of the main factors behind China's rapid poverty reduction after 1985.[17]

It is generally recognised that Ghana's success owes a great deal to stable, good governance over the past 15 years and sound macroeconomic policies including market liberalization. This has allowed investments in rural infrastructure and agricultural development. While a quarter of the growth has been through expansion of cropped land, there have also been significant increases in maize and cassava yields, new pest-resistant cassava varieties and the growth of smallholder export crops i.e. cocoa and pineapple. As a result, Ghana's national poverty rate has fallen from 52% in 1991/92 to 29% in 2005/06.[19]

It is often said that there is enough food in the world; hunger can be eliminated by better distribution. There is some truth in this and that is why FAO's food balance sheets (see above) measure the equality of access to food. But they also take into account the amount of food available. Drought, floods and other natural disasters reduce harvests and the lack of technology results in low crop yields of poor quality and low resistance to pests and diseases. The ability of poor farmers both to feed their own families, and to produce a surplus to sell, not only serves rural and economic growth generally, it also provides a valuable protection during adverse times.

4. Progress towards the health MDGs

People may become ill for a wide variety of reasons. They may catch infectious diseases, such as malaria, HIV and TB. They may fall ill with a non-communicable disease, such as cancer or a cardiac condition. They may suffer from an environmental contaminant such as arsenic in the water supply, or they may be afflicted by an inherited illness. But, often, the condition is made worse than it might otherwise be because they lack an adequate, well-balanced diet. From among these various conditions the MDGs focus on a limited set where the mortality and morbidity rates are especially high – the so-called 'Killer Diseases' (Box 4.1).

There are three goals within the MDGs devoted to health, and they are as follows:

Box 4.1 The so-called 'Killer Diseases'[11,16,20-23]	
	Deaths per year (millions)
HIV	2.0
Malaria	0.9
TB	1.7
Maternal conditions	0.6
Childhood conditions:	
Diarrhoea	1.5
Pneumonia	2.0
Measles	0.9
Neonatal	4.0

Note: there is some double counting: for example child deaths may be caused by malaria.

- Goal 4: Reduce child mortality

    Target 4.A: Reduce by two-thirds, between 1990 and 2015, the under-five mortality rate.

- Goal 5: Improve maternal health

    Target 5.A: Reduce by three quarters, between 1990 and 2015, the maternal mortality ratio;

    Target 5.B: Achieve, by 2015, universal access to reproductive health.

- Goal 6: Combat HIV/AIDS, malaria and other diseases

    Target 6.A: Have halted by 2015 and begun to reverse the spread of HIV/AIDS

    Target 6.B: Achieve, by 2010, universal access to treatment for HIV/AIDS for all those who need it;

    Target 6.C: Have halted by 2015 and begun to reverse the incidence of malaria and other major diseases.

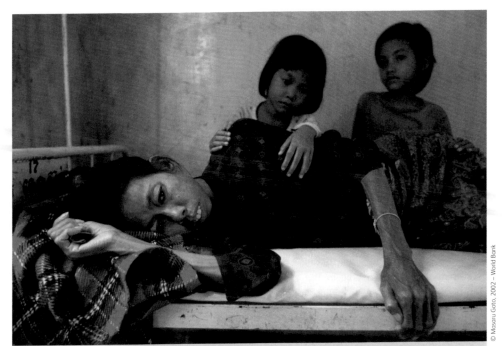

Figure 4.6 – HIV – one of the killer diseases responsible for 2 million deaths a year

This is an ambitious set of goals. Their attainment depends on improved economic conditions and the creation of good health care systems, but also on changes in behaviour and the environment and the discovery and delivery of new vaccines, medicines and other treatments. Progress towards each of the individual goals, as described below, is usually a product of all these factors.

Reducing child mortality

Child mortality is commonly measured using the under-five mortality rate (U5MR), which is the probability that a newborn will die before reaching the age of five (expressed as a rate per 1,000). But three indicators are used: the under-five mortality rate itself, the infant (under one) mortality rate and the proportion of one year-old children immunised against measles.

Vital registration systems which record births and deaths are the best sources of data on infant and under-five mortality rates but these are rarely well functioning and instead household surveys of child histories are employed. The proportion of infants immunised at least once against measles derives from national level reports of vaccinations performed and from household surveys.

Globally considerable progress has been made.[24] In 2006, for the first time since mortality data has been gathered, annual deaths among children under-five fell below 10 million. Nevertheless, the levels in developing countries remain unacceptably high: a child born in a developing country is over 13 times more likely to die within the first five years of life than a child born in an industrialised country. Between 1990 and 2006, about 27 countries – the large majority in Sub-Saharan Africa – made no progress in reducing childhood deaths.

South Asia is doing reasonably well, but Sub-Saharan Africa is significantly off-track (Figures 4.7 and 4.8).

Figure 4.7 – Lack of progress towards MDG 4 child mortality. Dotted lines show the necessary trajectory to meet the goal, while solid lines show actual progress[11]

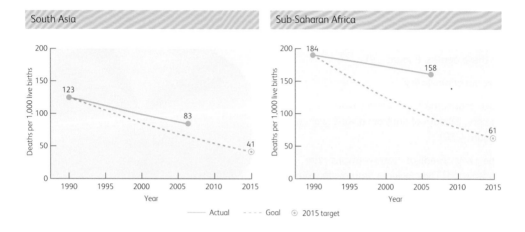

Actual   ---- Goal   ⊙ 2015 target

Figure 4.8 – All Sub-Saharan African countries have shown no progress, or insufficient progress towards achieving MDG 4[16]

© UNICEF 2007

Progress towards the MDG 4, with countries classified according to the following thresholds:

● **On track:** U5MR is less than 40, or U5MR is 40 or more and the average annual rate of reduction (AARR) in the under five mortality rate observed for 1990-2006 is 4% or more.

● **Data not available**

● **Insufficient progress:** U5MR is 40 or more and AARR is between is between 1% and 3.9%

● **No progress:** U5MR is 40 or more and AARR is less than 1%

The major causes of child mortality are complications during the first 28 days of a newborn's life (the neonatal period), pneumonia, and diarrhoea. But undernutrition, which limits a child's ability to fight off disease, is estimated to be the underlying cause in 35 % of these deaths. (Figure 4.9).

Neonatal mortality

Each year some four million children die within the first 28 days of life from a variety of causes (Figure 4.10).

The key medical interventions are well understood. They include: *'improving women's health during pregnancy, providing appropriate care for both mother and newborn during and immediately after birth, and caring for the baby during the first weeks of life. Cost-effective, feasible interventions include: initiating breastfeeding within one hour of birth, ensuring proper cord care, keeping the baby warm, recognizing danger signs and seeking care, and giving special care to infants with low birthweight.'*[16] In addition, significant attention must be paid to addressing gender equality, so that women's needs during pregnancy and birth are given more priority.

As yet no clear indicators for neonatal mortality (as distinct from infant mortality) have been formulated, but it is evident that neonatal deaths remain very high at 44 per 1,000 live births in both Sub-Saharan Africa and South Asia.[16]

The causes of child mortality

Figure 4.9 – The causes of child mortality.[25] Undernutrition has been estimated to be an underlying cause in 35 % of all under-five deaths[26]

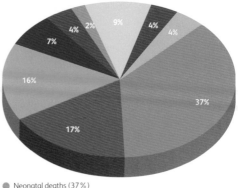

- Neonatal deaths (37 %)
- Acute respiratory infections (post-neonatal) (17 %)
- Diarrhoeal diseases (post-neonatal) (16 %)
- Other infectious and parasitic diseases (9 %)
- Malaria (7 %)
- Measles (4 %)
- Noncommunicable diseases (post-neonatal) (4 %)
- Injuries (post-neonatal) (4 %)
- HIV/AIDS (2 %)

Figure 4.10 – Global causes of neonatal mortality[25]

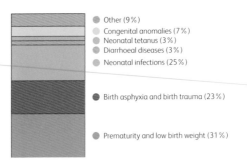

- Other (9 %)
- Congenital anomalies (7 %)
- Neonatal tetanus (3 %)
- Diarrhoeal diseases (3 %)
- Neonatal infections (25 %)
- Birth asphyxia and birth trauma (23 %)
- Prematurity and low birth weight (31 %)

Once past the neonatal period, pneumonia is responsible for one in five child deaths. Part of the challenge is to provide access to appropriate antibiotics but it is also crucial that a child is seen by a health provider trained to detect those symptoms of pneumonia (fast breathing and difficult breathing) that indicate a need to receive immediate treatment. Over half of all infected children in developing countries are now seen by such a person but the proportion is only 40 % in Sub-Saharan Africa.

Diarrhoea is nearly as important as pneumonia. It is caused by at least 20 viral, bacterial and protozoan pathogens (including *Salmonella spp, Shigella spp, Vibrio cholerae*, and rotavirus).[27] These multiply in the human gut, exit in excreta, contaminate water and other elements of the environment from which they infect human beings causing diarrhoea. *Shigella* related diarrhoea alone could be responsible for as many as a million deaths and rotavirus for half a million.[28,29]

Improved sanitation and drinking water is thus critical to reducing child mortality from diarrhoea but, as we shall report under MDG 7, progress here is unsatisfactory and appears to have had little effect.

The biggest success in combating child mortality has been in reducing the incidence of measles and malaria. A measles vaccine is available which is highly effective. The combination of improved routine measles immunization and follow-up campaigns, that provide a second opportunity for children to be immunized, has led to a steep reduction in the number of measles deaths: by 93 % in Sub-Saharan Africa between 2001 and 2008.[30]

Equally successful has been the control of malaria, which causes 8 % of child mortality.

Maternal mortality

The goal of MDG 5 is to improve maternal health, by aiming to reduce, by three quarters, the maternal mortality ratio (MMR), which is measured by two indicators, the MMR and the proportion of births attended by a skilled health professional.

Maternal mortality is most commonly expressed using the MMR, which records the number of women who die either during pregnancy or delivery due to pregnancy-related conditions per 100,000 live births. This is difficult to measure in part because it is a relatively rare event, thus requiring large sample sizes for household surveys.

A woman in Sub-Saharan Africa has a risk of 1 in 22 of maternal death compared with 1 in 8,000 in industrialised countries.[31] This difference in risk represents the widest disparity seen for any human development indicator.[32]

Figure 4.11 – Maternal mortality rates (MMR) per 100,000. Sub-Saharan Africa has an average MMR of 992, compared with 9 in the developed countries[16]

© UNICEF 2007

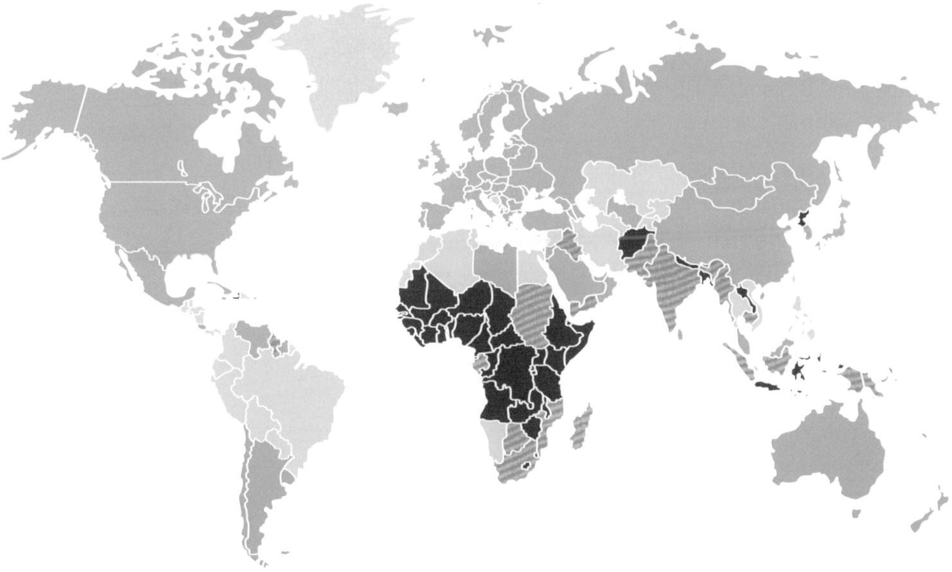

● Low MMR (less than 100)   ● Moderate MMR (100-299)   ◕ High MMR (300-549)   ● Very high MMR (550 or more)

○ Data not available

Maternal mortality has decreased globally but not at a rate to achieve the MDG and there has been little progress in Sub-Saharan Africa (Figure 4.12).

Figure 4.12 – Poor progress towards reducing maternal mortality in Sub-Saharan Africa[11]

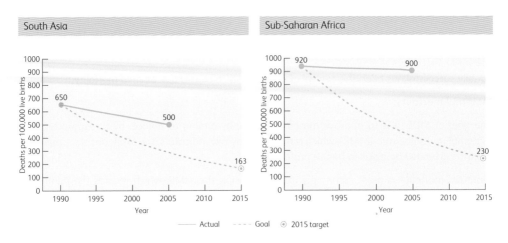

The causes of maternal deaths

In Sub-Saharan Africa and South Asia haemorrhage is the main cause of maternal mortality. This is partly why skilled attendance at delivery is critical to reducing deaths. Overall, nearly 60% of births in the developing world are attended by doctors, nurses or midwifes but the figures are only 43% for Sub-Saharan Africa and 41% for South Asia. In general this indicator is a better measure of progress than the relatively crude estimates of maternal mortality.

Combating HIV/AIDS

MDG 6 aims to combat HIV/AIDS, malaria and other diseases.

For HIV/AIDS the target is to halt by 2015 and begin to reverse the spread of HIV/AIDS. The principal indicator is the percentage prevalence, that is the proportion of the population 15 to 49 years of age living with HIV, obtained by methodologies developed by UNAIDS and WHO. It has shown a significant decline over the past seven to eight years in Sub-Saharan Africa (Figure 4.13), although it still remains high especially in southern Africa; 26% of the population of Swaziland is infected.

Figure 4.13 – The stabilisation of the prevalence of HIV (the percentage infected) in Sub-Saharan Africa[22]

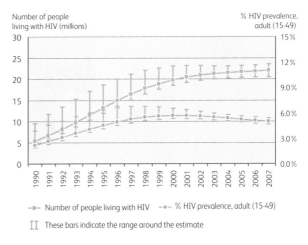

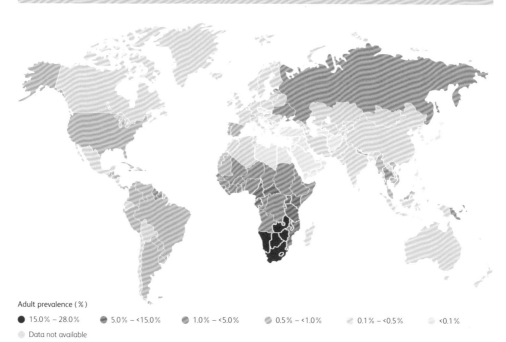

Adult prevalence (%)

● 15.0% – 28.0%   ● 5.0% – <15.0%   ● 1.0% – <5.0%   ● 0.5% – <1.0%   ● 0.1% – <0.5%   ● <0.1%
● Data not available

However, the absolute number (as opposed to the proportion of the population) of people living with HIV worldwide has continued to rise. Worldwide, nearly 33 million people are infected, 50% of whom are women. Sub-Saharan Africa is most affected, containing two thirds of those living with HIV.

In part this rise in the numbers infected is due to the decline in the death rate (from a total of 2.2 million in 2005 to 2.0 million in 2007) resulting from the substantial increase in access to antiretroviral therapy in recent years. In six years the number receiving antiretroviral drugs has risen ten-fold (Figure 4.15). The second target is to achieve by 2010 universal access to treatment for HIV/AIDS for all that need it.[22]

Figure 4.15 – The rapid increase in the numbers of people receiving anti-retroviral drugs in low and middle income countries.[33]

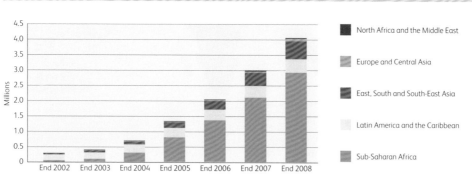

More encouragingly, in a number of heavily affected countries – such as Kenya, Rwanda, Uganda, and Zimbabwe – dramatic changes in sexual behaviour (see Box 6.6) have been accompanied by a decline in the number of new HIV infections. Since the late 1990s the percentage of adults aged 15 to 49 who are infected with HIV in these countries has fallen. However these gains have not been consistent within and between regions.[22]

Campaigns against Tuberculosis (TB)

Under MDG 6, TB is a target similar to HIV/AIDS – the aim is to have it halted by 2015 and then to begin to reverse the incidence of TB. The specific indicators are:

1. The incidence, prevalence and death rates associated with TB;

2. The proportion of TB cases detected and cured under directly observed treatment short course (DOTS).

These are computed by WHO based on data submitted in various forms through a consultative and analytical process[34]. Incidence is the number of new cases per 100,000 of the population, while prevalence is the proportion of the population infected, again per 100,000.

The global incidence of TB appears to have peaked in 2004 and is now levelling off. However, although incidence rates are dropping in all regions, progress has not been fast enough to keep pace with population growth. As a result, the absolute number of new infections is still rising. Globally, there were an estimated 9.3 million new cases of TB in 2007, up from 9.2 million cases in 2006. Most occurred in Asia (55 %) and Africa (31 %) (Figure 4.16). About 15 % of the new cases were among people who were HIV-positive, most of whom (79 %) lived in Africa.[10]

Figure 4.16 – Incidence of TB is falling in Sub-Saharan Africa but the levels remain very high[35]

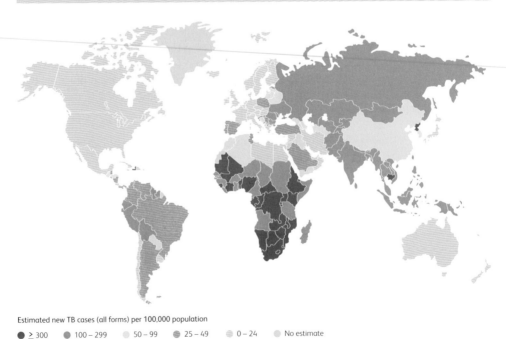

Estimated new TB cases (all forms) per 100,000 population

● ≥ 300   ● 100 – 299   ○ 50 – 99   ● 25 – 49   ○ 0 – 24   ○ No estimate

South Asia has already achieved a halving of prevalence, but the incidence is only slowly falling. In Sub-Saharan Africa, incidence and prevalence are only just beginning to fall.[20]

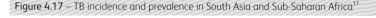

Figure 4.17 – TB incidence and prevalence in South Asia and Sub-Saharan Africa[11]

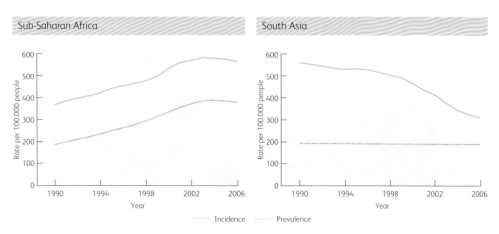

The good news is that non-drug resistant TB is actually fully treatable. Much of the success in reducing mortality and prevalence has been due to the DOTS strategy (directly observed treatment, short course). This involves microscopic examination of the sputum samples of symptomatic patients followed by treatment with antibiotics for six to eight months. In the absence of HIV/AIDS, cure rates have reached as high as 95 %, even in the poorest countries.[36] This has been partly due to high levels of detection and high levels of successful treatment.

In 2007 some 5.5 million cases were identified in DOTS programmes. The percentage of estimated cases which were identified by DOTS and non-DOTS programmes combined was 63 %. Treatment success for new cases was 85 % globally.

However, while DOTS is effective in treatment, and hence reduces mortality and prevalence, there is no evidence that the DOTS strategy is reducing transmission or contributing to the fall in incidence.[20,37] In Sub-Saharan Africa incidence appears to be falling mainly because HIV/AIDS prevalence is falling. In addition, resistance to main-line drugs has been steadily increasing and practitioners are increasingly challenged to come up with strategies beyond DOTS to treat those with multiple drug resistant TB (MDR-TB) (discussed further in Chapter 6).

Tackling malaria

Under MDG 6 the goal is to have halted by 2015 and begun to reduce the incidence of malaria. There are three principal indicators:

1. Incidence and death rates associated with malaria;

2. Proportion of children under five sleeping under insecticide-treated mosquito nets;

3. Proportion of children under five with fever who are treated with appropriate anti-malarial drugs.

Malaria differs primarily from the other 'killer diseases' in that the causative agent is transmitted from person to person via a mosquito.

About half the world's population (over 3 billion people) is at risk from malaria. Some 250 million cases develop each year with nearly a million deaths, mostly of children under five (Figure 4.18). Over 100 countries are endemic for malaria, 45 in Africa.

Figure 4.18 – Continued high levels of malaria incidence (numbers per 1,000) in Sub-Saharan Africa[21]

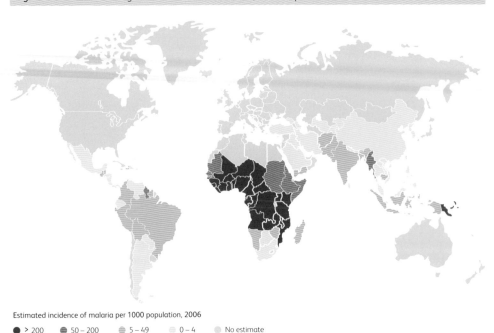

Estimated incidence of malaria per 1000 population, 2006

● > 200   ● 50 – 200   ● 5 – 49   ● 0 – 4   ● No estimate

Nearly a million people died of malaria in 2006 of which 95 % lived in Sub-Saharan Africa. The vast majority were children under five. Between 190 million and 330 million episodes of malaria occurred that year, with 88 % in Sub-Saharan Africa, 6 % in Southern Asia and 3 % in South-Eastern Asia.[10]

According to the UN, *'the risk of dying from malaria is considerably higher in Sub-Saharan Africa than other parts of the world for several reasons: transmission of the disease is more intense, the more lethal form of the malaria parasite – Plasmodium falciparum – is more abundant, and the region tends to have weak health systems.'*[10]

In the case of malaria the estimates for cases and deaths are especially problematic. This is, in part, because over 60 % of cases use facilities in the private sector, shops and pharmacies, or do not seek treatment at all. Also, in many African countries, only a small proportion of suspected malaria cases have laboratory investigation. As a result the diagnosis is unreliable being based only on clinical signs and symptoms. Since slide positivity rates are generally below 50 %, more than half of all clinically diagnosed cases do not have malaria.[21]

However, there is now a well developed suite of tools and methods for combating malaria: long-lasting insecticidal nets (LLIN) and artemisinin-based combination therapy (ACT), supported by indoor residual spraying of insecticide (IRS) and intermittent preventive treatment in pregnancy (IPT) (see Chapter 6).[21] WHO has set a target of 80 % coverage for each of these interventions in the belief that this will result in a reduction of cases and deaths per capita by 50 % between 2000 and

2010, and by 75% between 2005 and 2015. In some Asian countries – which are on track to achieve the goal by 2010 – there is evidence of links between interventions and the outcomes, such as with the use of ITNs.[21]

In Africa, the levels are far below these targets (Box 4.2).

Box 4.2   Lack of attainment of targets for malaria interventions in Africa – the WHO goal is 80% coverage. Data for 2006[21]

- 34% of households with insecticide treated nets in 19 countries;
- 38% of children with fever treated with anti-malarial drugs in 18 countries (but only 3% with ACT);
- 18% of women using IPT in pregnancy in 16 countries;
- Only 5 countries reported IRS coverage sufficient to protect 70% of those at risk.

Cases of malaria and associated deaths have reduced by 50% between 2000 and 2006/7 in at least seven out of 45 African countries or areas of countries, but these have relatively small populations, good surveillance and high intervention coverage. In a further 22 countries in other parts of the world, malaria cases fell by 50% or more, over the same period. However, it is not clear whether these 29 countries are on course to meet targets for reducing the malaria burden by 2010.[21]

In general the record of attainment of the health MDGs is mixed. In some cases, notably malaria, child and maternal mortality, the interventions are relatively well developed and the challenge is to better implement them. In other instances – against HIV/AIDS and TB – there is still a need for new technologies and interventions.

5. Progress towards the environment MDGs

MDG 7 – to ensure environmental sustainability – incorporates a variety of different environmental targets:

1. Integrate the principles of sustainable development into country policies and programmes and reverse the loss of environmental resources;

2. Reduce biodiversity loss, achieving, by 2010, a significant reduction in the rate of loss;

3. Halve, by 2015, the proportion of people without sustainable access to safe drinking water and basic sanitation;

4. By 2020, to have achieved a significant improvement in the lives of at least 100 million slum dwellers.

The presentation of MDG 7 differs between international organisations, particularly because the first two targets are inter-related and involve a very diverse range of environmental elements. Below we use the presentation used by UNSTATS, the official UN site for MDG targets and indicators.[38]

The first two targets have seven indicators:

- Increasing land area covered by forests;
- Combating climate change through reducing CO_2 emissions (total, per capita and per US$ GDP);
- Reducing the consumption of ozone-depleting substances;
- Restoring fish stocks depleted by over-exploitation;
- Using water resources in a sustainable manner;
- Protecting terrestrial and marine areas;
- Decreasing the proportion of species threatened by extinction.

Increasing forests

Our growing scientific understanding of the importance of forests in combating climate change places renewed emphasis on the objective of increasing forest cover. Land use change, principally deforestation, is responsible for the release of large amounts of carbon into the atmosphere. Mature forests contain huge carbon stores in the trees, understorey vegetation and within the decaying matter in the soil, and when they are logged or burnt the carbon is released. Deforestation currently accounts for an estimated 17% of global greenhouse gas (GHG) emissions, more than the entire transport sector.[39]

Most of this is generated in developing countries – in recent years, deforestation in

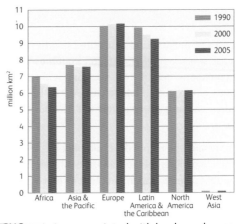

Figure 4.19 – Total forest area by region, note that net forest losses are greatest in Latin America and Africa.[40]

Brazil and Indonesia has produced over half of all GHG emissions associated with land use change. The role of forest conservation in carbon capture and climate change mitigation adds to the critical role played by forests in water conservation and management and in sustaining valuable, harvestable biodiversity for food, fuel, shelter and industrial uses.

Forest cover continues to decrease on a global scale. Between 1990 and 2005 the global surface of forests was reduced by 1.3 million square kilometres, or 3% of its total. Some 40% of the world's forests are located in Latin America and Sub-Saharan Africa, which are the two most important regional contributors to global deforestation. Latin America and the Caribbean lost 7% of their forests during this 15 year period and Sub-Saharan Africa lost 9%.[11]

While the losses from deforestation are about 13 million hectares per year (roughly equivalent to the land area of Bangladesh), this is partially counterbalanced by forest planting, landscape restoration and the natural expansion of forests. This has significantly reduced the net loss of forest area. Over the period 2000-2005 the net global loss is estimated at 7.3 million hectares per year, down from 8.9 million hectares per year in 1990-2000. Net losses have been particularly severe in Latin America and Africa. In Asia major afforestation programmes have been underway particularly in China, which has partly compensated for the continued deforestation in Indonesia (Figure 4.19). For the most part, continued losses in tropical countries are attributable to conversion into agricultural land.

Conserving water resources

As with forests, countries vary greatly in their supply of water resources. Much water is present as groundwater and difficult to measure and monitor.

Nevertheless, it is evident that available water resources continue to decline as a result of excessive withdrawal of both surface and groundwater, as well as decreased water run-off due to global warming. Already, in many parts of the world, such as West Asia, the Indo-Gangetic Plain in South Asia and the North China Plain, human water use exceeds annual average water replenishment. Use of freshwater for agriculture, industry and energy has increased markedly over the last 50 years. Freshwater shortage has been assessed as moderate or severe in more than half the regions studied in the Global International Waters Assessment (GIWA).[41]

UN Water estimated in 2007 that, by 2025, two-thirds of the world's population could be under conditions of water stress, defined as 1,700 m³/person/year – the threshold for meeting the water requirements for agriculture, industry, domestic purposes, energy and the environment. And among that group, 1.8 billion people will be living in countries or regions experiencing absolute water scarcity, with only 500 m³/person/year available.[42]

The International Water Management Institute (IWMI) also recently assessed global environmental water needs. They went beyond traditional calculations which compare water withdrawals to mean annual run-off, measuring the water needs at a river basin level and finding the amount of water needed to maintain ecosystem functionality. Figure 4.20 below shows areas where human use was found to be in conflict with environmental requirements.

Figure 4.20 – World map of water stress measured by the environmental Water Stress Indicator (WSI), which takes into consideration the amount of water needed for ecosystem sustainability[43]

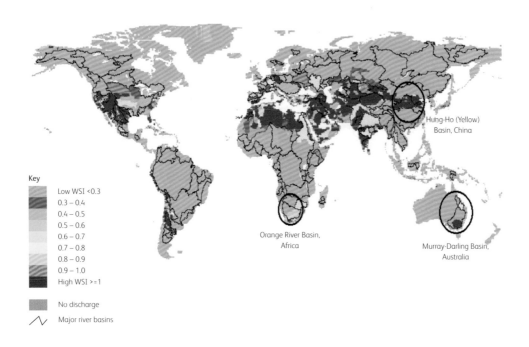

Key

Low WSI <0.3
0.3 – 0.4
0.4 – 0.5
0.5 – 0.6
0.6 – 0.7
0.7 – 0.8
0.8 – 0.9
0.9 – 1.0
High WSI >=1

No discharge

Major river basins

Hung-Ho (Yellow) Basin, China

Orange River Basin, Africa

Murray-Darling Basin, Australia

Managing fisheries

Developing countries are highly dependent on marine and freshwater fisheries. Fish provide 2.6 billion people with over 20 % of their protein intake. Two-thirds of world fisheries production comes from fish capture. Together China, Peru, Chile, Indonesia, and India accounted for 45 % of inland and marine fish catches in 2004.[11]

Currently about half of all stocks are fully exploited, implying that production is close to maximum sustained yield. The share of overexploited fish populations has increased, from 10 % in 1974 to 25 % and the most commercially successful species are all fully exploited or overexploited (see Figure 4.21).

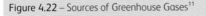

Figure 4.21 – The percentage of fully exploited fish stocks are increasing[11]

Underexploited, moderately exploited   Fully exploited   ◆ Overexploited, depleted, recovering

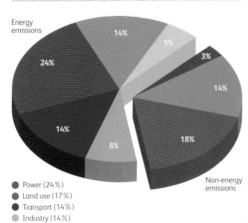

Figure 4.22 – Sources of Greenhouse Gases[11]

Energy emissions

14%
5%
3%
24%
14%
14%
8%
18%

Non-energy emissions

● Power (24 %)
● Land use (17 %)
● Transport (14 %)
◐ Industry (14 %)
● Agriculture (14 %)
◐ Buildings (8 %)
○ Other energy related (5 %)
● Waste (3 %)

Reducing greenhouse gas (GHG) emissions

Greenhouse Gas (GHG) emissions have continued to increase since 1990. Globally about 65 % come from energy consumption and industrial processes, 18 % from land use change (deforestation), and the remaining 17 % from agriculture and waste (Figure 4.22).

Deforestation and fossil fuel consumption primarily produce CO_2, while agriculture and waste are the main source of methane and nitrous oxide emissions. For the very poorest countries, most GHG emissions come from agriculture and changes in land use. When emissions from land use change are included, the top ten emitters account for two-thirds of CO_2 emissions, and include China, India, Brazil, Indonesia and Malaysia.[44]

But in general, even taking into account land use change, the amount of GHGs emitted per capita are far higher in the developed than in the developing countries (Figures 4.23 and 4.25).

Figure 4.23 – CO_2 emissions from land use changes, 1850-2000[11]

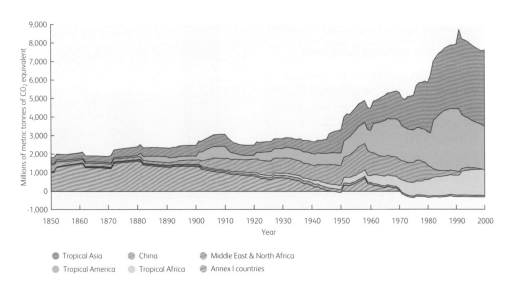

- Tropical Asia
- Tropical America
- China
- Tropical Africa
- Middle East & North Africa
- Annex I countries

Figure 4.24 – Per capita GHG emissions including from changes in land use in 2000, ranging from zero tonnes CO_2 emissions/capita (dark green) to 93.9 tonnes CO_2 emissions/capita (dark red)[45]

No data   0   93.9 tonnes CO_2 emissions per capita

Carbon emissions by both high-income and developing countries are predicted to rise by over 60% by 2035 from 2004 levels under the A1FI scenario (see Chapter 8 for description of scenarios). Moreover, developing countries' CO_2 emissions from fossil fuels – as a whole – will soon equal those of high-income countries.

Reducing ozone depleting substances

One of the most remarkable achievements in recent years has been the reduction, by 97% between 1986 and 2007, in the consumption of substances that deplete the Earth's ozone layer (Figure 4.26).[10]

177 parties to the Montreal Protocol have put in place national regulations or legislation to promote effective protection of the ozone layer. In addition, the Montreal Protocol Multilateral Fund has supported national capacity-building which has helped to transfer essential technologies that enable developing countries to 'leapfrog' to new, energy-efficient technologies and export their wares to the global market. According to the UN this has come about because of the integration of sustainable development principles into national policy frameworks (MDG 7) and the funding from an appropriate global partnership for development (MDG 8).

The challenges that remain include the continued phasing out of chlorofluorocarbons (CFCs) and the less active transitional CFC replacements, hydrochlorofluorocarbons (HCFCs), while avoiding the use of alternative compounds with a high potential for global warming. Alternatives must also be developed for the few remaining uses of HCFCs for which no acceptable substitute has been found, such as the Halon fire suppression system used in aircraft. Finally, existing stocks of ozone-depleting substances must be destroyed.[10]

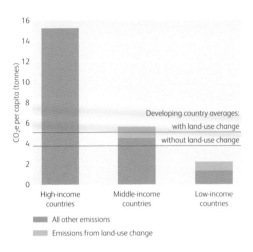

Figure 4.25 – The difference in emissions between low, middle and high-income countries as of 2005[38]

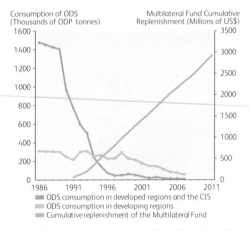

Figure 4.26– Greatly reduced consumption of all ozone-depleting substances (ODS) funded by the Montreal Protocol Multilateral Fund[10]

Reducing biodiversity loss

The second target under MDG 7 is to reduce the current rapid rate of biodiversity loss. If successful, it will secure the biological resource base on which much of our future agricultural, health and other scientific innovation depends. It will also maintain the integrity and functionality of terrestrial and marine ecosystems in which particular, often poorly known, species play key roles that cannot be easily replaced.

The target has two specific indicators, to:

- Increase the proportion of terrestrial and marine areas protected;
- Decrease the proportion of species threatened with extinction.

Despite significant increases in the protection of biodiversity areas the amount protected remains very low (Figure 4.27).

Figure 4.27 – Slow increase in the proportion of terrestrial and marine area protected[11]

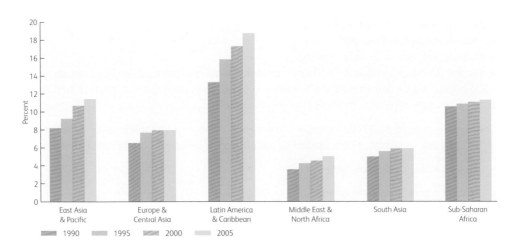

East Asia & Pacific | Europe & Central Asia | Latin America & Caribbean | Middle East & North Africa | South Asia | Sub-Saharan Africa

1990   1995   2000   2005

Only 12% of the planet is under some form of protection: about 18 million square kilometres of protected land and over three million square kilometres of protected territorial waters. Protected areas are also often poorly managed and suffer from pollution and climate change, irresponsible tourism, infrastructure development and increasing demands for land and water resources.[10]

Measuring the diversity of animals, plants and other organisms is inherently very difficult. Some progress has been made by the World Wildlife Fund (WWF) which summarises changes in populations of vertebrate species in its Living Planet Index (LPI). This tracks over 3,600 populations of 1,313 vertebrate species.[46]

© Eskinder Debebe – UN Photo

Figure 4.28 – Tropical rainforests are one of many threatened ecosystems

Separate indexes are also computed for terrestrial, marine and freshwater organisms using data from a variety of sources, and for different biogeographic regions of the world. The LPI indicates a downward trend since 1970 with no signs of recovery (Figure 4.29)

Improving water supply and sanitation

Access to clean potable water and basic sanitation is a key target for human development. Over 880 million individuals lack access to safe drinking water and 2.5 billion individuals lack access to basic sanitation. Improvements in these two areas could help to reduce dramatically the burden of disease, particularly diarrhoea, which contributes to approximately 1.5 million childhood deaths annually.[23]

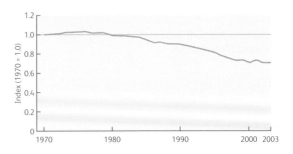

Figure 4.29 – Downward trend in the Living Planet Index for vertebrate animals[11]

The target is to halve, by 2015, the proportion of people without sustainable access to safe drinking water and basic sanitation. This is tracked by measuring the proportion of the population:

- Using an improved drinking water source;

- Using an improved sanitation facility.

Access to improved sources of water refers to the percentage of the population with reasonable access to a permanent source of safe water in their dwelling or within a reasonable distance from it. Access to sanitation refers to the percentage of the population with at least adequate access to excreta facilities (private or shared, but not public) that can effectively prevent human, animal and insect contact with excreta.

Lack of safe drinking water is more serious a problem for rural dwellers. A person living in an urban area of the developing world is more than twice as likely to have a piped drinking water supply, than a person living in a rural area. Nearly one quarter of the rural population obtain their drinking water from 'unimproved' sources: surface water such as lakes, rivers, dams or from unprotected dug wells or springs. But even using an improved water source is no guarantee that the water is safe from contamination.[10]

There has been significant progress in improving access to drinking water: Europe and Central Asia and South Asia have achieved the target for 2015 and East Asia and the Pacific have exceeded the target. The population with access has risen from 69% in 1990 to 87% in 2006. Sub-Saharan Africa is farthest from the target (Figure 4.31).

Figure 4.30 – Family collecting water from a local community pump in Mozambique

© Moira Hart

Figure 4.31 – Number of people per year requiring access to improved drinking water to reach the MDG target[10]

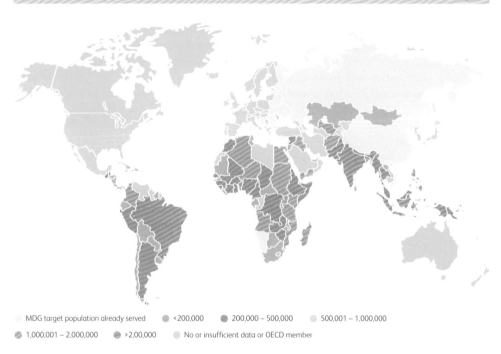

MDG target population already served   ● <200,000   ● 200,000 – 500,000   ● 500,001 – 1,000,000

● 1,000,001 – 2,000,000   ● >2,00,000   ○ No or insufficient data or OECD member

In 2006, 2.5 billion people worldwide were still without access to basic sanitation. 18 % of the world's population – 1.2 billion people – practice open defecation, the vast majority (87 %) living in rural areas. The biggest challenges are in Southern Asia and Sub-Saharan Africa, but there has been significant progress. In Southern Asia, the population that gained access to an improved sanitation facility more than doubled since 1990; in Sub-Saharan Africa, it increased by over 80 %.

While the indicators are for 'use' of improved water and sanitation facilities, this is in practice very difficult to measure. The target is therefore tracked in practice by the number of households with access – which is indeed the first step. However, particularly with sanitation facilities, access does not always lead to use. Long-standing hygiene habits are often hard to change, as will be discussed in later chapters, and this increases the difficulty of achieving this already challenging goal.

Figure 4.32 – Population that gained access to an improved sanitation facility 1990-2006 (millions) and population that needs to gain access to an improved sanitation facility to meet the MDG target, 2006-2015 (millions)[10]

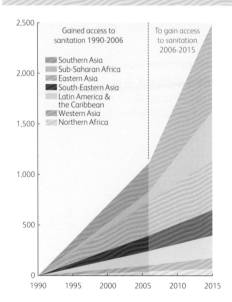

Improving the lives of slum dwellers

The proportion of the global urban population in developing regions living in slum conditions, defined as a lack of access to one of four basic amenities, clean water, improved sanitation, durable housing and adequate living space, has reduced from almost half in 1990 to around 36 % in 2005. Much of this progress is due to expanded access to water and sanitation, especially in Asia. Continued urbanisation will make this target a continuing challenge and investments in appropriate low-cost infrastructure as well as enabling policies will be important for progress.[10]

6. Conclusion

As is abundantly clear there are no silver bullets which will attain the MDGs. Political commitment, good governance and sound macro-economic policies are essential. In this context good governance embraces a wide range of attributes – fair and democratic elections (at all levels), accountable, efficient and responsive government, protection of human rights, absence of abuse of power and a lack of corruption.

Economic growth is also crucial. The MDGs can, in many instances, be attained by donor funding but maintaining progress depends on local resources, government budgets and the private sector. In general, as incomes rise individuals can purchase food and afford health care.

Nevertheless many of the goals are dependant on the application of new or existing technologies and the natural sciences that underpin them.

For example, reducing hunger will continue to depend on the production of new crop varieties, livestock breeds and agricultural systems that give higher yields, better nutritional quality, reduce pest and disease attack, and are tolerant of heat and drought. It is also clear that although reasonably effective forms of intervention exist for most of the 'killer diseases' there will need to be further and continued development of vaccines and medicines and other forms of health intervention. Finally, environmental management will depend on scientists' continued discovery and evaluation, often using new sensing technologies, of ecosystems and our effects on their functionality.

A more thorough analysis indicates that, in addition, when effective solutions do exist they are often not ideal and, in particular, are not in a form that can be easily implemented in developing countries. The need, therefore, is for interventions that are more efficient and user-friendly. We discuss these in the next three chapters.

Chapter 4 references and further reading

1   Hulme, D., (2007) *The Making of the Millennium Development Goals: Human Development Meets Results based Management In an Imperfect World*, Brooks World Poverty Institute, Working Paper 16.

2   World Bank. (1990) *Poverty; World Development Report 1990*, World Bank, Washington.

3   UNDP. (1990) *Overcoming barriers: Human mobility and development*. Human Development Report. United Nations Development Programme, New York.

4   Streeten, P. et al., (1981) *First Things First: Meeting Basic Human Needs in Developing Countries*. Oxford, Oxford University Press.

5   Sen, A., (1999) *Development As Freedom*. Knopf, New York.

6   Haq, M., ul (1995) *Reflections on Human Development*. Oxford, Oxford University Press.

7   UN. (2000) *A Better World for All*. United Nations, New York.

8   UN. (2001) *Road map towards the implementation of the United Nations Millennium Declaration*. United Nations, New York. Available at: unpan1.un.org/intradoc/groups/public/documents/UN/UNPAN004152.pdf [Accessed 16 Nov 2009].

9   Locke, E. & Latham, G., (1990) *A theory of goal setting & task performance*. Prentice Hall Englewood Cliffs, NJ.

10 UN. (2009) *The Millennium Development Goals Report, 2009*, United Nations, New York.

11 World Bank. (2008) *Global Monitoring Report 2008. Agenda for Inclusive and Sustainable Development. MDGs and the Environment*, World Bank, Washington, DC.

12 DFID Hunger Fact Sheet. (2008) Available at: www.dfid.gov.uk/Documents/publications/mdg-factsheets/hungerfactsheet.pdf [Accessed 16 Nov 2009].

13 Collier, P., (2007) *The Bottom Billion: Why the poorest countries are failing and what can be done about it*. Oxford University Press, Oxford.

14 UN. (2009) *The Millennium Development Goals Report 2009*. Statistical Annex. UN, New York. Available at: mdgs.un.org/unsd/mdg/Resources/Static/Data/2009 % 20Stat % 20Annex.pdf [Accessed 16 Nov 2009].

15 UN. *The Millennium Development Goals Indicators*. Country Level Data. Available at: mdgs.un.org/unsd/mdg/Data.aspx [Accessed 16 Nov 2009].

16 UNICEF. (2007) *Progress for Children: A world fit for children. Statistical review no 6*. UNICEF, New York, NY.

17 Von Braun, J. Gulati, A. & Fan, S., (2005) *Agricultural and economic development strategies and the transformation of China and India*. Annual Report, 2004-2005, International Food Policy Research Institute, Washington, DC.

18 IHT. (2008) Report to the Government of Ireland. Irish Hunger Task Force. Available at: www.irishaid.gov.ie/uploads/hunger_task_force.pdf [Accessed 16 Nov 2009].

19 Breisinger, C. et al., (2008) *Agriculture for Development in Ghana: New Opportunities and Challenges*. Discussion Paper No. 784, International Food Policy Research Institute, Washington, DC.

20 WHO. (2008) *Global Tuberculosis Control: Surveillance, planning, financing*. WHO, Geneva.

21 WHO. (2008) *World Malaria Report 2008*. WHO, Geneva.

22 UNAIDS. (2008) *Report on the Global AIDS Epidemic, 2008*. UNAIDS, Geneva.

23 WHO/UNICEF. Joint Monitoring Programme for water supply and sanitation. (2008) *Progress on Drinking water and sanitation – Special Focus on Sanitation*. UNICEF and WHO, New York.

24 UNDP. *Global progress, Are we on track to meet the MDGs by 2015?* Available at: www.undp.org/mdg/basics_ontrack.shtml [Accessed 16 Nov 2009].

25 WHO. (2008) *The global burden of disease: 2004 update*. WHO, Geneva.

26 Black, R. et al., (2008) Maternal and child undernutrition: global and regional exposures and health consequences. *Lancet*, **371**, 243–60.

27   Curtis, V. & Cairncross, S., (2003) Effect of washing hands with soap on diarrhoea risk in the community: a systematic review. *Lancet Infect Dis*, **3**, 275-81.

28   Kotloff, K. et al., (1999) Global burden of Shigella infections: implications for vaccine development and implementation of control strategies. *Bull World Health Organ*, **77**, 651-66.

29   WHO. (2007) Rotavirus vaccines, WHO position paper. *Weekly Epidemiological Record*, 10 August. **32**, 82, 285-296. Available at: www.who.int/wer/2007/wer8232.pdf [Accessed 16 Nov].

     CDC. (2009) Progress Toward Measles Control – Africa Region, 2001-2008. *MMWR Weekly*, 58 (37), 1036-1041. Available at: www.cdc.gov/mmwr/preview/mmwrhtml/mm5837a3.htm [Accessed 25 Nov 2009].

31   WHO, UNICEF, UNFPA, The World Bank. (2007) *Maternal mortality in 2005: Estimates developed by WHO, UNICEF, UNFPA and The World Bank*. WHO, Geneva.

32   DFID. (2004) *Reducing maternal deaths: Evidence and action*, DFID, London.

33   WHO, UNAIDS and UNICEF. (2009) *Towards Universal Access. Scaling up priority HIV/AIDS interventions in the health sector*, 2009 Progress Report. WHO, Geneva.

34   UN. Series Metadata – Tuberculosis detection rate under DOTS, percentage. Available at: unstats.un.org/unsd/mdg/Metadata.aspx?IndicatorId=0&SeriesId=718 [Accessed 16 Nov 2009].

35   WHO. (2009) *Global Tuberculosis Control – Epidemiology, Strategy, Financing*. WHO, Geneva.

36   Levine, R., (2004) *Millions Saved: proven successes in global health*. Center for Global Development, Washington, DC.

37   Dye, C. et al., *Determinants of trends in tuberculosis incidence: an ecological analysis for 134 countries*. Unpublished manuscript quoted in WHO 2008 *Global Tuberculosis Control: Surveillance, planning, financing*. WHO, Geneva.

38   Official list of MDG indicators. (2008) Available at: millenniumindicators.un.org/unsd/mdg/Host.aspx?Content=Indicators/OfficialList.htm [Accessed 16 Nov 2009].

39   World Bank. (2009) World Development Report 2010: Development and Climate Change. World Bank, Washington DC.

40   UNEP. (2007) *Global Environmental Outlook, Environment for Development, GEO4*, United Nations Environment Programme, Nairobi, Kenya.

41   UNEP. (2006) *Challenges to International Waters – Regional Assessments in a Global Perspective*. United Nations Environment Programme, Nairobi, Kenya.

42   UN Water. (2007) *Coping with water scarcity: challenge of the twenty-first century*. Prepared for World Water Day 2007 Available at: www.unwater.org/wwd07/ [Accessed 16 Nov 2009].

43   Smakhtin, V. Revenga, C. & Döll, P., (2004) *Taking into account environmental water requirements in global-scale water resources assessments*. Comprehensive Assessment Research Report 2. Colombo, Sri Lanka, Comprehensive Assessment Secretariat.

44   WRI. (2007) *Climate Analysis Indicators Tool (CAIT) database 5.0*. World Resources Institute, Washington, DC.

45   Burgoo, V., (2007) *Greenhouse gas emissions per capita 2000*. Available at: commons.wikimedia.org/wiki/Image:GHG_per_capita_2000.svg [Accessed 16 Nov 2009].

46   WWF. (2006) *Living Planet Report 2006*. World Wildlife Fund, Geneva, Switzerland.

05

Combating Hunger

Cooking pots in a village in the Ivory Coast. © iStockphoto

Hunger is a powerful word that encompasses the complex patterns of undernutrition amongst the world's poor. The hungry include:

- About a billion people who are chronically undernourished (i.e. consuming less than 1,800 calories per day);[1]
- 130 million children under five who are underweight for their age (more than two standard deviations below the median);[2]
- 400 million women who are anaemic;[3]
- Over 200 million children who are vitamin A deficient.[2]

In the developed countries hunger is a feeling of slight discomfort when a meal is late or missed. By contrast, in the developing countries hunger is a chronic problem. Television images convey the realities of hunger – emaciated and starving children – in war-torn countries or in the aftermath of droughts, floods or other calamities. But hunger in the developing countries is a day-to-day occurrence, both persistent and widespread. Children are especially vulnerable, from their time in the womb until the age of five. During this period of rapid physical and cognitive development, even short-term dietary deprivation can have lasting effects. Undernutrition during this time leads to stunted growth, low brain development, low life expectancy, poor educational attainment and inter-generational poverty. Hunger and poverty are inextricably linked, one resulting in the other, so creating a trap from which escape is very difficult.[2,4,5]

It is the persistence of hunger and its consequences that have made hunger a key target of the MDGs. While many of the Asian developing countries are going to reach the MDG of halving the proportion of hungry people by 2015, in Sub-Saharan Africa only Ghana is going to achieve this (see Chapter 4).

1. The chronic crisis

Hunger has grown much worse as a result of the 2008 food price crisis, which has added over a hundred million people to the numbers of chronically undernourished.[6] This is because even the poorest people are dependent on purchased food. They spend a much higher proportion of their income on food than wealthier people, making them particularly vulnerable to price increases.

A five-person household living in Bangladesh on the poverty line of US$1 a day per person typically spends its US$5 as follows:

- US$3.00 on food;
- US$0.50 on household energy;
- US$1.50 on non-foods.

A 50% increase in food and energy prices means there is virtually nothing left over for other expenditures.[7] In practice people eat less: they have one less meal a day, women may reduce their food intake or children drop out of school.

Figure 5.1 depicts the dramatic trajectory of the 2008 food price crisis. Prices started to rise at the end of 2006, accelerated through 2007, reaching a peak in June 2008. Then they fell back to a low at the beginning of 2009.

In many respects the food price increase of 2008 was a classic price spike. First, a commodity becomes, or is perceived to be, scarce; second, prices rise; third, producers respond by producing more of the commodity and finally, prices fall. But while food prices fell at the end of 2008 they were still 20 % up on the 2006 prices and grew throughout 2009.

The drivers of hunger and poverty

The food price crisis was not a simple transitory event.[9] It grew out of the underlying chronic crisis and that made it deeper and probably more persistent. It also raised awareness of the underlying drivers. These are not distinct processes. They may share common underlying causes and, most important, they feed on each other creating the hunger-poverty trap that was mentioned above.

The key drivers are as follows:

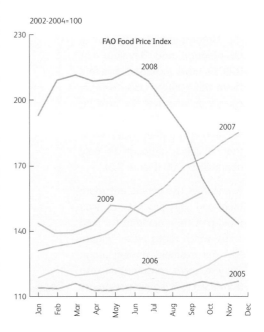

Figure 5.1 – The trajectory of food prices in 2008[8]

2002-2004=100

FAO Food Price Index

- *Rising populations.*

    According to the latest UN estimates, the global population is set to rise to about eight billion, plus or minus a billion by 2050 (Figure 5.2).[10] Thereafter it may begin to stabilize and fall.

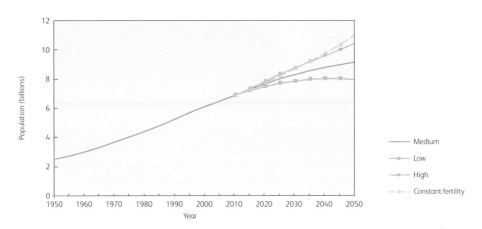

Figure 5.2 – Global population estimates – high, medium and low variants[10]

Population (billions)

Year

- Medium
- Low
- High
- Constant fertility

Inevitably this estimated rise in the population (from 5 billion now) will create an ever increasing demand for food. The International Food Policy Research Institute (IFPRI) model estimates that global cereal demand will therefore need to increase from about 260 million tonnes to over 450 million tonnes by 2050.[11]

• **Rising per capita income and its affect on diet.**

Per capita incomes in countries in the Organisation for Economic Cooperation and Development (OECD) have increased five-fold (from US$5,000 to US$40,000 in current dollars) over the past 30 years. In South Asia and Sub-Saharan Africa they have more than doubled, although to only about US$1,000 (Figure 5.3).[12]

As incomes rise people eat more meat and dairy products, causing rapid growth in demand for feed crops, which raises prices (Figure 5.4). For example, among urban Chinese, meat consumption rose from 25kg to 32kg per person per year in the decade from 1996.[13]

With rising incomes, people buy more processed and higher value foods but not more raw agricultural commodities. Globally, meat consumption is expected to grow from 55 million tonnes to 310 million tonnes/year over the next decade. Meeting this demand will require feed grain usage to increase from about 50 million tonnes to about 640 million tonnes/year.[15]

Figure 5.3 – The steady, worldwide growth in per capita incomes over the past 30 years[12]

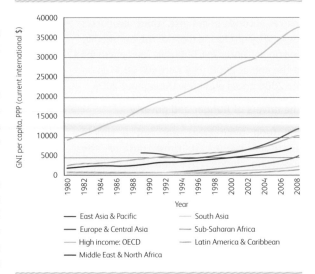

Year

— East Asia & Pacific   — South Asia
— Europe & Central Asia   — Sub-Saharan Africa
— High income: OECD   — Latin America & Caribbean
— Middle East & North Africa

Figure 5.4 – The rise in meat consumption over the past 40 years[14]

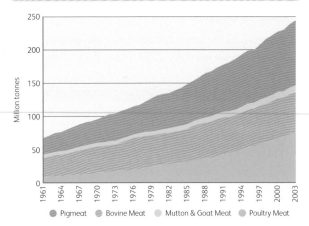

● Pigmeat   ● Bovine Meat   ● Mutton & Goat Meat   ● Poultry Meat

• **Growing demand for biofuels.**

Growing crops to produce biofuels reduces land and production directed towards growing crops for human consumption, so contributing to rising prices. But how much of the 2008 price spike was due to the rapidly increasing demand for biofuels is strongly disputed (IFPRI estimates that demand for biofuels was responsible for 30% of the rise in average grain prices).[16]

'The rapid increase in demand for, and production of biofuels – particularly bioethanol from maize and sugarcane – has had a number of effects on grain supply-and-demand systems. Expanded production of ethanol from maize, in particular, has increased total demand for maize and shifted land area away from production of maize for food and feed, stimulating increased prices for maize. Rising maize prices, in turn, have affected other grains.'[16]

What is not disputed is that biofuel production quadrupled between 2000 and 2008 (Figure 5.5)

Figure 5.5 – The rapid rise in biofuel production[17]

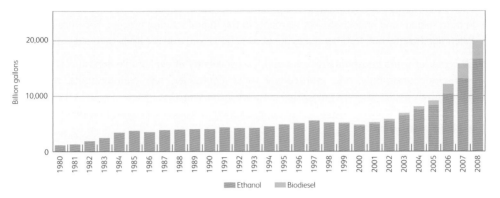

Figure 5.5 – The rapid rise in biofuel production[17]

Moreover this rise is to continue. The proportion of US maize for bioethanol increased to 33 % of the expected corn crop in 2009-10 and it is set to continue rising to meet national targets. Challenging new targets have also been proposed for biofuels in Europe. In 2008, EU members agreed that biofuels will constitute 10 % of transport fuel in the EU by 2020.[18]

- *Oil and fertiliser prices.*

Rising oil prices were one of the key elements of the 2008 food price spike. Indeed their rise was a precursor of the food price increase. The effect was, and still is, felt through the demand for biofuels together with the increased costs of transportation. This affects both agricultural input and output prices, and in particular the production, transportation and costs of fertilisers.

Figure 5.6 – Sweet potatoes are grown and consumed extensively in Sub-Saharan Africa

© HarvestPlus

One of the biggest fertiliser price increases was in diammonium phosphate (DAP), a commonly used source of nutrients in developing countries (Figure 5.7). It rose nearly six fold in early 2008, due to the energy prices involved in the production of the ammonium, and because of shortages in both sulphur and phosphate, key elements in the manufacturing process. The price has since fallen significantly but, fertiliser prices are above 2006 levels and are likely to remain at this level.

Estimates of world phosphate reserves and the availability of exploitable deposits vary greatly. High-grade phosphate ores, particularly those containing few contaminants, are being progressively depleted whilst production costs are increasing. One review concludes that within a time span of some 60 to 70 years about half the world's current economic phosphate resources will have been exhausted.[19]

Figure 5.7 – The rise and fall of fertiliser prices in 2008[20]

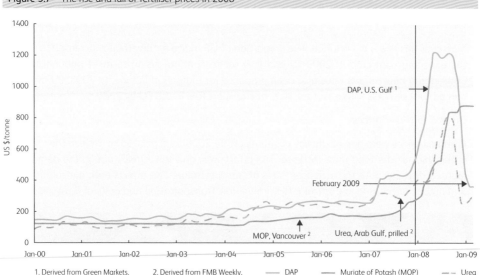

1. Derived from Green Markets.   2. Derived from FMB Weekly.   —— DAP   —— Muriate of Potash (MOP)   - - - Urea

- *Increasing water and land scarcity.*

The amount of arable land worldwide divided by the total population has halved to about 0.2 ha over the past 40 years.[21,22] At the same time large areas of land are being degraded as a result of erosion, loss of fertility and desertification. Similarly, water is in short supply (see Chapter 7).[23] Many river basins do not have enough water to meet all the demands. About a fifth of the world's people – more than 1.2 billion – live in areas of physical water scarcity. Rivers are drying up, groundwater levels are falling, freshwater fisheries are being damaged, and salinisation and water pollution are increasing. Growing water scarcity and declining land for crops will make agriculture less productive and food more expensive.

- *Impact of climate change.*

The 2008 price spike was not a result of climate change, although there is some evidence that the catastrophic drought in Australia – the worst for over 100 years – was made more severe in its effect on crop yields due to higher evapotranspiration resulting from higher land surface temperatures.[24-26] In Chapter 9 we will show how future climate change will have an increasingly adverse effect on food production.

- **The slowing of productivity increases.**

Growth in grains and oilseeds production has been slowing, from an average of 2.2% in the period 1970 to 1990, to an average of 1.3% since 1990.[27] Growth in global aggregate yield averaged 2% between 1970 and 1990, but declined to 1.1% between 1990 and 2007. The factors mentioned above have contributed to this slowed growth. In addition, the recent decline in agricultural research and development, and the fall in the rate with which plant breeding has increased productivity of some staple crops, have also had an impact.

- **Price fluctuations.**

Finally, food commodities are notoriously subject to severe price fluctuations. It is a phenomenon

Figure 5.8 – A farmer in northern Vietnam sifting seeds

that has long been recognised and was the rationale for establishing government purchase and storage schemes such as the various editions of the US Farm Bill and the European Common Agriculture Policy (CAP) which aim to smooth the fluctuations. In the 2008 price spike some argue that there was a strong element of speculation. Certainly the perception of shortage was particularly acute in the case of rice, for which only a small proportion of the total harvest is normally traded. This resulted in the Philippines buying large quantities at high prices.

As Joachim von Braun has argued the interactions between these drivers were intensified by the linkages between social unrest and food riots that spread from country to country.[28] Not only is hunger a cause of unrest and conflict but so is the fear of hunger.

Hunger and technology

Some conclude from these events that problems of food security can be primarily, indeed exclusively, solved by resorting to appropriate social and economic policies. They often quote from Amartya Sen's study of the great Bengal famine of 1942 to 1944. He stated that *'Starvation is the characteristic of some people not having enough food to eat. It is not the characteristic of there not being enough food to eat.'* This implies that we do not need to invest in food productivity or in the technologies this requires.[29] Globally it may well be true that there is enough food for all if it were evenly shared. But this would suggest large and continuing shipments of free grain that would create a lasting dependency and hamper the creation of indigenous production and markets.

In practice, the causes of hunger vary from place to place. In some situations the principal factors may be growing demand for, and lack of access to, food. In others poor yields, highly destructive pests, diseases and weeds may mean there is insufficient food, even if it were evenly shared.[30,31] Yet, as the Green Revolution demonstrated, greatly increasing food production had a transformative effect on Asia's food security, as Amartya Sen recognised.[32] Appropriate social and economic policies are critical, as is the provision of secure rights to land and water. But equally there is a need for enabling technologies. Sen emphasised that one of the entitlements of poor people is access to technologies.[33] The challenge is illustrated by the conditions under which a woman farmer, such as Mrs. Namarunda, who represents a composite of situations existing in Africa, struggles to feed herself and her family (Box 5.1, page 126).

Box 5.1   A one hectare farm in Kenya[34]

Several years ago, Mrs Namurunda's husband died from a meningitis infection. Her eldest son inherited the family farm, a single hectare running up one side of a hill, in the Siaya district near Lake Victoria. The soils are moderately deep and well drained, but they are acidic, highly weathered, and leached. Mrs Namurunda's first son married and moved to Nairobi, where he is a lorry driver and has children of his own. Her elder daughter also married and now farms near her husband's village, closer to the Tanzanian border. Mrs. Namurunda was left on the farm – still officially owned by her absent son – with four younger children and the responsibility to produce food, fetch water, gather fuel, educate the children and take care of the family. But shortages of almost everything – land, money, labour, plant nutrients in soil exhausted from many years of continual crop production – mean that she is often unable to provide her family with adequate food. The two youngest children in particular suffer from undernourishment and persistent illnesses.

Like many others in Africa, Mrs Namurunda's farm provides an "insecure" livelihood and her family does not have food security. Fertiliser is too expensive so she starts each growing season with a maximum potential harvest of only about two tonnes from mixed cropping on her one hectare of land.

To survive, her family requires a harvest of about one tonne, so if everything goes right and the maximum harvest is achieved, it would be sufficient to meet their needs and to generate a modest income. But, during the course of every growing season, she faces innumerable threats to her crops which reduce her yields. Weeds are her most persistent and pervasive problem. It takes 40 to 50 days of weeding each crop, by her and the children, to keep the weeds under control. Her staple crop, maize, is attacked by:

- Streak virus, where leaves develop long, white, chlorophyll-depleted lesions;

- The parasitic weed Striga, which sucks nutrients from the roots and poisons its host;

- Boring insects, which weaken the stem;

- Fungi which rots the ears that do develop, before and after harvest.

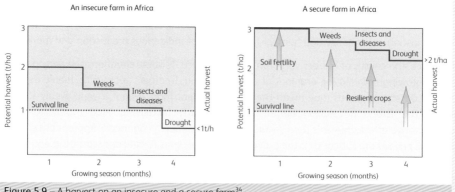

Figure 5.9 – A harvest on an insecure and a secure farm[34]

Mrs Namurunda has tried growing cassava as an "insurance crop." But it, too, was attacked, first by mealy bugs and green mites, exotic pests from Latin America, with no indigenous predators in Africa. Then it was totally devastated by a new super-virulent strain of African cassava mosaic virus that originated in Uganda, carried to Kenya by its white fly vectors.

The banana seedlings she obtained from neighbours were already infected with weevils, nematodes and the fungal disease Black Sigatoka (another import from Latin America) when she bought them. Her beans, which are intended as a source of protein for the family and nitrogen for the soil, suffer from fungal diseases that rot the roots, deform leaves, shrivel pods and lower nitrogen fixation. She also faces drought at some time during the growing season that again reduces crop yields. At the end of each season, what she actually harvests is usually less than one tonne. She and her children are often hungry, and there is no money for schooling or for health care.

It does not have to be this way for Mrs Namurunda and her children. Traditional, conventional or new platform technologies can provide answers, but they have to be accessible and affordable.

In this chapter we look at the ways in which science and innovation can develop technologies that go some way to mitigating the effects of the drivers of hunger. We begin with what has already been accomplished.

2. Past successes

The challenges highlighted by the food price crisis of 2008 must be placed in the context of the progress already made over the past 50 years in reducing hunger in the developing world. During that period the proportion of the global population that is chronically hungry has fallen from 37 % to 17 % and the total numbers from 1.4 billion to 1 billion.[35] We owe much of that to the Green Revolution, one of the great technological success stories of the 20th century (Box 5.2).

Box 5.2 The innovators of the Green Revolution[36]

Norman Borlaug was awarded the Nobel Peace Prize in 1970 for his work but sadly died in 2009. He was justly credited with being the Father of the Green Revolution. At the core of his innovations was the transfer to improved wheat varieties of a dwarfing gene – originally from Japan – by a speeded up, but conventional, process of plant breeding.

For nearly 20 years Borlaug worked with a team of Mexican and American scientists, in Mexico to improve local wheats. They achieved a great deal, especially in disease resistance, but were frustrated by the inability of the wheats to take advantage of high levels of fertiliser; the plants would 'lodge' and the ears rot. The new semi-dwarf varieties took up the nitrogen and produced yields of up to seven tonnes per ha.

In 1965, Norman Borlaug took the new seeds to India and Pakistan. In India M.S. Swaminathan became their champion; within ten years, average yields had more than doubled (Figure 5.10, page 128).

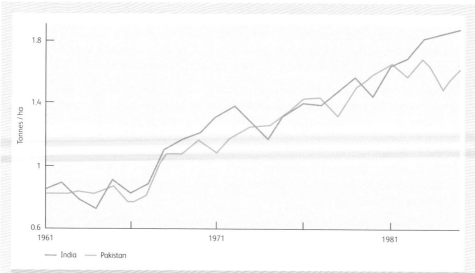

Figure 5.10 – The doubling of wheat yields in south Asia following the introduction of the new short-strawed wheat varieties in 1965[36]

Also in the 60s a similar innovation with dwarfing genes – originating in China – was applied to rice. The results were dramatic. In Indonesia rice yields doubled within ten years.[36] Again national innovators oversaw the transformations. Vo Ton Xuang's leadership took Vietnam from being a rice importing country in 1989, to the second largest exporter in the world by 1996.[37]

Figure 5.11 – Some of the Leaders of the Green Revolution (from left to right) – Norman Borlaug, M.S. Swaminathan and Vo Ton Xuang

Yields and production rose dramatically wherever new Green Revolution seeds were sown. By the end of the 1960s India and Pakistan were no longer dependent on foreign food aid. Food production began to outstrip population growth and the prices of the staple cereals fell progressively in real terms, benefiting both rural and urban consumers (Figure 5.12).

Figure 5.12 – After the oil price induced food price spike of the mid-70s cereal prices fell steadily[38]

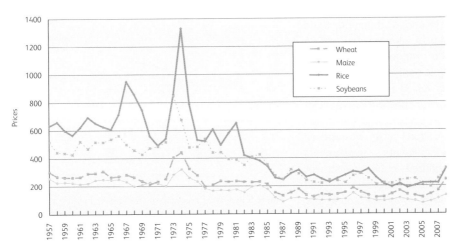

The Green Revolution succeeded because it focused on three interrelated actions:

- Breeding programmes for staple cereals to produce early maturing, day-length insensitive and high-yielding varieties;

- The organisation and distribution of packages of high pay-off inputs, such as fertilisers, pesticides and water regulation;

- Implementation of these technical innovations in the most favourable agro-climatic regions and for those classes of farmers with the best expectations of realising the potential yields (notably Sonora in Mexico, the Punjab in India and Pakistan, and Luzon and Java in Southeast Asia).

But limits to the success soon became apparent. While the better placed farmers greatly benefited as did the labourers they employed, many small farms in less favourable environments missed out as did millions of the rural landless. There were environmental consequences too, arising from the intensive levels of inputs, particularly from heavy pesticide use in the early years.

Most important, while the benefits were apparent in much of Asia, the Middle East and Latin America, virtually all of Sub-Saharan Africa missed out. As a consequence there is still a great deal of hunger in the world (see Chapter 4). On present trends there is little likelihood of Sub-Saharan Africa halving the proportion of hungry by 2015; Ghana is the only exception.

But the challenges are not confined to Africa. Recent agricultural growth in India has also been disappointing (Box 5.3).

Box 5.3   Agricultural growth in India has slowed over the past 20 years

The early benefits to India of the new varieties and input packages and the investments in irrigation were built upon in the 1980s with a set of targeted investments that went beyond national food security and began to tackle poverty in the more marginal rural areas. By the end of the decade, growth in agricultural GDP per annum had increased from 1.4%, at the beginning of the Green Revolution, to 4%.[39]

Progress slowed in the 1990s, however, as a national fiscal crisis and a changing world political climate brought a wide range of structural adjustments. The previously over-valued exchange rate and import substitution policies were removed, and the Indian agricultural sector was opened up.[40] Private investments stagnated, public investment continued to decline, and growth slowed to around 2% over the decade, with rain-fed areas being hardest hit.[39]

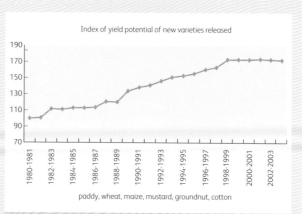

Index of yield potential of new varieties released

paddy, wheat, maize, mustard, groundnut, cotton

Figure 5.13 – The stagnation of yield growth in India as measured by the index of yield potential of new varieties of rice, wheat, maize, mustard, groundnut and cotton[41]

From 2000 growth slowed even further. Yield potentials stagnated and by 2004 per capita food grains production was back to 1970s levels (Figure 5.13).[41]

Indian farmers are increasingly vulnerable to declining water tables, ageing and poorly managed transportation and irrigation infrastructure as well as unstable markets. Inequality is also increasing in some areas, as richer farmers continue to make better use of the available technologies and overuse water resources.[39]

3. The need for a Doubly Green Revolution

Some have argued that what is needed is a repeat of the Green Revolution – a search for new technologies similar to those of the semi-dwarf cereal varieties that will deliver a quantum leap in yields and production. For a number of reasons this is unlikely to be an effective strategy.

The environments that were ideal for the Green Revolution varieties are already fully exploited. The poor and hungry live today in very different circumstances. Both in South Asia and Sub-Saharan Africa the challenge is to develop technologies that will deliver for relatively small farmers in more diverse, poorly endowed, risk-prone environments. This will require a variety of locally adapted technologies targeted on specific needs.

In brief we need a Doubly Green Revolution that:

'repeats the success of the Green Revolution on a global scale in many diverse localities and is equitable, sustainable and environmentally friendly.'[36]

The goal is an agriculture that is:

- Highly productive – by 2050 we will need to have increased grain production by over 70% and it will need to be produced efficiently and cheaply;
- Stable – less affected by the vagaries of the weather and the market;

- Resilient – resistant or tolerant of stress or shocks, especially those generated by climate change (see Chapter 9);

- Equitable – providing food and incomes to the poor and hungry.

To produce this revolution we need to develop and implement new technologies and production processes that provide farmers with productive, stable, resilient and equitable farming systems (Box 5.4).

Box 5.4   The nature of sustainable agriculture

Agricultural systems, from the field to the watershed, can be characterised by four properties – productivity, stability, resilience and equitability. Each of these may be at high or low levels and typically in development they trade-off against each other. Thus, during the Green Revolution, high productivity was achieved at the expense of resilience and equitability. Sustainable agriculture aims to minimise these trade-offs and to produce as large as possible an overlap where all the properties are high.

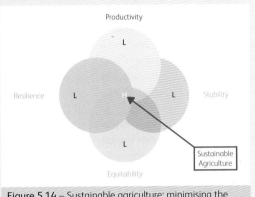

Figure 5.14 – Sustainable agriculture: minimising the trade-offs

---

The technologies for sustainable agriculture need to focus on five broad needs:

1. New crop varieties (and livestock breeds) that are more productive and of better nutritional quality;

2. Improved soil fertility and crops and livestock better able to use existing nutrients;

3. More efficient water use;

4. Better pest, disease and weed control without environmental damage;

5. Cropping and livestock systems that combine these qualities in ways that bring benefits to both small and large farmers.

As we discussed in Chapter 2 the technologies may be drawn from a wide range of sources. They may be:

- Traditional – encompassing everything from bird scaring to designing intricate home gardens;

- Intermediate – including treadle pumps for water supply and mixed cropping to reduce pests and increase nutrients;

- Conventional or industrial – comprising conventional breeding techniques and industrial agrochemicals;

- Advanced – including nanotechnology and the various forms of modern biotechnology.

In the following sections, we explore how science and innovation are contributing in these five areas.

4. Breeding for yields and quality

The Green Revolution resulted in dramatic increases in the yields of the main cereal crops. These translated into rising average national yields, for example in South Asia and China, but not in Sub-Saharan Africa (Figure 5.15).

Increasing yields

The yield increases in South Asia and China have partly come from plant breeding.[43] New varieties have been developed with a higher harvest index (the ratio of grain to total crop biomass), shorter stature and increased stalk strength that reduces susceptibility to lodging, so making them able to take up high amounts of nitrogen. Plants which mature earlier can exploit shorter growing seasons and make it possible to grow more than one crop a year in some environments. Annual double-crop systems with rice, wheat and maize are now the main cropping system where the soil, climate, and water environment are favourable. For maize and rice the development of hybrids has made a significant contribution.

But there is now evidence that the annual increase in cereal yields is declining.[43] As is evident from Figure 5.16 in South Korea, where all rice is produced with irrigation, the yields increased rapidly until 1980 but thereafter have plateaued at 80 % of the yield potential which has not changed. In Indonesia yields are continuing to rise because of increasing irrigation, while the yields in Thailand have remained low because 75 % of the rice is rain-fed on poor quality soils.

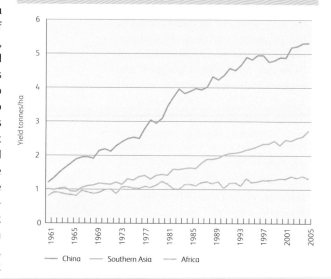

Figure 5.15 – Average cereal yields have increased steadily since the Green Revolution in China and South Asia but remained stagnant at 1 tonne/ha in Sub-Saharan Africa[42]

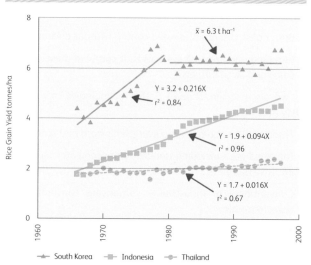

Figure 5.16 – Average rice yields in three Asian countries[43]

This has led some breeders to suggest we are reaching plateaux in yield potential for several crops (the yield potential is the yield under ideal conditions, i.e. when stresses are at a minimum) (Box 5.5). Kenneth Cassman argues that much of the gains over the past 30 years have been made through 'a brute-force' selection approach, and this may be increasingly unproductive.[43]

Crop	Potential in tonnes/ha	Comments
Rice	9 – 10	IRRI farm in the Philippines.[44]
Maize	16 – 20	Irrigated, yield contest winners, Nebraska.[44]
Spring wheat	10 – 11	Maximum yields in farmers' fields.[45]
Winter wheat	12 – 15	Maximum yields in farmers' fields.[45]

Table 5.1   Yield potentials of major cereals have plateaued at about the following levels. In the case of rice the potential is not much greater than in 1966

As in rice, there has been a similar slowing down in improving wheat yield potential. Investments have been targeted on traits such as quality and disease resistance rather than yield; further increases in yield may be possible with renewed efforts.[45] It has been argued that the high average yields of maize (about 9 tonnes/ha) attained in the US have been the result of the strong interest of the private sector in the crop (in contrast to rice and wheat).[46] Average annual US yields were about 1.5 tonnes/ha prior to the 1930s and only began to increase with the introduction of hybrids. Since then increasing yields have, in part, been due to plant breeding and in part due to improved agronomic practices.[47]

Hybridisation

The production of hybrid crop varieties has been one of the major successes of plant breeding over the past hundred years, but its full potential in the developing countries has yet to be realised.

Hybrids make use of the property of 'hybrid vigour' (or heterosis), where the decline in quality which comes from self-pollination, is overcome by crossing different lines of the species to provide an extra yield increment (Box 5.5). Often the more distant the relatedness of the crosses, the higher the heterosis. This property was discovered in maize some 100 years ago,[48] and has since been exploited across the developed world and, to a limited extent, in Asia and Africa.

Box 5.5   The steps in producing hybrid maize[49]

The superiority of hybrids over self-fertilised (inbred) plants and animals has been known for thousands of years, but modern hybrid maize breeding began in 1909, through the work of George Shull of the Carnegie Institute. Some of the first hybrids were bred by Henry Wallace, later to become Secretary of Agriculture, in 1923. Adoption took off in the US in the 1930s: in Iowa, the proportion of hybrid maize grew from less than 10% in 1935 to well over 90% only four years later.

The process is relatively straight forward:

1. Elite inbred lines are crossed;

2. Their progeny are then self-pollinated over five generations or so to find the best performing lines;

3. Some of the best, unrelated inbreeds are crossed to produce the hybrids which are tested in different environments over several years;

4. Each year the two best parents are crossed to produce the hybrid seed for sale.

In Kenya, for example, the first steps in hybrid maize production began in 1955, under the country's chief maize breeder, who decided to widen the genetic base by crossing an Ecuadorian line with a local improved variety.[50,51] In 1964 the new Hybrid 611 provided a remarkable 40 % yield advantage over previous varieties, and enjoyed a rapid uptake by both large- and small-scale farmers. This spawned what has been termed in Kenya the 'Maize Green Revolution', with continued increases in yields and spread of innovative hybrid varieties across the country from 1965 through to 1980 (Figure 5.17). The technological breakthroughs were supported by government policies which provided an extension programme, credit and subsidised inputs for smallholders, as well as a controlled export market.

But with the decline of support for public agricultural research through the 1980s, and pressure to reduce state subsidies and market support, the growth declined.[51]

Elsewhere in the developing countries, hybrids are less common and yields are accordingly lower. In India over half of the planting is of open-pollinated varieties which cross at random and generate an average yield of only two tonnes/ha.

In Malawi a large-scale programme of subsidies for maize seed and fertilisers was introduced in 2005/6.[52] Farmers could choose from among the following:

- Their local landraces whose seed they keep from year to year;

- Open-pollinated (OPV) or composite maize – essentially mixtures of different varieties whose seeds can be re-used for at least three to four years without significant deterioration in yield;

- Hybrid maize – where the seeds need to be obtained and planted every one or two years to maintain high yields.

Yields under optimal conditions are three, five and eight tonnes/ha respectively for local, open-pollinated and hybrid seeds. Significantly, by the 2006/7 season

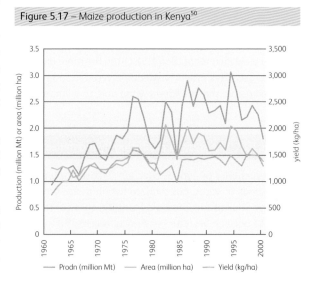

Figure 5.17 – Maize production in Kenya[50]

the farmers were predominantly choosing the hybrids, many thousand farmers for the first time. The result was a spectacular increase in total maize production from under two million to over three million tonnes for the country as a whole.

It is clear that wider adoption of hybrid maize will greatly increase yields. This is true for small farmers as well as large (in Malawi small farmers are readily producing five tonnes from a one ha plot sown with hybrid seeds and using adequate fertilisers). There is no fundamental reason why developing country maize yields should not approach those of the US.

The same argument also applies to hybrid rices which have been developed more recently in China.[53] For some time there has been disappointing progress in improving the yields of tropical rices. But the new hybrids have a high yield potential when grown in tropical lowland environments.[54] They account for about 50% of the rice area in China with average yields of seven tonnes/ha. Attention has now turned to the development of super hybrid rices with average yields over nine tonnes/ha and in some trials 12 tonnes being achieved. Adoption is beginning to occur in Vietnam, India, the Philippines and Bangladesh. There are impediments to further growth of hybrid rice varieties, including low hybrid seed production, high seed cost, and poor grain quality but these can be overcome.[44]

Beyond hybridisation

In the US breeding improvements, beyond hybridisation, have relied on marker-aided selection (MAS) (see Box 2.17 in Chapter 2) and the use of recombinant DNA engineering to produce genetically modified (GM) crops.

So far MAS has focussed on individual traits such as resistance to maize streak virus or that which enables the introduction of certain nutritive proteins in the grain (see below). Breeding for yield is more complicated because it is controlled by numerous genes. Nevertheless, MAS has demonstrated improvements in yields of maize and soybean in the US utilising traits for grain moisture and the prevention of stalk lodging.[55] Currently GM technologies increase yields by targeting the pests and weeds that reduce yields, but new generations of GM crops will soon be released in the US that have direct yield enhancing traits.

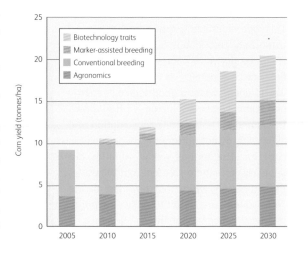

Figure 5.18 – Predicted relative contribution of agronomic methods and different breeding technologies to improving maize yields in the US[46]

Companies, such as Monsanto, that are intimately involved in the development of biotechnological approaches, believe that by 2030 approximately half the yield increases of crops such as maize will come from biotechnology (Figure 5.18).[46] In due course this could also hold true for the developing countries.

Improving nutritional value

Hunger is not only due to a lack of calories, but also a result of deficiencies in a range of proteins and micronutrients in the diet – sometimes referred to as hidden hunger. Most of these deficiencies can be improved by having a varied diet including meat, milk, fruits and vegetables in addition to cereals. Yet such diets are often not available or affordable for poor people and they have to rely almost exclusively on the staple cereals. This is particularly true of infants and young children where malnutrition is widespread in Sub-Saharan Africa and South Asia.

Perhaps surprisingly, most cereals and other staples are deficient in a number of proteins and other micronutrients. For instance, maize is deficient in the amino acids lysine and tryptophan which are essential for building proteins in the body. However, the capacity to produce these amino acids exists in the maize genome and only needs the right genetic background for expression. In this case, a suitable mutant has been found and this has been used in a long meticulous programme of conventional breeding to produce new high yielding maize with these amino-acids present.[56] Marker-aided selection is now being used to transfer these genes into a wide range of locally adapted maize in Africa.

Vitamin A

Another major deficiency is vitamin A (Chapter 6). While provision of supplements and fostering dietary variety are effective, they often do not reach the urban or rural poor.[57] Breeding beta-carotene, the precursor of vitamin A, into staple foodstuffs, for example sweet potato or rice, can provide a more stable and sustainable source at little or no extra cost. (Box 5.6)

Box 5.6   Breeding for vitamin A

Sweet Potatoes

This root vegetable is grown and consumed extensively throughout Sub-Saharan Africa. It can be grown in poor soil conditions, has few natural enemies, is highly tolerant of weeds, and provides a good source of energy and carbohydrates. The crop is often grown by women for both family consumption and extra cash. Sweet potatoes come in multiple varieties. The orange-yellow varieties are relatively rich in beta-carotene, but the white-fleshed, starchy types that have less of the compound, are traditionally favoured amongst African populations. Research is now focussed on breeding a variety with high beta-carotene levels that will be acceptable to African palates, are virus resistant and grow well in the local climate. Markers have been identified for high beta-carotene

© Harvest Plus

Figure 5.19 – Women enjoying orange sweet potato

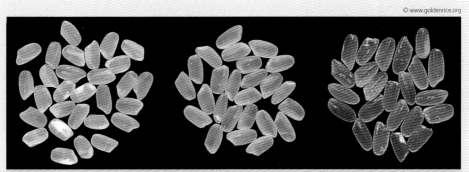

© www.goldenrice.org

Figure 5.20 – Rice grains with and without beta-carotene. Golden Rice 1 was the first generation, Golden Rice 2 the second. (from left to right) Wild type, Golden Rice 1, Golden Rice 2

content and the first releases of improved 'biofortified' sweet potatoes were made in Uganda and Mozambique in 2007.[57-59]

The breeding has been conducted by scientists at the International Potato Centre in Lima, Peru as part of the CGIAR's HarvestPlus programme and implementation is being led by the Vitamin A Partnership for Africa (VITAA), formed by bringing together scientists with health and nutrition agencies, NGOs and private businesses. Together these groups are working with communities to explain the benefits of the new varieties and promote their uptake.

Rice

In Asia, and many parts of Sub-Saharan Africa, poor families consume rice as the basic staple of their diet and babies are often weaned on rice gruel. But the rice grain lacks beta-carotene; there is plenty in the leaves and stems, but none in the grain endosperm. And no amount of traditional breeding has been able to get it there (Brown, unmilled rice contains only minute amounts of beta-carotene).

Here the approach has been to find suitable genes elsewhere and to use recombinant DNA to insert them into a new variety of rice named, after its distinctive colour, 'Golden Rice.' (Figure 5.20).

Ingo Potrykus of the Swiss Federal Institute of Technology, and his colleague Peter Beyer of the University of Freiburg, first transferred two daffodil and one bacterial gene into rice to ensure the grain contained beta-carotene. The biochemical pathway leading to beta-carotene is largely present in the rice grain but lacks two crucial enzymes: phytoene synthase (*psy*) – provided by a daffodil gene – and carotene desaturase (*crt1I*) – provided by a bacterium gene.[60] In the greenhouse this transfer gave beta-carotene levels of about 1.6 µg/g, significant but not large. Subsequently, scientists at Syngenta have found new versions of the *psy* gene in maize; which when introduced to rice increased the beta-carotene levels to 31 µg/g, although this high level degrades slowly during storage.[61]

Given a conversion ratio of beta-carotene to vitamin A of 4:1, the new golden rice (Golden Rice 2) will be able to provide the necessary boost to daily diets, even after six months of storage.[61] Currently the new golden rice varieties are undergoing field and feeding trials and being assessed on bio-safety criteria.

5. Improving the productivity and quality of livestock

Livestock are frequently ignored in discussions of food security. The emphasis in agricultural policies tends to be focused on cereal grains and this is equally true of donor programmes and projects. Yet for the rural poor, livestock are often a critical element in their livelihoods. It is estimated that about 600 million people, or 70 % of the rural poor, depend on livestock.[62,63] For many communities in arid environments, livestock such as cattle, sheep, goats and chickens are the main source of food and income. Besides meat, cattle are a valuable source of milk and blood, traction and fertiliser for the fields. They also serve as a traditional means of banking, being sold when times are hard or to finance a special celebration.

Despite their obvious importance, there has been insufficient coordinated effort to improve livestock productivity in developing countries in the past decades. While livestock systems in industrialized countries have evolved into highly efficient and planned commercial enterprises, most production in the developing world still relies on small flocks or herds, often free grazing. According to IFPRI, '*although three-quarters of the world's cattle and two-thirds of the world's pigs, poultry, sheep, and goats lived in developing countries in 1993, those countries produced less than half of the world's meat and a third of the world's milk.*'[64]

One success story is the progress made from 1970 to 1996 in India during 'Operation Flood,' which revolutionised milk production and consumption in a way that benefited the poor. The 30 year project was a coordinated effort by India's National Dairy Development Board to better connect milk producers to consumers through the establishment of dairy cooperatives and a national 'milk grid'. Measures were also taken to increase the productivity of cattle by improving veterinary services, ensuring better feed and nutrition for the cattle, extending artificial insemination for breeding and the development of vaccines for diseases such as tropical theileriosis.[65]

Productivity in other areas is growing slowly, especially in Asia where a scarcity of land increases the pressure to improve efficiency of livestock production.[64] Traditional systems are also beginning to be squeezed in other regions as grazing land decreases, changes in crop production methods leave less residue for crop feed, and more cereals are required for feed, which are often imported.[64] Solutions to these challenges can come through better quality feed and nutrition, improved management of stocking densities and better awareness of the entire livestock-crop-environment system (Box 5.21 on crop-livestock systems).

Breeding also plays a role in improving livestock productivity by helping to find and incorporate traits which better address changes in demand for meat products, expanding industrialisation and climate change issues.[66,67]

Developing breeding programmes

Farmers have been selecting for useful traits in their herds for thousands of years, since the first domestication of animals. Cattle have been selected for such obvious characteristics as size, colour and the shape of their horns, sheep for their wool, chickens for the amount of eggs they produce and livestock of all kinds for the taste and quality of their meat. They also select for animals that are resistant to disease. This process, like conventional breeding in plants, can be slow.

Artificial insemination has been used for more than 50 years to economically and efficiently improve herds. The practice is slowly growing in the developing world, especially in Asia, in sectors such as dairy cattle in India.[64] Another improvement technique is cross-breeding with foreign or exotic species, such as crossing Kenyan dairy cattle with European breeds. This has resulted in some improvements in productivity, especially in yields of marketable products such as milk and meat. Yet, while taking traits from foreign productive animals can bring quick results, it is expensive and desirable traits of local animals, such as adaptation to the local climate and diseases, can be lost in the cross-breeding process.[68-70]

Advances in applied genetics, molecular biology and reproductive technologies are making it possible to more efficiently select for high quality characteristics, and to address the loss of genetic diversity among livestock worldwide. Since 1990, 300 out of 6,000 breeds identified by FAO have become extinct and many more are at risk, largely as a result of unplanned intensive selection and cross-breeding.[71] Traditional breeds, which have evolved over generations to be particularly well adapted to local conditions, are being lost. Here, genetic mapping and markers can be used to gain an understanding of the current state of diversity in various breeds. This information can be fed into the design of conservation and breeding programmes, making difficult choices such as the prioritization of sheep breeds in Ethiopia (Box 5.7) easier.[72,73]

Box 5.7   Conservation of sheep breeds in Ethiopia

Ethiopia is believed to have the largest livestock population in all of Africa, with the sector accounting for around 15 % of total GDP and contributing to the livelihoods of around 70 % of the total population. Sheep play a particularly important role, with a herd population of around 24 million, largely kept by smallholders, both in the cooler highlands (25 %) and the more arid lowlands (75 %). Despite their significant role, to date, there has been no coordinated national sheep breeding strategy.[74]

To help address this problem, researchers from the Agricultural Research Centre in Ethiopia, Wageningen University in the Netherlands and the International Livestock Research Institute (ILRI) recently teamed up to prioritise the 14 traditional Ethiopian sheep breeds. As criteria they used the breed's vulnerability to extinction, its contribution to farmer livelihoods (as ranked by the farmers) and its contribution to genetic diversity (based on a breed's uniqueness). Rather than just ranking the breeds by one of these criteria, the team aggregated the results to provide overall rankings (Table 5.2).

Breed	Contribution to diversity	Extinction probability	Average breed merit to farmers	Total utility	Conservation priority rank
Simien	0.4355	0.3	0.33	0.60	1
Gumz	0.1170	0.9	0.23	0.44	2
Adilo	0.0000	0.4	0.17	0.17	14

Table 5.2 – Extract from ranking table for Ethiopian sheep breeds

Rankings like this can provide a more scientific means of balancing the trade-offs between genetic conservation and present-day livelihood concerns, and can be used as a starting point for regional or national conservation plans.[75] Recommendations from the research team included:

- Supporting genetic improvement programmes to increase market competitiveness of indigenous breeds of lower productivity;

- Separating production zones to avoid indiscriminate cross-breeding;

- Implementing management strategies which conserve within-breed variation.

© Belay Duguma

Figure 5.21 – Horro Sheep in their centre of origin, Horro Guduru Wollega, Ethiopia

Efforts to better understand and map livestock genetic characteristics should be used to improve breeding programmes, and to help livestock owners decide whether to select from local or exotic stock, and where artificial insemination or other modern technologies are appropriate. National programmes also need to prioritise local needs for productivity, adaptability and genetic conservation, and find new ways of extending this information to local owners.

6. Improving the fertility of soil and its utilisation

The provision, uptake and utilisation of nitrogen were critical to the success of the Green Revolution. In part this was due to the high application of inorganic fertilisers, but also because the Green Revolution lands were inherently rich in soil fertility. For example, a typical irrigated rice soil in Asia contains about 2,800 kgs nitrogen (N) per ha in the top 20 cms of soil.[76]

By contrast much of Africa's soil is derived from ancient granite rocks, which have been subjected to thousands of years of weathering and are therefore inherently low in plant nutrients. For example, the loamy sand and clayey soils of sorghum and millet plantations in central Mali, peak at around 20 and 40 kg N/ha respectively in the topsoil,[77] and sampled maize fields in Malawi contain 40 kg/Nha at the most.[78]

Whatever the original level of nutrients, agricultural activity can reduce soil fertility by depleting nutrients or contributing to soil erosion. Globally some 2,000 million ha of the Earth's land area is estimated to be degraded in one way or another.[79,80] 84% of the loss is due to water or wind erosion.[80] More than 80% of all degraded land is located in Africa, Asia, South and Central America.[43]

The net consequence is a continuous depletion of soil fertility. Most African countries lose more than 30 kg of nutrients (nitrogen, phosphorus and potassium) per ha per year (Figure 5.22). For some countries the figure is even higher: Rwanda was losing over 100kg of nutrients/ha/per year in the 1990s.[81]

Figure 5.22 – Most African countries are losing over 30 kgs of nutrients (nitrogen, phosphate and potassium) per ha per year[81]

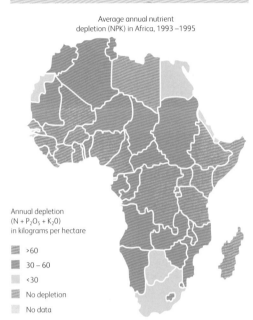

Average annual nutrient
depletion (NPK) in Africa, 1993 –1995

Annual depletion
(N + P₂O₅ + K₂O)
in kilograms per hectare

$(N + P_2O_5 + K_2O)$

- >60
- 30 – 60
- <30
- No depletion
- No data

Clearly part of the answer lies in significantly adding more inorganic fertiliser to the soils. In Africa, traditional fallow-based or rotational agriculture, which allowed soils to recover their fertility between cropping periods, has given way to continuous cropping without the application of fertilisers. On average, farmers in Sub-Saharan Africa (excluding South Africa) apply less than 10 kg of nutrients/ha, compared with 100 kg/ha in South Asia and 135 kg/ha in Southeast Asia.[82]

There is considerable evidence from African trials on farmers' fields that adding fertilisers will result in marked increases in yields.[83] Farmers in Malawi who are supplied with hybrid seed and adequate fertiliser can easily produce over five tonnes/ha on one ha plots, compared to less than one tonne using traditional methods.[84]

However, as indicated in Figure 5.7, fertilisers – such as diammonium phosphate – are now considerably more expensive and are only going to be affordable if technologies are developed that use techniques such as precise targeting to increase fertiliser efficiency. Far too often, extension systems advocate national fertiliser recommendations which may not be appropriate for local conditions.

One consequence of the high price of synthetic fertilisers, and the attendant environmental problems with their use in some parts of the world, has been to stimulate scientific research into making their use more efficient and into improving other, natural sources of soil nutrients, as has long been practised in organic agriculture.

Precision nutrients

In Chapter 2, we showed how farmers can substitute more selective placement of fertilisers instead of the widespread practice of broadcasting them. Urea super granules (USG), inserted in the middle of every four rice plants in Bangladeshi paddy fields, resulted in an extra tonne of paddy with a reduction of fertiliser by over a third.[85] Another simple but powerful selective approach is to apply a small and measured amount of fertiliser in the planting hole when the seeds are planted (Box 5.8).[86]

Box 5.8 Micro-dosing: using Coca-Cola bottle caps to apply fertiliser

Farmers in Niger have recently benefited from experiments to discover how to reduce the amount of fertiliser they need to use and still give the crops the necessary nutrients. While farmers in the area already knew well the benefits of fertilisers, most could not afford to buy the large amounts typically recommended, and therefore were not using them at all, causing yields to suffer.

To address this and to avoid the negative effects of over-fertilising on the environment, the International Crops Research Institute for the Semi-Arid Tropics (ICRISAT), along with the FAO, the University of Hohenheim in Germany and the National Agricultural Research Institute of Niger undertook research to discover the amount and mixture which was optimal for individual millet plants, a technique known as 'micro-dosing.'

© Jessie Luna

Figure 5.23 – Women working a field in the Sahel

Soil scientists and an estimated 5,000 farmers took part in the research and participatory trial of the idea between 1998 and 2000.[87] The result was a tailored fertiliser mix and measuring technique for the area. They found that using a mix of phosphorus and nitrogen fertiliser the dose for each plant was about six grams and could be measured out with a Coca-Cola bottle cap – a very easy item to obtain. This fertilising technique equates to using 4 kg/ha, three to six times less than used in Europe and North America, but still very effective.[86]

The practice has been credited with boosting millet yields by 50% to 100% in the Sahel, thereby helping to reverse a 50-year trend of declining yields and rising soil degradation.[86] Researchers are continuing to work with farmers to monitor trends in soil nutrients and yields and to fine-tune, and even further reduce, the amount of fertiliser used.

Better precision also depends on what is already in the soil. At a regional and national level, soil surveys can identify areas where fertiliser application is most needed. In Malawi the Rockefeller Foundation funded a nationwide soil and cropping survey that resulted in recommendations for over a 1,000 distinct regions.[88,89]

Finally, precision can be increased by the timing of application. While it is common to recommend fertiliser application at the time of sowing or planting this may not be the optimal time for crop uptake. Typically, in Asia, rice farmers make a relatively large initial fertiliser application followed by a single top dressing later. An experiment on 180 farmers' fields in six Asian countries showed that yields could be significantly increased by a relatively small initial application of prilled urea (the usual fertiliser) and two to three subsequent top dressings based on the readings from a chlorophyll meter. This produced an increase in the nitrogen recovery efficiency, from the 30% typical of farmer's traditional practices, to some 40%. On average yields rose by 500kg/ha, fertiliser use was reduced by 5 kg N/ha and returns were up by US$46/ha.[76,90]

Cropping systems

Productive soils are not only rich in nutrients but also in organic matter. This provides structure to the soil, improving stability, water-holding capacity and the ability of plants to absorb nutrients. It also prevents problems such as soil acidification that can result from inorganic fertiliser application. These functions not only improve plant health and drought tolerance, but lessen environmental impacts by reducing soil erosion and nutrient leaching into surrounding water sources.

Unfortunately many soils, and particularly those in Africa, are inherently low in organic carbon – and the amount declines with continuous cropping.[91,92] Even with high levels of organic carbon input, losses can be over two thirds of a tonne per ha per year.[93]

Crop residues and animal manure are important potential sources of both nutrients and organic matter for poor farmers. And, unlike synthetic fertilisers, they are renewable. But large amounts are needed to maintain soil fertility and to support increased production with improved crop varieties. A 10 tonnes/ha maize crop contains about 100 kg N/ha and at least this amount of nitrogen must be added back to the field to maintain fertility.[46]

Over much of Africa, crop residues, the mix of stalks and leaves – referred to as the stover – are insufficient in amount and nutrient value to maintain more than a very low level of grain yield. For example, reasonable yields of pearl millet in Niger are only obtained with the addition of the manure from transmigrant cattle.[94] Elsewhere organic matter has to be imported, often entailing high labour costs.

An alternative approach to renewable sources of nutrients and organic matter is to design cropping systems that incorporate nitrogen fixing legumes which can provide both organic matter and nutrients. These may be green manures, such as clover, sunn hemp and jack-beans that are incorporated in the soil at the end of their growth. Alternatively legume crops, such as cowpeas or groundnuts – that will also produce a yield – can be grown in rotation, or by intercropping or relay cropping along with grains. This second option requires farmers to carefully plan the timing and combination of their planting, so that the two crops complement each other and nitrogen sources are used as efficiently as possible. See Box 5.9 for an example.

Box 5.9 MBILI intercropping

In western Kenya a local NGO has been experimenting with methods of improving the traditional legume-maize intercropping used by farmers in the area. The Sustainable Agriculture Centre for Research, Extension and Development in Africa (SACRED-Africa) noticed that the second maize crop often failed due to insufficient late rains. It pioneered an approach which uses faster maturing maize varieties, mixed with higher-value legumes such as green gram and groundnut.[95]

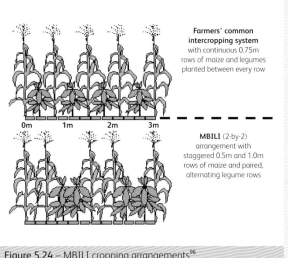

Farmers' common intercropping system with continuous 0.75m rows of maize and legumes planted between every row

0m   1m   2m   3m

MBILI (2-by-2) arrangement with staggered 0.5m and 1.0m rows of maize and paired, alternating legume rows

Figure 5.24 – MBILI cropping arrangements[96]

The system, known as MBILI (literally meaning 'two' in Swahili), consists of intercropping double rows of maize and legumes, allowing for better light and soil conditions within the understorey legumes, while maintaining the same plant populations, as shown in Figure 5.24.[96]

This provides several advantages, including higher efficiency of land use, disruption of normal pest cycles and the ability to grow crops with different light requirements.

By intercropping with high value legumes, the maize is able to take advantage of the nitrogen which is returned to the soil from the falling leaves and decomposing roots of the bean plants. The legumes can also be sold for a profit.[97] Studies over the past few years by SACRED staff and farmers have shown that planting in the MBILI arrangement can improve legume yield and total crop value by 12% without the need for additional investment by the farmers or reducing the yield of maize.[96] Yields from the system can be over five tonnes of maize and over one tonne of groundnuts per ha.[98]

© Eusebius Mukhwana

Figure 5.25 – Women evaluating the MBILI trials

Breeding for nutrient uptake

An approach which complements efforts to increase soil fertility is to breed plants which are more effective at taking up and utilising nutrients. Box 5.10 explores this challenge and the progress made so far.

Box 5.10 Getting more from nitrogen

Breeding for nitrogen use efficiency has traditionally been neglected by plant breeders, because the processes and the genetics involved are extremely complicated. The desired trait is a higher nitrogen use efficiency, or NUE, defined as the yield of grain per unit of available N in the soil. Currently, average NUE in cereals production is only around 33%,[99] and many believe there is a good potential for this to be significantly improved.

Unfortunately, NUE is a very complex trait. Nitrogen is taken up, transferred, stored and recycled through the roots, shoots, leaves and grains of a plant in response to a wide variety of triggers throughout its life cycle. Events such as leaf formation, flowering and grain filling require very specific regulation and control of the nutrient – a process which is managed differently in each individual grain crop species.[100]

Furthermore, most studies of nitrogen management have been conducted in high-N conditions. Plants behave quite differently when N is limited. Breeders also cannot select for high NUE in isolation, as they may risk inadvertently choosing cultivars which are weaker in other areas, such as yield potential or drought tolerance.[100,102]

Despite these challenges, some progress has been made. Breeders have been able to identify markers for the variability of NUE.[99] For example, scientists have discovered that the glutamine synthetase (GS) enzyme in maize not only plays a central role in N assimilation and recycling, but is also linked to yield and kernel size in both high and low N conditions.[101]

Future progress will depend on utilising tools such as micro-dissection, ^{15}N labelling, and more sophisticated crop simulation models to speed up discovery and also ease the transition of knowledge to the field.[100]

The alternative approach is to use recombinant DNA technology to incorporate in the major staple cereals a capacity to fix nitrogen that is similar to that in legumes (Box 5.11).

Box 5.11 Creating nitrogen fixing cereals

Legumes are capable of fixing nitrogen, taking it from its inert molecular form N_2, and converting it to nitrogen compounds such as ammonia, nitrate and nitrogen dioxide which can be used for plant growth. They do this through a symbiotic relationship with rhizobial bacteria that live in root nodules.

Unfortunately, the task of putting this capacity in cereal crops is considerable. Some 17 genes code the enzymes involved in nitrogen fixation. Since these genes, as well as the genes necessary for nodule formation, need to be transferred, the process is complex and its realization will be costly. Furthermore,

Reprinted by permission from Macmillan Publishers Ltd:

Figure 5.26 – Nodules form spontaneously in the absence of rhizobial bacteria on a root through removal of an inhibiting factor in the signalling pathway[104]

there is an energy cost in fixing nitrogen. It is estimated that the amount of energy required to fix 150 kg of nitrogen per hectare could reduce wheat yields by 20 % to 30 %.[100]

While these challenges have made progress difficult, a few interesting discoveries have been made along the way. Scientists in Brazil have found that while the N-fixing bacteria *Gluconacetobacter diazotrophicus* occurs naturally in the roots, it is also present in the stems, leaves and trash of sugar cane and other tropical grasses growing in low-fertility soils. However, these occurrences are not widespread, and only seem to take place in low-fertility soils, where particular plant species have evolved to grow in the absence of fertilisers. Most modern varieties have evolved to make use of added fertiliser, thus minimising the potential for developing nitrogen fixing associations. For this reason, scientists may look to more ancient germplasm for breeding programmes in the future.[103]

Recently, work by scientists in Giles Oldroyd's laboratory at the John Innes Centre in Norwich, UK, has led to an important breakthrough. They managed to identify the genes which trigger the formation of nodules in legumes, and use this knowledge to induce the formation of nodules in the absence of the bacteria (Figure 5.26).[104]

While still a distant prospect, this could be an important step in transferring nodulation, and ultimately creating nitrogen fixing cereals.

7. Optimizing water use

The third key component of the Green Revolution was the massive investment in irrigation infrastructure that took place, mostly in Asia. Agriculture uses 85 % of fresh water withdrawals in developing countries, and irrigated agriculture accounts for about 40 % of the value of agricultural production in the developing world.[105] Today, much of Asia's grain harvest comes from the irrigated, annual double- and triple-crop, continuous rice systems in the tropical and subtropical lowlands of Asia, and from the irrigated, annual rice-wheat, double-crop systems in northern India, Pakistan, Nepal, and southern China.

However, many of these areas in Asia, the Middle East and North Africa are now maintaining irrigated food production through unsustainable extractions of water from rivers or the ground.[106] In China the groundwater overdraft rate exceeds 25% and it is over 56% in parts of northwest India.[107] Much of this excess is driven by subsidized or free electricity. Sub-Saharan Africa has large untapped water resources for agriculture. Only 4% of cultivated land (5.3 million hectares) is irrigated, of which 70% is in Madagascar, Nigeria and Sudan. The potential exists to bring an additional 20 million hectares of land under irrigation but, so far, technical, financial and socio-economic constraints have slowed this expansion. At the same time, almost a quarter of the African population live in water-stressed countries, and the proportion is rising.[106]

There is considerable room for improvement in existing irrigation practices; in most instances the major challenge is to improve the governance of irrigation systems by using a river basin or watershed approach.[108,109] However, the World Bank has pointed to a number of innovative technologies that can also improve the quality of irrigation services. It cites the potential of canal automation and satellite data to accurately measure water use in irrigation. Remote-sensing technologies can measure the amount of water from surface and groundwater schemes actually applied to the fields.[110] It also believes that moving from manually operated to automated channel control of irrigation, as applied in Australia, could be used in some developing countries.[111] Although such technologies require a substantial initial investment, they can be cost effective in the long run.[112]

Challenges to water management in rain fed systems

In many developing countries, particularly in Africa, the principle challenge for optimising water use in agriculture is to improve water capture and use by crops in predominantly rain fed systems. As with soil fertility, opportunities for scientific innovation range from enhancing traditional water capture technologies to improving crops through biotechnology.

In some cases, crop production can be greatly increased by simple, small-scale irrigation or water capture systems that either extend the growing system or make water available at times of stress. There are many traditional agricultural practices which attempt to do this, such as drip-irrigation techniques which deliver water directly to plants,[113,114] and the Zai system common in West Africa (Box 5.12).

Box 5.12 The *Zai* system

The *Zai* system is a traditional technology pioneered by farmers in the dry, sun-baked, encrusted soils of north-west Burkina Faso decades ago as a way to create more arable land. The technique has now spread throughout similar climates in the rest of Burkina and in Mali and Niger. Farmers first dig medium size holes or *Zais* (20 to 30 cms in diameter and 10 to 15 cms deep) in rows across the fields during the dry season. The *Zai* is allowed to fill with leaves and sand as the winds blow across the land. Farmers add manure to each *Zai*, which during the dry months attracts termites; these dig an extensive network of underground tunnels beneath the holes and bring up nutrients from the deeper soils. Stone earth bunds are constructed around the field, in order to slow run-off when the rains come.[115]

When the rains arrive, run-off is captured in the *Zais*. Sorghum or millet seeds are sown in the holes where the water and manure are now concentrated. Water loss through drainage in the

Figure 5.27 – *Zais* in the sandy soil of Niger

often sandy soils is limited by the manure, and deep infiltration is made possible by the termites' porous tunnels. Thus, even in the drought-prone environment of the Sahel, sufficient water capture is ensured.[116]

Farmers have consistently reported greatly increased yields using this technique. In a study done in Bafaloubé, Mali, sorghum yield increased by 80 % and 168 % in 2000 and 2002 respectively, while millet yields increased by 83 % in 2001 and by 111 % in 2003.[117] The labour required to build the zais in the first year is quite high, but after that farmers may reuse the holes, or dig more between the existing ones. In many cases, after around five years the entire land surface will be improved.

One of the greatest recent successes in water and soil management has involved the substitution of a long-standing conventional technology, soil cultivation, with zero-tillage regimes in both developed and developing countries. Cultivation processes, especially use of the plough, can be implicated in high levels of both soil erosion and water loss. There is now a range of no- or minimum-tillage systems in development and use, that are grouped under the generic name of Conservation Agriculture, discussed further in Chapter 9 (Box 9.12).

Parallel to research into improved water capture and retention in crops, has been a growing interest in breeding plants which are more water efficient, and particularly drought tolerant. While some argue that increased infiltration and reduced run-off will have much greater impact on crop yields than can be expected from genetic improvement,[43] breeding for drought tolerance has achieved some success to date. It is of growing interest because global warming will cause some regions to become too dry for the staple crop varieties currently grown there (see Chapter 9).

8. Better pest, disease and weed control

The fourth main challenge to improved production is the collective deleterious effects of numerous pests, diseases and weed species on crop and livestock production. Some of these are particularly devastating. In many respects they are analogous to the great killer diseases of humans such as HIV/AIDS, malaria and TB. Indirectly they are responsible for a great deal of human mortality and morbidity. Like human diseases they often display the same capacity to outwit human attempts at their control. Box 5.13 details some of the more recent crop pest outbreaks in Africa.

Box 5.13 Some recent pest outbreaks in Africa

- **Cassava Mealybug** – This South American insect feeds on cassava shoots, reducing growth and tuber size. It was introduced accidentally into Africa on cassava breeding material in the 1970s, and spread, in only a decade, across the entire African cassava growing region, causing widespread suffering. The pest caused yield losses of up to 60%. It was finally suppressed by an African-wide biological control programme costing US$34 million. This proved a good investment, potential losses to African farmers from this single pest, discounted over 40 years, have been estimated at US$8 billion to US$20 billion.[118,119]

- **Cassava Mosaic Virus** – A new and highly virulent strain of this indigenous virus appeared in Uganda in 1988. The virus grew to epidemic proportions between 1989 to 1999, causing the loss of an estimated 60,000 ha. of cassava, equivalent to over 600,000 tonnes (US$6 million) of fresh cassava roots in the country. There were massive food shortages: in 1994 an estimated 3,000 people died of starvation as a result of famine caused by the plant disease epidemic. All the local varieties (over 500) were eliminated because they were highly susceptible.[120]

- **Banana Xanthomonas Wilt (BXW)** – This disease appeared in the Mukono district of Central Uganda in early 2000. It spread throughout the country and has since covered the Great Lakes region of Eastern Africa. It is estimated that the recent spread of BXW within Uganda will have an economic cost, borne by smallholders, of US$4 billion by 2010, and an even greater impact on household livelihoods.[121,122]

- **Coffee Wilt Disease** – This disease was first reported in Africa in 1927 and there have been periodic outbreaks in various regions. An outbreak in the Democratic Republic of Congo (DRC) in the 1970s, associated with abandonment of coffee plantings, spread into Uganda in the 1990s. In Uganda, smallholder income declined by up to 50% and losses in 2003 were estimated at US$9.6 million.[123]

- **Wheat Stem Rust** – A new strain of this fungus, Ug99, appeared in Uganda in 1999 and has since been detected across East Africa and the Middle East, reaching Iran in 2007. Kenya wheat areas suffered severe losses in 2007: field trials have shown Ug99 to cause yield losses of up to 80%. The predicted cost of a 10% loss in areas immediately at risk is estimated to exceed US$7 billion (See Box 5.16).[121,124]

At the time of the Green Revolution the most widely used approach to pest and disease control in crops was to use synthetic chemical pesticides. These were often effective, at least in the short term, but in the long term, some products made many pest problems worse.[125] Excessive or inappropriate use of pesticides often led to pesticide resistance in populations of pests, diseases and weeds. At the same time, insecticides, and some fungicides, eliminated important predators and parasites of pests and diseases. The loss of this natural control was not immediately recognised. In the case of the brown planthopper on rice (Box 5.14), farmers were surprised to see a resurgence of pest populations after spraying, due to the elimination of their natural enemies. Growing pesticide resistance and pest resurgence led farmers to apply more pesticides. This exacerbated the situation, leading to "pesticide treadmills". The growing costs of pest control, in the face of falling yields, began to make production unsustainable. In addition to these agricultural effects, there were also significant human health problems arising from pesticide use.[126,127]

In response to these pesticide-related problems, integrated pest management (IPM) was developed. IPM aims to control pests, diseases and weeds through a combination of appropriate, selective and sustainable methods. Usually, this meant a reduction in the reliance on chemical pesticides and a move to natural, sustainable methods of pest management, including reliance on natural enemies of pests and on traditional methods such as intercropping. Observation of pest populations over the season allowed farmers to restrict pesticide use to situations where pest abundance was damaging crops and yields. One of the earliest applications of IPM was to control cocoa pests in northern Borneo,[128] but the first large scale use of IPM on a staple crop was for the control of the insect pest brown planthopper that attacks rice (Box 5.14).

Box 5.14 IPM and the rice brown planthopper: science and farmer empowerment

In 1974, only a few years after the fertiliser and pesticide intensive Green Revolution planting programmes began, outbreaks of the rice brown planthopper, *Nilaparvata lugens*, started to occur in Indonesia. This sucking insect was, previously, a very minor pest but it soon spread throughout the rice growing areas of Asia. The initial response was to draw upon plant breeding and pesticides. New varieties resistant to planthopper quickly lost their resistance.[129] And government pesticide subsidies led to farmers becoming stuck on "pesticide treadmills," where they were continually paying more and more for chemicals which delivered less benefit.

There were many scientific theories about the cause of planthopper outbreaks, including: indirect stimulation of plants by pesticides, emergence of pest resistance to pesticides, and development and migration of new, virulent pest strains. In the 1980s, scientists at the International Rice Research Institute (IRRI) demonstrated that pesticide use caused planthopper outbreaks by killing predators, such as spiders, which fed on the pest.[130] Predators sit on plant surfaces and standing water and are highly exposed to sprays. They reproduce slowly, so just a few sprays can eliminate them from fields for long periods. The planthopper, by contrast, spends much of its life protected inside or under rice plants. It reproduces rapidly, so it can recover quickly after a spray, particularly in the absence of predators.

An IPM programme was developed which involved reducing pesticide use and recognising and conserving predators. Its implementation, however, faced opposition from entrenched government dependency on pesticides and the influence of the pesticide industry.

An FAO-supported programme identified that delivering IPM messages via national extension systems would not bring rapid change, and they embarked upon an ambitious plan for direct training of farmers through adaption of methods developed for participatory, community health programmes.

Figure 5.28 – A brown planthopper colony on rice stems

The 'farmer field school' approach developed by Peter Kenmore, was based on three principles to be conveyed to the farmers: (1) grow a healthy crop, (2) observe fields weekly, and (3) conserve natural enemies. In the schools, farmers participated in season-long programmes of experiential learning: designing, executing and interpreting experiments in their rice crops. As a result, they developed an understanding of crop, pest and natural enemy ecology and became experts in pest management in their own fields.

Farmers soon realised large economic benefits within a single season, because of reduced pesticide costs and sustained or even increased yields,[131] and they began to undertake their own IPM research. The concept gradually spread across Asia, Africa and Latin America and to other crops with intensive pesticide use, including, vegetables and cotton.[132]

Many years after the scientific research that led to the development of IPM, further ecological research has finally revealed why rice systems were so sensitive to pesticides in the first place. Work in Indonesia demonstrated that the flooding of rice fields creates an ideal environment for small insects and other invertebrates. Early in the season, spiders and other predators invade the fields to feed on these harmless organisms. When the rice grows and pests like the planthopper invade, the predators are already present in abundance and suppress pests before their populations can grow. But pesticide spraying suppresses this natural biological control system.[133]

Sometimes effective control can be brought about by agronomic means, in particular using interplanting with crops or other plants that deter or destroy the pest. A recent example has been the use of the legume *Desmodium*, interplanted to control the devastating weed *Striga*. This does however require skills and labour. An alternative is to use a herbicide but in such a targeted way that it is not only effective but has little if any environmental consequence (Box 5.15)

Box 5.15 The control of *Striga*

Striga, or witchweed, is a devastating parasitic weed that sucks nutrients from the roots of maize, sorghum and other crops. It infests as many as 40 million hectares of farmland in Sub-Saharan Africa and causes yield losses ranging from 20% to 100%. It affects the livelihoods of more than 100 million people, causing US$1 billion in annual crop losses.[134]

Two approaches to control *Striga* are being developed:

© Rothamsted Research

- The first involves intercropping maize with silverleaf, *Desmodium*, a legume which effectively controls *Striga* resulting in yield increases of two tonnes per hectare. Root exudates from the *Desmodium* cause suicidal germination of *Striga* seeds before they can attach to the maize roots. The intercrop also improves soil fertility and repels stemborers because of the odours that the plant releases. It is part of the 'push-pull' system which uses biological methods to combine *Striga* control with stem borer control.[135,136]

Figure 5.29 – The purple parasitic weed *Striga*

- *Striga* is also readily controlled by a herbicide, imazapyr, but this kills the crop. Recently, a mutant gene in maize has been discovered that confers resistance to the herbicide and is being bred into local maize varieties. The seed is then dipped into the herbicide before being planted. This kills the parasitic spores in the ground, allowing the maize to grow whilst minimising the environmental impact of the herbicide. Early trials are showing increases in yield from half a tonne per hectare to over three tonnes.[134]

© AATF

Figure 5.30 – Maize interplanted with *Desmodium* to control *Striga*

Both these approaches are very promising but because of the scale and difficulty of the problem new technologies are urgently required. This is true of many of the other devastating pests, disease and weeds listed in Box 5.13, the ideal solution is to put resistance to these pests into the seed. It is by far the easiest and most convenient – and often the cheapest – approach, providing of course that the resistance is not too rapidly overcome.

There has been a long history of plant breeding for disease resistance, going back to the earliest days of modern agriculture. In many cases it is possible to find resistance in collections of varieties maintained in various parts of the world. At the present time there is a hunt on for resistance to an extremely serious disease, wheat stem rust, that threatens to devastate wheat in Asia (Box 5.16).

Box 5.16 The hunt for resistance to wheat stem rust

The causative agent of wheat stem rust is the fungus *Puccinia graminis*. The risk from this fungal pathogen is considerable. It is able to completely decimate wheat crops and infect distant fields via its windborne spores. Historically, the disease has been controlled through the propagation of resistant cultivars and the removal of the plants on which the fungus lives for the other part of its life cycle.[137] In spite of this, a novel strain of wheat stem rust, identified in 1999 in Uganda, was found to overcome both of the widely utilised rust resistant genes, *Sr31* and *Sr38*.[138]

This strain, known as Ug99 (Uganda 99), attacks the majority of the world's wheat varieties and therefore presents a serious threat to global food security. Since 1999 the spread of wheat stem rust has been alarming, with systemic cases reported in Uganda, Kenya, Ethiopia, Sudan, Yemen, and Iran.[139] The seriousness of these developments has led to the formation of the Borlaug Global Rust Initiative,[140] the Durable Rust Resistance in Wheat project at Cornell University[139] and the AGP-FAO Wheat Rust Programme.[141]

In the short-term the urgent need is to identify the small number of wheat cultivars that remain resistant to Ug99. However, the ability of the fungus to mutate and evolve means that protracted resistance will be unlikely. In the long-term there remains cause for optimism as researchers have discovered that rice is resistant to the entire taxon of rust fungi. The challenge is to identify the genetic information that confers the observed resistance of rice to rust and to successfully achieve its translocation into the wheat plant. This may enable the creation of a range of durable resistant varieties.[137,139]

The gene transfer technology is currently available to make this process feasible, but the severity of the current threat means researchers face a race against time.

This may prove successful and then the task will be to cross-breed the resistance into the wide range of existing mainstream varieties, maintaining their superior qualities while adding the resistance. However, in the case of many of the worst pests this approach will not work, either because no resistant genes are present in the crop genome (cowpeas in Africa are a good example[142]) or because they are not easily transferred. The alternative then is to utilise GM techniques.

In Chapter 2 we described the use of GM techniques for the control of cotton bollworm which has proven highly successful for millions of small farmers in China, India, South Africa and Mexico. One of the earliest forms of GM disease control was against the papaya ring spot, developed at

Cornell University, which saved the papaya industry in Hawaii and is being developed for countries in Southeast Asia. A current effort is targeted at controlling the Diamondback moth, a highly damaging pest of cabbages and its relatives, in tropical countries (Box 5.17).

Box 5.17 Developing GM crops for Diamondback moth[143]

Figure 5.31 – Diamondback moth and its caterpillar

Cabbages, cauliflower, kale, mustard and other brassica crops are important food plants in developing countries. In India cabbage and cauliflower are grown by more than 20 million small-holders. But across Asia and Africa they are devastated by insect pests and particularly by the Diamondback moth caterpillar, *Plutella xylostella*, which can cause 90 % crop loss. Even when sprayed with insecticides, often every other day, with 12 to 24 applications normal in a three-month season, there can still be up to 35 % loss. The moth has developed resistance to almost all insecticides. One consequence of the heavy and frequent spraying is the serious health risk posed to farmers as well as to consumers and the environment.

The aim is to breed into cabbages a Bt gene that confers resistance to the Diamondback moth. Bt (the bacterium *Bacillus thuringiensis*), produces a toxin, a protein in the form of a crystal, which, when ingested, kills the caterpillar (see also Box 2.18 on Bt cotton). Because the protein toxin is so specific there is little or no effect on other wildlife and spraying of the bacterium against pests is approved in organic agriculture. One problem, however, is insect resistance to the toxin.

A new project to develop a Bt cabbage, managed through the public-private partnership Collaboration on Insect Management for Brassicas in Asia and Africa (CIMBAA), is introducing two different Bt genes. The caterpillars have not been widely exposed to these two proteins before and it is believed they cannot readily develop resistance to both toxins simultaneously.

It is intended that caterpillar resistant plants will be introduced within a full IPM programme (including the promotion of the use of natural enemies of the pests, and traditional, as well as technology-based practices), so maximizing their profitability, effectiveness and long-term sustainability.

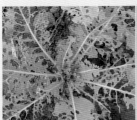

Figure 5.32 – Diamondback moth damage on an untransformed plant (left) and an undamaged Bt plant (right)

Control of major diseases of livestock

Livestock diseases have a serious impact on the livelihoods of farmers in developing countries. Many of these diseases are of global significance, e.g. foot and mouth disease of cattle and Newcastle disease of poultry. Strict international trade regulations restrict movement of animals from areas affected by disease. Outbreaks can be eradicated in wealthier countries but the same diseases are often endemic in poorer countries, causing substantial losses and limiting their capacity to trade. A focus of policy in wealthy countries on eradication has reduced impetus for research on vaccines, which would be of particular value in poorer regions where diseases are endemic. Financial constraints on farmers in developing countries also provide a disincentive for private sector investment in vaccines for tropical livestock diseases.

As we will see with human diseases in the next chapter, animal diseases can be managed by modifying the environment of the pathogen, or by targeting the pathogen directly. A good example of environmental management is vector control. Box 5.18 illustrates how innovative research on insect vector behaviour may help to reduce the impact of trypanosomiasis, a particularly serious disease of livestock in Africa.

Box 5.18 Selective control of tsetse fly in Africa[144]

Tsetse are large biting flies which live by feeding on the blood of animals and humans. They infest some 10 million km² of Sub-Saharan Africa, extending from Mali and Ethiopia in the north to South Africa and Namibia in the south. The flies transmit trypanosomes, tiny protozoa which cause trypanosomiasis, otherwise known as sleeping sickness in humans and nagana in cattle.

Figure 5.33 – The *Glossina pallidipes* tsetse fly

There are currently no vaccines against the disease and only a few drugs. Resistance against these is widespread and consequently one long-term solution would be to control tsetse. Effective control has successfully brought down infection rates in cattle. In Zimbabwe, cases have fallen from around 10,000 per year in the early 1980s, to less than 100 today. The methods used to control the flies have also evolved and are now more cost-effective, efficient and environmentally-friendly. Figure 5.34 shows the evolution of methods used in Zimbabwe during the 1980s.

In the early 1980s, the mainstay of tsetse control was the application of DDT to the resting sites of tsetse. This was supplemented by the aerial application of the highly toxic insecticide endosulfan. In the mid 1980s, in an effort to cut back on the amount of chemicals used, scientists began experimenting with the use of targets. These are cloth screens impregnated with insecticide and baited with artificial host odours, as tsetse flies are attracted to animals by vision and smell. They discovered that targets deployed at densities of just 4/km² could eradicate tsetse populations in a year.

In order to improve the effectiveness of the targets, scientists at the Natural Resources Institute (NRI) in London, in collaboration with Zimbabwean scientists, identified the pheromones which attract tsetse to their hosts. They also used GIS mapping and simulation techniques to study the relationship between the flies and the cattle and decide how to best deploy the targets.

To further reduce costs, researchers began looking at the option of treating the cattle themselves with insecticide. While it is costly and difficult to treat all of the cattle in a herd, they discovered that the flies predominantly attack the older and larger animals, and that for a typical herd, 80% of meals are from 25% of animals. Thus a big impact could be made by selective treatment.

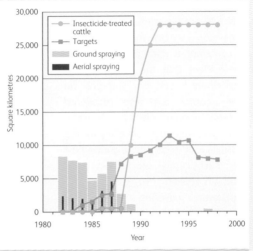

Figure 5.34 – Evolution of tsetse control in Zimbabwe[144]

Building on this, they looked at *where* on the animals the flies tended to land and bite. They found that 75% to 99% of tsetse feed on the legs or belly of cattle. So, by treating just the legs and belly of older cattle, very big impacts are made, costing less than US$1 per animal each year, and with less pesticides.

The other approach is to control the pathogen in the host, and this is usually done with vaccines or medicines. There have been very successful vaccination campaigns against animal diseases, including against the cattle plague, rinderpest, one of the most long-standing of livestock diseases. A highly contagious and lethal viral disease related to the human measles virus, rinderpest is thought to date back to the first domestication of cattle in Asia. It spread throughout Asia and Europe over the centuries, often through travelling military campaigns. It was introduced to Eastern Africa in the late 19th century.

Animals infected with rinderpest develop fever, discharges from the eyes and nose, erosions on mucous membranes of organs, diarrhoea and often death from weight loss and dehydration after 10 to 12 days. In its most severe form it is capable of killing 95% of all animals it infects. The disease is spread when animals inhale aerosolized particles that contain the virus, or through contact with secretions from infected animals.[145] Cattle which recover, however, gain lifelong immunity.

A series of campaigns against the disease have now led to its global eradication (Box 5.19).

Box 5.19 The successful eradication of cattle plague[146]

The battle against rinderpest, described as 'the most dreaded bovine plague known,' has been long and hard-fought. Pandemics of the disease swept through communities in Europe, Asia and Africa over the centuries, bringing devastation similar to human plagues such as the Black Death. The disease served as one of the main motivating factors in the establishment of formal veterinary service institutions, such as the national veterinary colleges that were begun in the 1700s and the World Organisation for Animal Health in 1924.

The discovery in the 1880s that serum from a recovered animal could be used to develop a vaccine marked the start of coordinated rinderpest control. It was evident that the nature of the virus (there is only one serotype, no other carrier and the recovered animals acquire ability to confer lifelong immunity) would allow for the possibility of eradication. Rinderpest was successfully eradicated from Southern Africa by 1905 through strict legislation covering zoosanitary procedures combined with vaccination campaigns, and in Europe by 1928. The virus persisted, however, in pockets in South Asia and in Africa through to the 1990s.

© Ray Witlin – World Bank

Figure 5.35 – Healthy cattle play an important role in rural livelihoods

In 1992 the idea of an internationally coordinated programme for worldwide eradication was conceived. The Global Rinderpest Eradication Programme (GREP) was launched through the FAO, set as a time-bound initiative to end in 2010. The GREP began a package of interventions including detection of existing cases and vaccination in infected areas with a transition to careful surveillance and national accreditations of rinderpest freedom. As of 2009, the GREP has pronounced that rinderpest is no longer circulating in domesticated or wild animals anywhere in the world, making it one of only two infectious diseases, along with smallpox, which we have succeeded in eradicating worldwide.

The eradication of such a damaging disease will bring many benefits to the lives of livestock owners in Asia and Africa, including security in their investments as well as added income from the lifting of trade restrictions. However, of perhaps even greater importance are the lessons learned during this widespread effort. While global eradication may not be appropriate for every disease, a number of both organisational and technical prerequisites for large-scale disease control have been proposed in a recently published paper. The technical elements include:

- A clear and evolving understanding of the epidemiology of the targeted disease;

- Safe, efficacious, affordable and quality-assured vaccines;

- A set of robust, validated laboratory diagnostic tools for agent detection;

- A world and regional reference laboratory network supporting the technology transfer to national diagnostic laboratories and technical fora for information exchange;

- Dynamic and innovative disease-control and eradication strategies based on epidemiological studies, adapted to local conditions and amended repeatedly;

- A clearly defined disease freedom accreditation process.

Solutions to controlling animal pathogens in developing countries will involve a mixture of conventional and new platform technologies. For instance, East Coast fever, which affects cattle across Eastern and Central Africa, has been the subject of many years of research at the International Livestock Research Institute (ILRI). Working with the Institute for Genomic Research in the US, IRLI has now succeeded in sequencing the genome of the protozoan parasite which causes the disease, *Theileria parva*. The sequencing, along with high-throughput immunological screens, has been used to identify potential vaccine antigens. The challenge now is to engineer these antigens into a sub-unit vaccine for the disease[147] (see Box 6.9 for a description of the main forms of vaccine). This would be the first experimental vaccine to protect mammals against a protozoan parasite, and findings from the research may help scientists make advances against related parasites such as malaria and TB.[148,149]

Meanwhile, in the course of this research, it has been observed that effective immunity can be conferred by infecting cattle with a mixture of live East Coast fever parasites and then treating them quickly with a long-acting antibiotic, which kills off the pathogen after the immune system has been stimulated. This mixture, known as the Infection and Treatment method, or the '*Muguga Cocktail*,' has been widely accepted by herders in East Africa. While not as elegant as the discovery of a vaccine, this approach is highly practical, and it is currently being scaled up with support from foundations and civil society organisations. Even here, continuing scientific research is needed to understand variation in the parasite, and hence the efficacy of control and immunization.[150,151]

The formation of a new public-private partnership, the Global Alliance for Livestock Veterinary Medicines (GALVmed), should help to progress work in this area.[152] The aim is to get existing diagnostics, medications and vaccines to farmers, as well as to understand better what influences farmer uptake of these products. The group will also be scaling up efforts to develop new preventatives and treatments which are safer, cheaper, more effective and protect against previously unpreventable diseases. New advances in biotechnology will also make it possible to develop vaccines which do not require refrigeration – a major benefit for rural small-holders.[153,154]

Attention is increasingly turning towards the need for integrated disease control packages, where multiple strategies, such as environmental control, community education, vaccination and treatment medications are applied together to control diseases with more complex transmission patterns. Box 5.20 (page 158) describes work to control the zoonotic tapeworm, *Taenia solium*, which infects both swine and humans.

© DFID

Figure 5.36 – Sheep are an important source of food and income for many rural communities in developing countries

Box 5.20 Integrated control of pork tapeworm[155,156]

Taenia solium, or pork tapeworm, is a zoonotic tapeworm transmitted between pigs and humans, common in non-Muslim regions of Asia, Latin America and Africa. When humans eat raw or undercooked meat of pigs infected with *T.solium*, they ingest the larval form of the tapeworm, which then develops into the adult form in the human gut, causing a disease known as taeniasis. Those infected may be largely asymptomatic, although intestinal upset, nausea and diarrhoea often occur. They will however discharge segments of tapeworm in their faeces, and this is how the disease spreads. Pigs which have access to human faeces will ingest the eggs of the tapeworm, so completing the cycle.

© Trevor Samson – World Bank
Figure 5.37 – A veterinarian in Africa

It is also possible for the disease to be transferred directly from human to human upon ingestion of infected faeces. This can lead to a more severe form of the disease, cysticercosis, in which the larvae lodge in the infected person's organs. The most severe consequences resulting from lodging in the brain. Neuro-cysticercosis is one of the largest causes of adult epilepsy in poor, pig-keeping countries.

Due to the nature of transmission of this disease between humans and animals, and the prolonged incubation period of the disease in humans (from a month up to ten years), effective reduction in prevalence cannot be achieved without using a variety of measures. These can include some or all of the following:

• Preventing access of pigs to human faeces through housing or tethering;

• Education, marketing and infrastructure for improved hygiene and safe disposal of human faeces;

• Testing and treating infected humans;

• Testing and treating infected pigs;

• Meat inspection and processing or condemnation of infected meat;

• Education on appropriate pork preparation practices;

• Vaccinating pigs;

• Market-based incentives for producing cysticercus-free pigs.

The first large-scale elimination programme is now underway in the Tumbes Region of Peru, funded by the Bill and Melinda Gates Foundation. The intervention, informed by sociology, farming system science and epidemiology, integrates treatment, vaccination and advanced detection methods and is proving to be highly effective.

Zoonoses, or diseases which infect both humans and animals are of increasing concern, and we discuss these in more detail in Chapter 6.

9. Improved agricultural systems

All of these approaches to increasing yields, increasing nitrogen supply and uptake, conserving moisture and controlling pests are simply components that have to be woven into a total farming system. It is a task undertaken by farmers, large and small, on a day-to-day basis but it can be assisted by research into the structure and dynamics of farming systems themselves. Examples include the rice-wheat systems of Asia and many different forms of crop-livestock systems throughout the world (Box 5.21).

Box 5.21 Examples of contemporary innovative farming systems[157-159]

Rice-wheat systems

The Indo-Gangetic floodplain (IGP), extending across the Himalayan foothills of India, Pakistan, Bangladesh and Nepal, is one of the most fertile and productive agricultural areas of the world. The climate is sub-humid with a distinct wet monsoon summer season and a dry, cool winter season. With the introduction of the shorter-duration improved Green Revolution varieties in the 1960s, it became possible for farmers on canal irrigated land to grow rice and wheat in a double cropping pattern in one calendar year: rice in the summer and wheat in the winter. This led to impressive increases in per capita production, and irrigated rice-wheat systems remain the major source of marketed grain surplus in the area, helping to feed a growing urban population. Rice-wheat production systems now occupy 24 million ha of cultivated land in the Asian subtropics, with 13.5 million ha extending in the IGP alone. They cover about 32% of the total rice area and 42% of the total wheat area in these four countries.

In the 1980s, however, yield increases from these systems began to stagnate. Inappropriate fertiliser applications, scarcity of surface and ground water, and late and inefficient planting of the wheat rotation combined to challenge farmers in the area. Of particular concern were problems associated with the wheat sowing. Farmers were broadcasting seed into ploughed land and then ploughing again because of the need to deal with crop residue left over from the previous rice crop. This led to seed placement at many different depths and varying soil moisture levels resulting in variable germination. In addition, many farmers were planting the wheat crop too late, because too much time was being spent ploughing or dealing with rice residues.

In 1994, the Rice-Wheat Consortium was formed to try to restore high productivity to this important system, bringing together several CGIAR centres (CIMMYT, IRRI, ICRISAT, CIP and IWMI), the national agricultural research centres of the four countries, and a number other institutes. The group has introduced zero-tillage methods – with direct seeding of wheat into rice residues immediately following the rice harvest using an inexpensive and locally manufactured seed drill. They have also begun experimenting with bed planting, an idea picked up by Indian scientists when visiting the CIMMYT programme in Mexico. In this system rice and wheat are planted on top of a ridge and furrow system, leading to significant water and herbicide savings.

Through these innovations it is possible to improve yields of both rice and wheat while maintaining good soil quality, leading to extremely high productivity and efficient use of the improved varieties.

Crop-livestock systems

Most farmers produce both food crops as well as raise livestock, and for resource-poor farmers, getting the most out of this combination is very important. First, livestock can act as an extremely beneficial and cheap form of additional nutrient supply for fields – collecting, transporting, converting and depositing nutrients. When farmers tether their animals in fields overnight, the animals will deposit up to 95% of the nitrogen and phosphorus they consume during the day through their urine and faeces. By selectively rotating the tethering location, entire fields can gain, with the manure also helping to improve soil structure, biological activity and water-holding capacity. Long-term fertility trials on the savanna soils of West Africa show how beneficial animal manures can be (Figure 5.38).

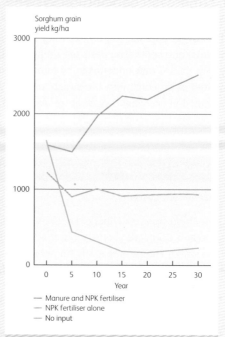

Figure 5.38 – The long term impact of the combination of fertilisers and manure on sorghum yields in Burkina Faso over 30 years[160]

In addition, farmers can further integrate animals and cropping productively by planting N-fixing, forage legumes, such as cowpea, intercropped with the crop plants. This improves soil quality and also the quality and quantity of animal feed. Careful ecological management of crop-livestock systems can create virtuous circles:

'Cowpea thus feeds people and animals directly while also yielding more milk and meat, better soils through nitrogen fixation, high quality manure, which, used as fertiliser, further improves soil fertility and increases yields.'[161]

Organic agriculture

Resource-poor farmers in developing countries have been practicing traditional forms of agriculture for centuries without reliance on synthetic fertilisers or pesticides. These traditional systems have much in common with the recently developed certified organic farming systems of the developed countries. Indeed, the FAO/WHO Codex Alimentarius guidelines define organic agriculture in a way that might apply equally as well to a modern certified organic farm in England as to a home garden in Indonesia that does not use synthetic inputs:

Organic agriculture is a holistic production management system which promotes and enhances agro-ecosystem health, including biodiversity, biological cycles, and soil biological activity. It emphasises the use of management practices in preference to the use of off-farm inputs, taking

Figure 5.39 – Development of certified organic agriculture[165]

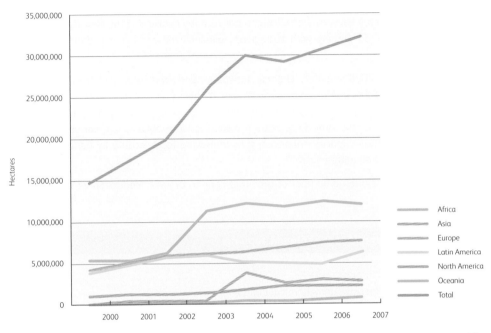

into account that regional conditions require locally adapted systems. This is accomplished by using, where possible, agronomic, biological, and mechanical methods, as opposed to using synthetic materials, to fulfil any specific function within the system.[162]

However, in the developed countries the certification of organic food production is considerably more stringent than the above definition. All synthetic fertilisers are banned and so are all herbicides and most insecticides and fungicides – the exceptions are various 'natural or simple' chemicals (in the UK the list includes sulphur, soft soap, copper and rotenone, some pyrethroids, iron orthophosphate and paraffin oil, and certain bacterial and other microorganisms).[163]

The amount of land under certified organic production has steadily grown over the past few decades. As of 2007, there were approximately 30.6 million hectares of certified organic farmland worldwide, representing about 1 % of total world production.[164] Figure 5.39 above shows how this practice has grown, largely in the developed countries.

However, official statistics do not include the millions of small producers who practice traditional non-certified organic agriculture. It is estimated that in developing countries, there are probably another 10 to 20 million hectares in this category.[166]

Certified organic farming in developed countries has a well established niche. Research supports the improvement of methods, and higher costs relative to conventional production systems are offset by the premium prices which organic products command. The question is whether an organic approach offers another route towards improvement of agriculture in developing countries. It certainly provides a profitable niche for the production of high value crops for export to the developed countries.

But is it a means whereby Africa and South Asia can transfer into highly productive yet sustainable agricultural production? In general yields from organic agriculture in the developed countries are lower than those using synthetic inputs, in part because the nitrogen levels are lower. However, a research group from the University of Michigan has recently challenged the view that more land is required to grow food entirely with biologically available nitrogen and without the use of synthetic fertilisers.[167]

In the UNEP/UNESCO 2008 report on 'Organic Agriculture and Food Security in Africa' an analysis was made of the 114 cases in Africa previously studied by Jules Pretty et al.[168] It showed that there was a 116% increase in productivity by converting to organic or near-organic production (not necessarily certified). At the same time natural resources were building up, communities were strengthened and human capacity enhanced, thus improving food security by addressing many different causal factors simultaneously.[169]

Nevertheless, there are a large number of pros and cons to organic production which should be considered (Box 5.22).

Box 5.22 The pros and cons of organic farming

Pros:

- Minimal use of expensive agrochemical inputs;

- Reduced environmental impact;

- Increasing biodiversity leading to more resilient systems.

And for resource-poor smallholders, these are:

- The emphasis on the use of local resources;

- The low degree of mechanisation and high utilisation of local and family labour;

- The suitability for the cultivation of small areas;

- The ability to build on existing traditional skills.

Cons:

- Lack of readily available crop residues or manure to provide nitrogen and other nutrients;

- 'Knowledge-intensity' requiring a high level of capacity from farmers and research and extension systems to produce high yields.

And a number of environmental and social constraints:

- Higher labour requirements in labour constrained environments;

- Risks of failure associated with handling particularly difficult pests, disease or weather threats without outside inputs;

- Desire of farmers to use a range or combination of techniques;

- Perception of farmers that organic agriculture is a step backward, rather than forward;

- Lack of supportive government policies.

Whilst many of the principles of organic agriculture do have the potential to make positive impacts in improving soil fertility, pest management and agricultural production, more work is needed in the areas of research, extension and policy in order for this to become a productive approach on a wider scale. Moreover, extensive soil degradation and loss of nutrients, common in many parts of the developing world, necessitates a rapid increase in inputs of targeted, synthetic fertilisers both to increase yields and to produce greater amounts of green matter that will be available for incorporation as crop residues.

We would argue, at least in the medium term, for a hybrid approach to increasing agricultural production, rather than the promotion of either a solely 'conventional' or 'organic' system. Innovations in the smart use of inputs – under the general headings of integrated nutrient and pest management as described above – can be combined with holistic ecological techniques as discussed here. And, further, scientific breakthroughs in plant breeding, including biotechnologies, may provide crops with greater ability for nutrient uptake or pest and disease resistance, thus reducing the need for either synthetic or organic fertilisers or pesticides.

© Thomas Sennett – World Bank

Figure 5.40 – With the right inputs yields from rice crops in Bangladesh can be greatly improved

10. Conclusion

The devastating food price spike of 2008 drew attention to the underlying chronic hunger crisis. There are now probably more than a billion chronically hungry people in the world. In the 1960s and 70s the hunger crisis was resolved by a Green Revolution that greatly increased cereal production and averted famine in Asia and elsewhere. Today there is a need for a new Green Revolution – but one that is in many respects very different; production has to increase but in a way that is sustainable, environmentally friendly and equitable, ensuring that more food becomes available to the poor.

The priorities are:

- Increasing yields and the quality of the food that farmers grow, in particular ensuring that the basic staples contain the necessary vitamins and other micronutrients that people need to keep healthy;

- Improving the soil, ensuring that there is optimal provision of both nutrients and organic matter, and that plants can make maximum and sustainable use of what is available;

- Utilising water in an optimal manner, particularly given the greater incidence of drought in the future;

- Combating the major pests, diseases and weeds that are so devastating to developing country crops, in a way that minimises the use of harmful or counterproductive pesticides.

In each instance, choosing the appropriate technology mix will be important. Conventional technologies, for example inorganic fertilisers and pesticides, will remain a mainstay of the approach but they need to be used in ways that are much more selective and precise. Traditional and intermediate technologies have much to offer, and there will be increasing utilisation of some of the new platform technologies, including biotechnologies where they are superior in terms of their selectivity, environmental sensitivity and cost.

Chapter 5 references and further reading

1   FAO. (2009) *1.02 billion people hungry*. FAO Media Centre 19 June. Available at:
    www.fao.org/news/story/en/item/20568/icode [Accessed 19 Nov 2009].

2   UNICEF. (2009) *Tracking Progress on Child and Maternal Nutrition*. UNICEF, Geneva.

3   WHO. (2009) *Worldwide prevalence on anaemia 1993-2005, Summary*. Available at:
    www.who.int/vmnis/anaemia/prevalence/summary/anaemia_status_summary/en/index.html
    [Accessed 19 Nov 2009].

4   Black, R. et al., (2008) Maternal and child undernutrition: global and regional exposures and health
    consequences *The Lancet*, **371**, 243 – 260.

5   Victora, C. et al., (2008) Maternal and child undernutrition: consequences for adult health and human
    capital, *The Lancet*, **371**, 340 – 357.

6   FAO. (2008) *Number of hungry people rises to 963 million*. FAO Media Centre. Available at:
    www.fao.org/news/story/en/item/8836/icode/ [Accessed 19 Nov 2009].

7   Von Braun, J., (2007) *The World Food Situation*. Presentation for the CGIAR Annual General Meeting,
    Beijing, December 3, 2007. Available at: www.slideshare.net/jvonbraun/the-world-food-situation
    [Accessed 19 Nov 2009].

8   FAO. (2009) *Food Price Indices*, October 2009. Available at:
    www.fao.org/worldfoodsituation/FoodPricesIndex/en/ [Accessed 19 Nov 2009].

9   Piesse, J. & Thirtle, C., (2009) Three bubbles and a panic: An explanatory review of recent food
    commodity price events. *Food Policy*, **34**, 119-129.

10 Population Division of the Department of Economic and Social Affairs of the United Nations Secretariat.
    (2009) World Population Prospects: *The 2008 Revision, Highlights*. UN, New York.

11 Sulser, T. et al., (2008) *IFPRI's IMPACT Model*: Update and Outlook. IFPRI Presentation at the 17th
    World Outlooks Conference in Washington DC. Available at:
    www.fapri.missouri.edu/woc2008/Day1_S3/IMPACTUpdate.pdf [Accessed 19 Nov 2009].

12 World Bank. (2008) World Development Indicators, Key Development Data and Statistics. Available at:
    go.worldbank.org/1SF48T40L0 [Accessed 19 Nov 2009].

13 von Braun, J., (2007) *The world food situation: new driving forces and required actions*. Food Policy
    Report 18. International Food Policy Research Institute, Washington DC.

14 FAOSTAT. 28 Sept 2009. Available at: faostat.fao.org [Accessed 19 Nov 2009].

15 Edgerton, M., (2009) Increasing Crop Productivity to Meet Global Needs for Feed, Food, and Fuel.
    Plant Physiology, **149**, 1, 7-13.

16 Rosegrant, M., (2008) *Biofuels and Grain Prices: Impacts and Policy Responses*. Testimony for the US
    Senate Committee on Homeland Security and Governmental Affairs. Washington, DC.

17 Coyle, W., (2007) The Future of Biofuels: A global perspective. *Amber Waves*, **5**, 25-29 Available at:
    www.ers.usda.gov/AmberWaves/November07/Features/Biofuels.htm [Accessed 19 Nov 2009].

18 Blas, J., Commodities Correspondent of the Financial Times. [Email] (Pers.Comm. 29 Sept 2009).

19 The Natural History Museum. (2009) *Phosphate Recovery*. Available at: www.nhm.ac.uk/research-
    curation/research/projects/phosphate-recovery/p&k217/steen.htm [Accessed 19 Nov 2009].

20 Roy, A., (2009) Global Fertiliser Situation and Fertiliser Access. IFDC presentation at the *Building
    Sustainable Fertiliser Markets Session* Agriculture and Rural Development Week 2009 The World Bank,
    Washington, DC, 3 March. Available at: siteresources.worldbank.org/INTARD/Resources/335807-
    1236361651968/ARDmeetingpresentation_WorldBank_March32009.pdf [Accessed 19 Nov 2009].

21 FAO. (2000) World Soil Resources Report 90. *Land Resource Potential and Constraints at Regional and
    Country Levels*. Based on the work of Bot, A. Nachtergaele, F. & Young, A., FAO, Rome.

22 FAO Terrastat. *Land resource potential and constraints statistics at country and regional level*.
    Available at: www.fao.org/ag/agl/agll/terrastat/#terrastatdb [Accessed 19 Nov 2009].

23 Comprehensive Assessment of Water Management in Agriculture. (2007) *Water for Food, Water for Life: A Comprehensive Assessment of Water Management in Agriculture*. London, Earthscan, and Colombo, International Water Management Institute.

24 Karoly, D. Risbey, J. & Reynolds, A., (2003) *Global Warming Contributes to Australia's Worst Drought*. WWF, Sydney.

25 Nicholls, N., (2004) The Changing Nature of Australian Droughts. *Climate Change*, **63**, No 3. 323-336.

26 Schneider, K., (2009) Warming Takes Center Stage as Australian Drought Worsens. *Yale Environment, 360* 2 April. Yale School of Forestry & Environmental Studies Available at: e360.yale.edu/content/feature.msp?id=2137 [Accessed 19 Nov 2009].

27 Throstle, R., (2008) *Global Agricultural Supply and Demand: Factors Contributing to the Recent Increase in Food Commodity Prices*. USDA Economic Research Service. Available at: www.ers.usda.gov/publications/WRS0801/WRS0801.pdf [Accessed 19 Nov 2009].

28 Von Braun, J., (2008) *The World Food Crisis: Political and Economic Consequences and Needed Actions*. Presentation for the Ministry of Foreign Affairs, Stockholm.

29 Sen, A., (1981) *Poverty and Famines: An Essay on Entitlement and Deprivation*. Clarendon Press, Oxford.

30 DFID. (2005) *Growth and Poverty Reduction: the Role of Agriculture*. DFID, London.

31 FAO. (2008) *The State of Food Insecurity in the World 2008*. FAO, Rome.

32 Sen, A., (2003) [Discussion] (Pers. Comm.).

33 Sen, A., (1999) *Development as Freedom*. Oxford University Press, Oxford.

34 Conway, G. & Toenniessen, G., (2003) Science for African Food Security. *Science*, **299**, 1187-1188.

35 FAO. (2006) *State of Food Insecurity in the World*. FAO, Rome.

36 Conway, G., (1999) The *Doubly Green Revolution*. (1999) *Doubly Green Revolution – Food for All in the 21st Century*. Cornell, Ithaca.

37 FAOSTAT – Trade Available at: faostat.fao.org/site/342/default.aspx [Accessed 19 Nov 2009].

38 Piesse, J. & Thirtle, C., (2009) Three Bubbles and a Panic: An Explanatory Review of the Food Commodity Price Spikes of 2008, *Food Policy*, **34**, (2), 119-29.

39 Ahluwhalia, M., (2005) *Reducing Poverty and Hunger in India: The Role of Agriculture*. IFPRI 2004-5 annual report. IFPRI, Washington, DC.

40 Mahadeven, R., (2003) Productively Growth in Indian Agriculture: The Role of Globalization and Economic Reform. *Asia-Pacific Development Journal*, **10**, (2).

41 India Planning Commission. (2007) *Agricultural Strategy for Eleventh Plan, Some Critical Issues*. Available at: planningcommission.gov.in/plans/planrel/53rdndc/AgricultureStrategy.pdf [Accessed 19 Nov 2009].

42 FAOSTAT. *Production*. Available at: faostat.fao.org/site/339/default.aspx [Accessed 19 Nov 2009].

43 Cassman, K., (1999) Ecological intensification of cereal production systems: yield potential, soil quality, and precision agriculture. *Proc. Natl. Acad. Sci*, USA **96**, 5952–59.

44 Cassman, K. et al., (2003) Meeting cereal demand while protecting natural resources and improving environmental quality. *Annu. Rev. Environ. Resour*, **28**, 315-358.

45 Braun, H., (2009) Director Global Wheat Program, CIMMYT. [Email] (Pers. Comm. 5 Oct 2009).

46 Edgerton, M., (2009) Increasing Crop Productivity to Meet Global Needs for Feed, Food, and Fuel, *Plant Physiology*, **149**, 7–13.

47 Duvick, D., (2005) The contribution of breeding to yield advances in maize (Zea mays L.). *Adv Agron* **86**, 83–145.

48 Crow, J., (1998) 90 Years Ago: The Beginning of Hybrid Maize. *Genetics*, **148**, 923-928, March 1998.

49 Pioneer. (n.d.) *Developing a superior maize hybrid*. Pioneer Hi-Bred International, Inc. Available at: www.pioneer.com/CMRoot/Pioneer/media_room/publications/documents/maize_hybrid.pdf [Accessed 19 Nov 2009].

50 De Groote, H. et al., (2005) The Maize Green Revolution in Kenya Revisited. *e-Journal of Agricultural and Development Economics*, **2**, No. 1, 32-49.

51   Smale, M. & Jayne, T., (2003) *Maize in Eastern and Southern Africa: Seeds of Success in Retrospect.* International Food Policy Research Institute. EPTD Discussion Paper No. 97.

52   Dorward, A. et al., (2008) *Evaluation of the 2006/7 Agricultural Input Subsidy Programme, Malawi, Final Report.* School of Oriental and African Studies, London.

53   Longping, Y., (2004) *Hybrid rice for food security in the world.* FAO Rice Conference 12-13 February, Rome. Available at: www.fao.org/rice2004/en/pdf/longping.pdf [Accessed 19 Nov 2009].

54   Peng, S. et al., (1999) Yield potential trends of tropical rice since the release of IR8 and the challenge of increasing rice yield potential. *Crop Sci,* **39**, 1552–59.

55   Eathington, S. et al., (2007) Molecular markers in a commercial breeding program. *Crop Sci,* (Suppl3) **47**, S154–S163.

56   HarvestPlus. (nd) *Provitamin a Sweet Potato for Uganda and Mozambique.* Available at: www.harvestplus.org/content/provitamin-sweet-potato-uganda-mozambique [Accessed 19 Nov 2009].

57   HarvestPlus. (nd) *Learn More, Why biofortification makes sense.* Available at: www.harvestplus.org/content/learn-more [Accessed 19 Nov 2009].

58   About VITAA. Available at: www.cipotato.org/Vitaa/about_vitaa.htm [Accessed 19 Nov 2009].

59   International Potato Center. (nd) *Sweetpotato.* Available at: www.cipotato.org/sweetpotato/ [Accessed 19 Nov 2009].

60   Golden Rice Humanitarian Board. (2007) *The science behind Golden Rice.* Available at: www.goldenrice.org/Content2-How/how1_sci.html [Accessed 19 Nov 2009].

61   Potrykus, I., [Email] (Pers. Comm. 27 Oct 2009).

62   ILRI (nd) *About ILRI.* Available at: www.ilri.org/home.asp?CCID=41&SID=1 [Accessed 19 Nov 2009].

63   Rege, E. & Marshall, K., (2007) *Animal Breeding for poverty impact: achieving more with available technologies.* ILRI. Presentation at the ILRI John Vercoe Conference, Nairobi, November 2007.

64   Delgado, C. et al., (1999) *Livestock to 2020, the Next Food Revolution.* IFPRI, FAO and ILRI, Washington, DC.

65   Indian Dairy. (nd) *Operation Flood.* Available at: www.indiadairy.com/ind_operationflood.html [Accessed 19 Nov 2009].

66   FAO. (2007) *People and animals. Traditional livestock keepers: Guardians of domestic animal diversity.* FAO, Rome. Available at: www.fao.org/nr/gen/gen_071201_en.htm [Accessed 19 Nov 2009].

67   ILRI. (nd) *Why livestock matter.* Available at:www.ilri.org/home.asp?CCID=52&SID=1 [Accessed 25 Nov 2009].

68   US Congress, Office of Technology. (1988) *Enhancing Agriculture in Africa: A Role for US Development Assistance.* US Government Printing Office, Washington DC.

69   Karugia, J. et al., (2001) *Economic Analysis of Crossbreeding Programmes in Sub-Saharan Africa*: A Conceptual Framework and Kenyan Case Study. FEEM Working Paper No. 106. Available at: www.feem.it/Feem/Pub/Publications/WPapers/WP2001-106.htm [Accessed 19 Nov 2009].

70   Thorpe, W. Morris, C. & Kang'ethe, P., (1994) Crossbreeding of Ayrshire, Brown Swiss and Sahiwal Cattle for Annual and Lifetime Milk Yield in the Lowland Tropics of Kenya. *Journal of Dairy Science,* **77**, 2415-2427.

71   Cardellino, R., (2006) Status of the world's livestock genetic resources: preparation of the first report on the state of the world's animal genetic resources. In: *The role of biotechnology in exploring and protecting agricultural genetic resources.* FAO. Available at: www.fao.org/docrep/009/a0399e/A0399E05.htm#ch1.1 [Accessed 19 Nov 2009].

72   CGIAR story of the month September 2007: *Practical Steps to Preserve the World's Barnyard Diversity.* Available at: www.cgiar.org/monthlystory/september2007.html [Accessed 19 Nov 2009].

73   Williams, J., (2003) *Molecular genetics and livestock selection: Approaches, opportunities and risks.* FAO/IAEA International Symposium on Applications of Gene-based Technologies for Improving Animal Production and Health in Developing Countries – Book of Extended Synopses. Vienna.

74 Duguma, B., (2005) *Sheep Production in Ethiopia*. Presentation made at Nova Scotia Agricultural College by Jimma University College of Agriculture and Veterinary Medicine, Jimma, Ethiopia. Available at: nsac.ca/international/International_Projects/Current_Projects/Ethiopia/SheepProd.pdf [Accessed 19 Nov 2009].

75 Gizaw, S. et al., (2008) Conservation priorities for Ethiopian sheep breeds combining threat status, breed merits and contributions to genetic diversity. *Genetics Selection Evolution*, **40**, 433-447.

76 Cassman, K. Dobermann, A. & Walters, D., (2002) Agroecosystems, nitrogen-use efficiency, and nitrogen management. *Ambio*, **31**,132–40.

77 Shahandeh, H. et al., (2004) Nitrogen dynamics in tropical soils of Mali, West Africa. *Biology and Fertility of Soils*, **39**, No. 4, 258-268.

78 Ikerra, S. et al., (1999) Soil nitrogen dynamics and relationships with maize yields in agliricidia–maize intercrop in Malawi. *Plant and Soil*, **211**, 155–164.

79 Oldeman, L., (1994) in *Soil Resilience and Sustainable Land Use*, eds. Greenland, D. & Szabolcs, I., CABI International, Wallingford, UK, 99–118.

80 UNEP. (2002) Chapter 2, Land. GEO: Global Environment Outlook 3. Available at: www.grida.no/publications/other/geo3/?src=/geo/geo3/english/141.htm [Accessed 19 Nov 2009].

81 Henao, J. & Baanante, C., (2001) Chapter 25 Nutrient Depletion in the Agricultural Soils of Africa. In: Pinstrup-Andersen, P. and Rosegrant, M., (eds) *The unfinished agenda: perspectives on overcoming hunger, poverty, and environmental degradation*. IFPRI. Available at: www.ifpri.org/sites/default/files/publications/ufa.pdf [Accessed 19 Nov 2009].

82 Kelly, V. A., (2006) *Factors Affecting Demand for Fertiliser in Sub-Saharan Africa: Agriculture and Rural Development*. Discussion Paper 23. World Bank, Washington, DC.

83 Bationo, A. et al., (2006) *African Soils: their productivity and profitability of fertiliser use*. Background paper presented for the African Fertiliser Summit 9 to13 June, Abuja, Nigeria.

84 Dorward, A. et al., (2008) Towards 'smart' subsidies in agriculture? Lessons from recent experience in Malawi. *Natural Resource Perspectives*, **116**, Overseas Development Institute, London.

85 Roy, A., (2008) Managing Access to farm inputs. Presented at the World Bank Symposium *Cultivating Innovation: A Response to the Food Price Crisis*. IFDC, Washington, DC.

86 ICRISAT. (2001) Things Grow Better with Coke. *SATrends*. Issue 2, January. Available at: www.icrisat.org/satrends/01jan/1.htm. [Accessed 19 Nov 2009].

87 ICRISAT. (2001) *Adoption of 'micro-dosing' soil fertility restoration technologies through the introduction of the warrantage credit facility in the Sudano-Sahelian zone of West Africa*. Research Brief 11 Sep. Available at: www.icrisat.org/gt-aes/ResearchBreifs3.htm [Accessed 19 Nov 2009].

88 Levy, S., (ed). (2005) Starter Packs: *A Strategy to Fight Hunger in Developing Countries? Lessons from the Malawi Experience, 1998-2003*, CABI, Wallingford.

89 World Bank. (n.d.) Jump-Starting Maize Production in Malawi through Universal Starter Packs, *Fertiliser Toolkit: Promoting Efficient and Sustainable Fertilizer Use in Africa*. Available at: www.worldbank.org/afr/fertilizer_tk/documentspdf/MalawiSP.pdf [Accessed 19 Nov 2009].

90 Dobermann, A. et al., (2002) Site-specific nutrient management for intensive rice cropping systems in Asia. *Field Crops Res*, **74**, 37–66.

91 Bationo, A. et al., (2003) Soil fertility management for sustainable land use in the West African Sudano-Sahelian zone. In: *Soil Fertility Management in Africa: A Regional Perspective*, 253–292. Academy Science Publishers (ASP), Nairobi, Kenya.

92 Bationo, A. et al., (eds) (2007) *Advances in Integrated Soil Fertility Management in Sub-Saharan Africa: Challenges and Opportunities*. Springer, Dordrecht.

93 Nandwa, S., (2003) Perspectives on soil fertility in Africa. In: *Soil Fertility and Management in Africa: A Regional Perspective*, 1–50. Academy Science Publishers, Nairobi, Kenya.

94 Akponikpe, P. Michels, K. & Bielders, C., (2008) Integrated nutrient management of pearl millet in the Sahel combining cattle manure, crop residue and mineral fertiliser. *Expl Agric*, **44**, 453–472.

95   Vanlauwe, B.et al., (eds) (2002) *Integrated Plant Nutrient Management in Sub-Saharan Africa: From Concept to Practice*. 322 CABI, Wallingford.

96   Lan'gat, M. Mukhwana, E. & Woomer, P., (n.d.) *Managing Beneficial Interactions in Legume Intercrops (MBILI)*. SACRED Africa. Available at: www.formatkenya.org/files/Organic % 20Resource % 20Notebook.htm [Accessed 19 Nov 2009].

97   Woomer, P. Lan'gat, M. & Tungani, J., Innovative Maize-Legume Intercropping Results in Above- and Below-ground Competitive Advantages for Understorey Legumes. *West African Journal of Applied Ecology*, **6**, 2004.

98   Woomer, P. L. & E. J. Mukhwana., (2004) Working with smallholder farmers to improve maize production and marketing in western Kenya, *Uganda Journal of Agricultural Sciences*, **9**, 491-500.

99   Agrama, H., (2006) Application of Molecular Markers in Breeding for Nitrogen Use Efficiency. *Journal of Crop Improvement*, **15**, 2, 175-211.

100 Hirel, B. et al., (2007) The challenge of improving nitrogen use efficiency in crop plants: towards a more central role for genetic variability and quantitative genetics within integrated approaches. *Journal, Exp. Bot*, **58**, 2369-2387.

101 Gallais, A & Hirel, B., (2004) An approach to the genetics of nitrogen use efficiency in maize. *Journal, Exp. Bot*, **55**, 295-306.

102 Muurinen, S. Kleemola, J. & Peltonen-Sainio, P., (2007) Accumulation and Translocation of Nitrogen in Spring Cereal Cultivars Differing in Nitrogen Use Efficiency. *Agron. J*, **99**, 441-449.

103 Ladha, J. Bruijn, F. & Malik, K., (eds) (1997) *Opportunies for Biological Nitrogen Fixation in Rice and Other Non-Legumes*. Kluwer Academic Publishers with IRRI, Dordrecht.

104 Gleason, C. et al., (2006) Nodulation independent of rhizobia is induced by a calcium-activated kinase lacking autoinhibition. *Nature*, **441**, 1149-1152.

105 World Bank. (2008) *World Development Report 2008*. World Bank, Washington, DC.

106 UNDP. (2006) *Human Development Report 2006. Beyond Scarcity: Power, Poverty and the Global Water Crisis*. Palgrave-McMillan. UN, New York.

107 World Bank. (2006) *Re-engaging in Agricultural Water Management: Challenges and Options*. World Bank, Washington, DC.

108 GWP. (2004) *Catalyzing Change*: A handbook for developing integrated water resources management (IWRM) and water efficiency strategies. Produced by the Global Water Partnership Technical Committee. Available at: waterwiki.net/images/9/9f/Catalyzing_change.pdf [Accessed 19 Nov 2009].

109 IWMI. (2007) *IWRM Challenges in Developing Countries: Lessons from India and elsewhere*. Water Policy Briefing Issue 24. Available at: www.iwmi.cgiar.org/Publications/Water_Policy_Briefs/PDF/WPB24.pdf [Accessed 19 Nov 2009]

110 Pongkijvorasin, S. & Roumasset, J., (2007) *Optimal Conjunctive Use of Surface and Groundwater with Recharge and Return Flows: Dynamic and Spatial Patterns*. University of Hawaii. Manoa, Hawaii. Working Paper No. 07-4. Available at: www.economics.hawaii.edu/research/workingpapers/WP_07-4.pdf [Accessed 19 Nov 2009].

111 Nayar, M. & Aughton, D., (2007) *Canal Automation and Cost Recovery: Australian Experience Using Rubicon Total Channel Control*. Discussion Paper 33. World Bank, Agriculture and Rural Development Department, Washington DC.

112 Bastiaanssen, W. & Hellegers, P., (2007) Satellite Measurements to Assess and Charge for Groundwater Abstraction. In: Dinar, A. Dayem, S. & Agwe, J., (eds.), *The Role of Technology and Institutions in the Cost Recovery of Irrigation and Drainage Projects*. Discussion Paper 33. Washington, World Bank, Agriculture and Rural Development, Washington DC. Available at: go.worldbank.org/W3216WCKB2 [Accessed 23 Nov 2009].

113 Practical Action. (2007) *Drip Irrigation*. Available at: dev.practicalaction.org/drip_irrigation [Accessed 19 Nov 2009].

114 USAID. (2005) *Drip Irrigation Turns Gravel into Green*. Available at: africastories.usaid.gov/search_details.cfm?storyID=390&countryID=30&sectorID=0&yearID=5 [Accessed 19 Nov 2009].

115 Cofie, O. Barry, B. & Bossio, D., (2004) *Human Resources as a driver of Bright Spots: the case of rainwater harvesting in West Africa.* International Water Management Institute, Ghana and Sri Lanka. Conference Paper 19, NEPAD/IGAD Regional Conference: Agricultural Successes in the Greater Horn of Africa, Nairobi.

116 IWMI. (2006) *Adoption Drivers and Constraints of Resource Conservation Technologies in Sub-Saharan Africa.* Technology Information Sheet #23 – Zai/Tassa. IWMI, FAO, Humbolt University. Available at: www.iwmi.cgiar.org/africa/West/projects/Adoption % 20Technology/RainWaterHarvesting/23-Zai.htm [Accessed 19 Nov 2009].

117 Doumbia, M. Berthe, A. & Aune, J., (2005) *Integrated Plant Nutrition Management in Mali Summary Report 1998-2004.* Drylands Conservation Group Report No. 36.

118 Zeddies, J. et al., (2001) Economics of Biological Control of Cassava Mealybug in Africa. *Agricultural Economics*, **24**, 209-219.

119 Neuenschwander, P., (2001) Biological control of the cassava mealybug in Africa: a review. *Biological Control*, **21**, 214-229.

120 Otim Nape, G. & Thresh, J., (2006) The recent epidemic of cassava mosaic virus disease in Uganda and Kenya. In: B. Cooke, B. Gareth Jones, D. & Kaye, B., (eds) *The Epidemiology of Plant Diseases.* Second Edition. Springer, Dondrecht , Netherlands, 521-550.

121 Smith, J. et al., (2008) The challenge of providing plant pest diagnostic services for Africa. *European Journal of Plant Pathology*, **121**, 3, 365-375.

122 Smith, J. et al., (2008) An analysis of the risk from *Xanthomonas campestris* pv. *musacearum* to banana cultivation in Eastern, Central and Southern Africa. Available at: bananas.bioversityinternational.org/files/files/pdf/publications/xanthomonas_campestris.pdf [Accecssed 25 Nov 2009].

123 Rutherford, M.A., (2006) Current knowledge of coffee wilt disease, a major constraint to coffee Production in Africa. *Phytopathology*, **96**, 663-666.

124 Expert Panel on Stem Rust Outbreak in East Africa. (2005) *Sounding the Alarm on Global Stem Rust,* An assessment of Ug99 race in Kenya and Ethiopia and potential for impact in neighbouring regions and beyond. CIMMYT. Available at: www.cimmyt.org/english/wps/news/2005/aug/pdf/Expert_Panel_Report.pdf [Accessed 25 Nov 2009].

125 Conway, G. & Pretty, J., (1991) *Unwelcome Harvest: Agriculture and Pollution.* Earthscan, London.

126 Loevinsohn, M., (1987) Insecticide use and increased mortality in rural Central Luzon, Philippines. *Lancet*, June 13, **1** 359-1 362.

127 Pingals, P. & Roger, P., (eds) (1995) *Impact of Pesticides on Farmer Health and the Rice Environment.* IRRI. Kluwer Academic Publishers, Massachusetts.

128 Conway, G., (1973) Ecological Aspects of Pest Control in Malaysia. In: Farver, M.T. & Milton, J., (eds) (1973) *The Careless Technology.* Tom Stacey, London.

129 Gallagher, K. Kenmore, P. & Sogawa, K., (1994) Judicial use of insecticides deter planthopper outbreaks and extend the life of resistance varieties in southeast Asian rice. In: Denno, R.F. & Perfect, T.J., (eds) *Planthopper: Their Ecology and Management.* Chapman & Hall, New York, 599-614.

130 Kenmore, P. et al., (nd) Population regulation of the rice brown planthopper (Nilaparvata lugens Stal) with rice fields in the Philippines. *Journal of Plant Protection in the Tropics*, **1**, 19-38.

131 van den Berg, H., (2004) *IPM Farmer Field Schools: A Synthesis of 25 Impact Evaluations.* Global IPM Facility, FAO Rome.

132 Ooi, P. & Kenmore, P., (2006) Impact of educating farmers about biological control in farmer field schools. In: Hoddle, M., Compiler, *Proceedings of 2nd International Symposium on Biological Control of Arthropods*, Davos, Switzerland. **1**, 277-289.

133 Settle, W. et al., (1996) Managing tropical rice pests through conservation of generalist natural enemies and alternative prey. *Ecology*, **77**, 1975-1998.

134 AATF. (2008) *Striga control in maize.* Available at: www.aatf-africa.org/aatf_projects.php?sublevelone =9&subcat=5 [Accessed 19 Nov 2009].

135 Hassanali, A. et al., (2008) Integrated pest management: the push-pull approach for controlling insect pests and weeds of cereals, and its potential for other agricultural systems including animal husbandry. *Philosophical Transactions of the Royal Society London*, **363**, 611-621.

136 Rothamsted Research Chemical Ecology Group. *Push-pull habitat manipulation for control of maize stemborers and the witchweed Striga*. Available at: www.rothamsted.ac.uk/bch/CEGroup/ChemEcolGroupArea6.html [Accessed 19 Nov 2009].

137 USDA-CSREES Coordinate Agricultural Projects. Wheat CAP: Disease resistance. Stem Rust Resistance. Available at: maswheat.ucdavis.edu/protocols/StemRust/index.htm [Accessed 19 Nov 2009].

138 Pretorius, Z. et al., (2000) Detection of virulence to wheat stem rust resistant gene *Sr31* in *Puccinia graminis f. sp. tritici* in Uganda. *Plant Disease*, **84**, 2, 203.

139 Durable Rust Resistance in Wheat Project at Cornell University. Available at: www.wheatrust.cornell.edu/about/index.html [Accessed 19 Nov 2009].

140 The Borlaug Global Rust Initiative. Available at: www.globalrust.org [Accessed 25 Nov 2009].

141 AGP-FAO Wheat Rust Disease Global Programme. *Wheat Rust – Threat to farmers and global food security*. Available at: www.fao.org/agriculture/crops/core-themes/theme/pests/wrdgp/en/ [Accessed 19 Nov 2009].

142 Purdue Collaborative Research Support Program. Breeding/Genetic Transformation of Cowpeas. Available at: www.entm.purdue.edu/entomology/research/cowpea/Breeding Pages/gentrans.htm

143 Collaboration on Insect Management for Brassicas in Asia and Africa (CIMBAA). Available at: www.cimbaa.org/index-0.html [Accessed 19 Nov 2009].

144 Torr, S. Morton, J. & Gibson, G., (2005) *Vectors of Animal and Human Disease: The Tsetse Story*. Presentation to Gordon Conway, 14 April 2005.

145 Canadian Food Inspection Agency. (2009) *Rinderpest*. Available at: www.inspection.gc.ca/english/anima/disemala/rinpes/rinpesfse.shtml [Accessed 19 Nov 2009].

146 Roeder, P. & Karl, R., (2009) *The global effort to eradicate rinderpest*. IFPRI Discussion Paper 923. IFPRI, Washington DC.

147 Vish N., Director of Biotechnology at ILRI. [Email] (Pers. Comm. 14 November 2009).

148 ILRI. *Why Livestock Matter*. Available at: www.ilri.org/home.asp?CCID=52&SID=1 [Accessed 19 Nov 2009].

149 Brown, K., (2006) *Genomics-based vaccine could prevent deadly cattle disease*. Innovations report 14.2.2006. Available at: www.innovations-report.de/html/berichte/biowissenschaften_chemie/bericht-55220.html [Accessed 19 Nov 2009].

150 RIU. (nd) *Pro-poor vaccine-based control of East Coat fever*. Research Into Use. Available at: www.researchintouse.com/nrk/RIUinfo/PF/AHP14.htm#L1 [Accessed 19 Nov 2009].

151 ILRI. (nd) *Collaborative Team Brings Vaccine against Deadly Cattle Disease to Poor Pastoralists for the First Time*. Available at: www.ilri.org/ilripubaware/Uploaded % 20Files/20061016716210. BR_ISS__045_VSFcollaborationOnECF.pdf [Accessed 19 Nov 2009].

152 GALVmed Available at: www.galvmed.org [Accessed 19 Nov 2009].

153 FFTC. (2000) *Biotechnology for Livestock Production*. Food and Fertiliser Technology Center for the Asian and Pacific Region. Available at: www.agnet.org/library/nc/129b/ [Accessed 19 Nov 2009].

154 Egerton, J., (2003) *Gene-based vaccine development for improving animal production in developing countries*. FAO/IAEA International Symposium on Applications of Gene-based Technologies for Improving Animal Production and Health in Developing Countries – Book of Extended Synopses. Vienna 2003.

155 Delia G., ILRI. [Email] (Pers Comm. 3 November 2009).

156 Tan, S., (2004) *Taeniasis*. Prepared for a course at Stanford University. Available at: www.stanford.edu/group/parasites/ParaSites2004/Taeniasis/index.htm [Accessed 19 Nov 2009].

157 Rice-Wheat Consortium. Available at: www.rwc.cgiar.org [Accessed 19 Nov 2009].

158 Hobbs, P. et al., (nd) *The adoption of Conservation Agriculture of Rice-Wheat Systems in South Asia*: A Case Study from India. Available at: www.css.cornell.edu/faculty/hobbs/File % 20posters/poster1.pdf [Accessed 19 Nov 2009].

159 Laxmi,V. Erenstein, O. & Gupta, R., (2007) *Impact of Zero Tillage in India's Rice-Wheat Systems*. CIMMYT, New Delhi.

160 ILRI. (1997) *Livestock and soil fertility: exploiting the natural balance*. Backgrounder paper. International Livestock Research Institute, Nairobi, Kenya. Available at: www.ilri.org/ILRIPubAware/ Uploaded Files/200410191145180.NR_BG_971201_001_ILRI_LivestockAndSoilFertility.pdf [Accessed 19 Nov 2009].

161 ILRI. (1999) *Livestock and Nutrient Cycling*. International Livestock Research Institute, Nairobi, Kenya.

162 Kristiansen, P. Taji, A. & Reganold, J., (2006) *Organic Agriculture: A Global Perspective*, CSIRO Publishing. Available at: www.publish.csiro.au/samples/OrganicAgSample.pdf [Accessed 19 Nov 2009].

163 Soil Association. (2007) *Pesticides and organic farming – a last resort*. Available at: www.whyorganic.org/web/sa/saweb.nsf/librarytitles/24E22.HTMl/$file/Pesticides % 20and % 20organic % 20farming % 20- % 20A % 20last % 20resort.pdf [Accessed 19 Nov 2009].

164 Research Institute of Organic Agriculture. (2007) *Statistics on global organic farming 2007*. Available at: www.organic-world.net/statistics-world.html [Accessed 19 Nov 2009].

165 Willer, H, Yussefi-Menzler, M. & Sorensen, N. (2008) *The World of Organic Agriculture, Statistics and Emerging Trends 2008*. International Federation of Organic Agriculture Movements (IFOAM) Bonn, and Research Institute of Organic Agriculture (FiBL), Frick.

166 Hine, R. & Pretty, J., (2006) Promoting Production and Trading Opportunities for Organic Agricultural Products in East Africa Capacity Building Study 3 in *Organic Agriculture and Food Security in East Africa*. University of Essex.

167 Badgley, C. et al., (2006) Organic agriculture and the global food supply. *Renewable Agriculture and Food Systems*, **22** (2), 86–108.

168 Pretty, J. et al., (2005) Resource-conserving agriculture increases yields in developing countries. *Environmental Science & Technology*, **40** (4), 1114-1119.

169 UNEP/UNESCO. (2008) *Organic Agriculture and Food Security in Africa*. UN, Geneva.

06

Improving Health

A baby receiving a vaccination at a health clinic in Guinea, Africa. © Giacomo Pirozzi – Panos Pictures

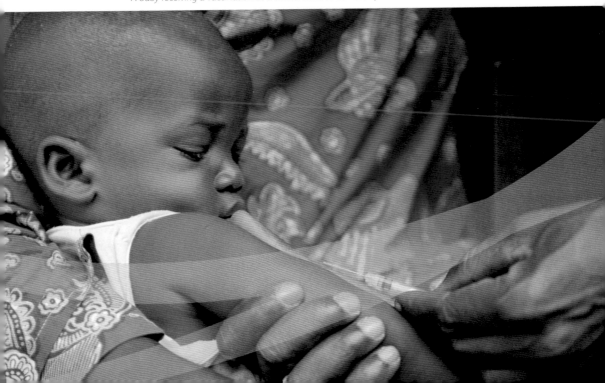

The global health gap remains very large. While life expectancy in industrialised countries is around 78 years it is only 55 years in the developing countries (50 years in Sub-Saharan Africa).[1] Chronic illnesses such as heart and circulatory conditions and cancer cause most morbidity and mortality in the developed countries, in contrast to developing countries where infectious diseases are more significant.[2,3]

Technological advances in controlling infectious diseases have therefore had considerable impact on the poor.

- The yellow fever vaccine, developed in the 1920s, helped eradicate the disease from Central and South America;

- Smallpox was eradicated using a vaccine by 1980;

- Penicillin and other antibiotics in the post World War II years brought down mortality from bacterial infections in both adults and children;

- Oral rehydration therapy, proven to be effective in Bangladesh in 1971, has produced a significant world-wide reduction in mortality from diarrhoeal diseases;

- Anti-retrovirals against HIV, developed in the 1970s, have saved millions of lives.

Recently, scientific research has been more directed at so-called "neglected diseases" largely restricted to the developing countries, and this has resulted in substantial further progress in their control.

Globally these and other technologies embedded in public health programmes, that also include such measures as the provision of clean drinking water and sanitation, have improved the health of many in developing countries.

The MDGs have identified three specific areas for improvement of health – decreasing child mortality, improving maternal health and combating infectious diseases (See Chapter 4). While infectious diseases, particularly HIV/AIDS, TB and malaria, have largely been addressed through campaigns to discover and develop new drugs and vaccines, supported by new funding mechanisms and public-private partnerships (described in Chapter 3), child and maternal health improvements have focused on the improvement of health systems and the extension of conventional technologies. Improving health has also been an element of MDG 7, with its target to improve the supply of clean water and sanitation, and MDG 1, with its commitment to reduce malnutrition.

We begin with this last target, as healthy diets which address malnutrition underpin child and adult health and the resilience to disease. They also underline the critical, but often neglected, link between agricultural and health development targets.

1. Improving health by improving diets

Improved diets are fundamental to improving health. They also play a significant role in preventing infection and reducing morbidity and mortality. Thus, advances in agriculture which increase the quantity and quality of food available to the poor can make a major complementary contribution to the direct efforts to improve health. It is difficult, if not impossible, however to identify the relative contribution of infectious disease and malnutrition to ill health – both are important and their interactions are crucial.

Children's health is usually assessed in terms of their weight and height. Low birth weight often stems from a mother's poor health and nutritional status before and during pregnancy. About 16% of infants in developing countries are born weighing less than 2.5kg and are 20 times more likely to die in infancy than heavier babies. Those who survive may be more susceptible to infectious diseases, inhibited growth and cognitive development, and are more likely to suffer from chronic illnesses in later life.[4]

Figure 6.1 – Improving diets is essential for improving health

© Edwin Huffman – World Bank

Stunting, or low height for age, which generally occurs before a child is two, is caused by long-term insufficient nutrient intake and frequent infections. Its effects, which include delayed motor development, impaired cognitive function and poor school performance, are largely irreversible. Nearly one third of children under five in the developing world are stunted. Wasting, or low weight for height, is a strong predictor of mortality among children under five. It is usually the result of acute significant food shortage and/or disease.[4]

Proteins and other micronutrients

While carbohydrates, which we derive largely from cereals, are critical to the provision of energy necessary for health and growth, they do not alone constitute a high quality diet. This requires consumption of protein and various micronutrients, particularly in childhood. Insufficient levels of micronutrients in the diet have distinctive effects which are particularly apparent in poor populations. Some of these are illustrated in Box 6.1.

Box 6.1 The consequences of micronutrient deficiency[4,5]		
Deficiency	**Effects**	**Incidence**
Iodine	Single greatest cause of preventable mental retardation: severe deficiencies cause cretinism, stillbirth and miscarriage; mild deficiency can significantly affect the learning ability of populations.	38 million newborns worldwide remain unprotected.
Zinc	Increases severity of diarrhoea, pneumonia, and possibly malaria, by one-third and causes stunting.	Over 70% at risk of low zinc intake in south and southeast Asia and Sub-Saharan Africa.

Deficiency	Effects	Incidence
Vitamin A	Results in night blindness and ultimately blindness, growth retardation, damage of mucous membrane tracts, and reproductive disorders. Children are also likely to be anaemic and be at increased risk of severe morbidity from common childhood infections such as diarrhoeal diseases and measles. Pregnant women with vitamin A deficiency have increased risk of mortality.	Some 127 million pre-school children are vitamin A deficient – about one-quarter of all pre-school children in high-risk regions of the developing world.
Iron	Deficiency during childhood and adolescence impairs physical growth, mental development, and learning capacity. In adults, it reduces the ability to do physical work. More than 2 billion people worldwide are anaemic and much of it is due to iron-deficiency. Severe anaemia increases the risk of women dying in childbirth.	In developing countries, the most affected population groups are pregnant women (42%) – although many women aged 15 to 59 years are also affected (30%) as well as school-age children and pre-school children.

Improving dietary intakes

There are three possible approaches to improving the quality of dietary intakes:

The first is to improve the diversity of the diet. As the FAO points out *'the share of dietary energy from animal foods, vegetable oils, sugar, fruits and vegetables increases with higher per capita income levels, while that from roots, tubers and pulses tends to decrease'.*[6] The poor rely more on staples and consume less meat and fewer dairy products, smaller amounts of oils and fats, and fewer fruits and vegetables that are rich in high-quality proteins and micronutrients, such as iron, zinc and vitamin A. Because such foods cost relatively more than the staples, poor people consume less in times of physical hardship (such as during a major drought) or financial crisis. In urban areas only an increase in income will permit inclusion of animal products, vegetables and fruits in diets. However, in rural areas efforts to encourage the cultivation of a greater diversity of edible foods may be productive, for example through the establishment and improvement of home gardens (see Box 2.7).

The second approach is to provide essential micronutrients in the form of dietary supplements. In the developed world, the science of supplements has long been established and much food, particularly cereals, is fortified with micronutrients. Extending these conventional technologies to developing countries has had some success, for instance in the provision of iodized salt (Figure 6.2) and Vitamin A pills (Figure 6.3).

Nevertheless, for the developing countries as a whole, the provision of good balanced diets, particularly for the poorest, remains a severe challenge. This is partly why recent efforts have focused on a third approach, that of improving the dietary quality of the basic staple crops through biofortification, either through conventional breeding or through recombinant DNA technologies as described in Chapter 5.

Figure 6.2 – In the developing world most countries have more than 50% of their households consuming adequately iodized salt.[4]

© UNICEF 2007

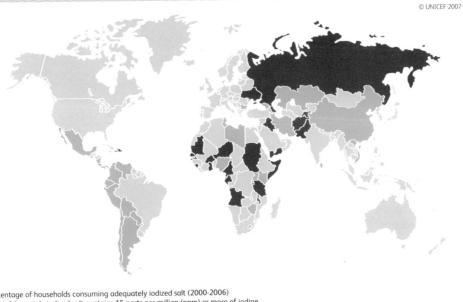

Percentage of households consuming adequately iodized salt (2000-2006)
Note: Adequately iodized salt contains 15 parts per million (ppm) or more of iodine.

● 90% or more   ● 50–89%   ● Less than 50%   ● Data not available

Figure 6.3 – Provision of two doses of vitamin A (For 103 countries where under five mortality rate or vitamin A deficiency is high).[4]

© UNICEF 2007

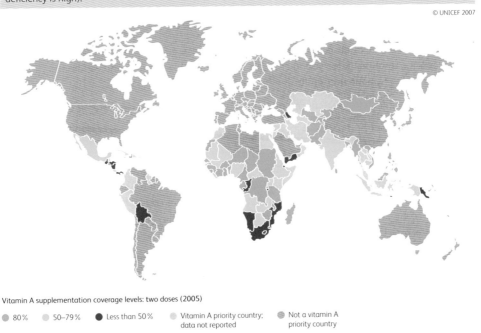

Vitamin A supplementation coverage levels: two doses (2005)

● 80%   ● 50–79%   ● Less than 50%   ● Vitamin A priority country; data not reported   ● Not a vitamin A priority country

2. Improving child and maternal health

Child mortality

As indicated in Chapter 4 considerable progress has been made in reducing the global death rate among under five year olds. To date, the greatest successes in combating child mortality have been in reducing the incidence of measles through vaccination and of malaria through the use of insecticide treated mosquito nets. Nevertheless the mortality rates in developing countries remain unacceptably high.[8] The major causes include neonatal complications, pneumonia and diarrhoea, with undernutrition acting as a significant underlying factor.

The contribution of undernutrition and how it can be tackled has been discussed above and in Chapter 5. Once past the neonatal period, deaths from pneumonia and other acute respiratory infections are currently the biggest concern. As was indicated in Chapter 4, this is largely due to a lack of access to correct diagnosis and antibiotics. Improvements in health system effectiveness are needed to make progress

Figure 6.4 – A woman feeds her child as part of a programme which teaches mothers ways to prepare nutritious meals for their children with the resources they have available

in this area. Diarrhoeal diseases, which cause 16 % of child deaths, will be dealt with first where we look at specific treatments for young children. Later on in this chapter, and in Chapter 7, we will discuss improving hygiene and sanitation for prevention.

Other childhood infections, such as malaria and HIV, will also be discussed later in this chapter.

Childhood treatment of diarrhoea

Whatever the basic cause, most diarrhoea-related deaths result from starvation or from the dehydration associated with diarrhoea. Acute, watery diarrhoea results in loss of both electrolytes and water; death occurs when the body fluid loss exceeds 10 %. Prior to the 1960s the only effective treatment was intravenous infusions which had to be administered in clinics, by trained personnel. They were costly and only available to a few patients. With the development of oral rehydration therapy (Box 6.2), this situation has changed.

The standard ORT packet consists of common salt, trisodium citrate dehydrate, potassium chloride and glucose, but the recommendations have changed in recent years reflecting a better understanding of what works in the home and community. Research has shown that home-made fluids – particularly those containing sodium and glucose, sucrose or other carbohydrates, like cereal based solutions – can be just as effective.

Box 6.2   The effectiveness of Oral Rehydration Therapy (ORT)[9]

In 1971 the war for independence in Bangladesh caused the flight of 10 million refugees to overcrowded camps where a deadly cholera outbreak occurred. *'Conditions were squalid and chaotic, intravenous fluid was in scarce supply, treatment facilities and transportation were inadequate, and trained personnel were limited.'*[10]

Dr Dilip Mahanabilis suggested trying an approach previously proven successful, but on a small scale, in Calcutta and Bangladesh. He and his team produced packets of table salt, baking soda and glucose which were distributed in one of the camps with instructions on how to dissolve the contents of the packets in water. There had been

© UNICEF, Nigeria

Figure 6.5 – A woman mixes ORT

scepticism among health professionals who cautioned that the treatment should only be administered by doctors and other trained personnel.[11] Yet the treatment was given by 'mothers, friends and patients themselves' and proved to be very cheap, highly effective and safe. Mortality fell to 4 % compared with 20 to 30 % in the camps using intravenous therapy.

ORT was heralded by the Lancet as *'potentially the most important medical discovery of the 20th century,'*[12] and in 1972 became the WHO's standard treatment. By 2000 deaths from diarrhoea had fallen by 3.1 million/year or 67 %.[13]

Recently there have been significant successes in countries such as Bangladesh and Egypt, nevertheless the proportion of affected children treated in this way worldwide still remains low (Figure 6.6).

Part of the problem is that treating a child with ORT does not immediately reduce the diarrhoea. In fact it may even make it worse before it improves. Inevitably, mothers will then resort to purchasing anti-diarrhoeal treatments which may be promoted by the private sector in preference to the much cheaper ORT. One answer, for the more severe and prolonged cases, may lie in developing cheaper, yet safer anti-diarrhoeal treatments for children. The Institute for

OneWorld Health in California, with a grant from the Bill and Melinda Gates Foundation, is currently working with the International Centre for Diarrhoeal Disease Research in Bangladesh, Novartis Institutes for BioMedical Research, Roche Pharmaceuticals and others to develop drugs which can be integrated with ORT to reduce

Figure 6.6 – The low proportions of children under five with diarrhoea who receive oral rehydration or increased fluids with continued breast feeding (2000-2006)[4]

© UNICEF 2007

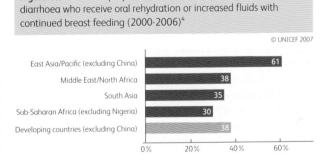

East Asia/Pacific (excluding China)	61
Middle East/North Africa	38
South Asia	35
Sub-Saharan Africa (excluding Nigeria)	30
Developing countries (excluding China)	38

0%   20%   40%   60%

fluid and electrolyte loss. They are also pursuing longer-term research and trials to find anti-microbial medications which are safe, effective and affordable for the types of diarrhoea affecting children in developing countries.[14] More generally there has been an emphasis, in recent years, on complementing ORT with a variety of other measures, including continued feeding (breast feeding in infants), clean drinking water, improved personal hygiene, and zinc treatment.[15,16,17]

Maternal mortality

Every year more than half a million women die as a result of complications during pregnancy and childbirth, 99 % of them in the developing countries.[18] In addition every year:[19]

- 80 million women face an unwanted or unplanned pregnancy;

- 20 million women risk an unsafe abortion rather than carry their pregnancy to term: 68,000 will die as a result;

- 50 million women suffer from a serious pregnancy related illness;

- 4 million women are disabled as a result of pregnancy or childbirth;

- 15 million adolescents give birth at an age when the risks are particularly high;

- 300 million women worldwide (25 % of the developing world's adult women) currently live with avoidable ill health and disability as a result of pregnancy. Problems include infertility, uterine prolapse (where the womb falls into the vagina) and vesico-vaginal fistula (holes in the birth canal that allow leakage of faeces and/or urine into the vagina). Many women become socially excluded as a result.

Maternal mortality has decreased globally but not at a rate to achieve the MDG and there has been little progress in Sub-Saharan Africa. There, and in South Asia, haemorrhage is the main cause of maternal mortality. Almost all maternal deaths could be prevented if professional care was available during pregnancy and childbirth, and the few weeks following delivery, as well as access to emergency obstetric care in the event of complications.

Experience from Thailand, Bangladesh and Sri Lanka shows that maternal mortality can be reduced in low-income settings – by increasing access to skilled attendants, emergency obstetric care and family planning services.[20] Evidence also indicates that preventing unplanned pregnancies alone could avert at least one quarter of maternal deaths each year. Over 130 million women, who have expressed a desire to space or limit their family size, are not using any form of contraception. A further 64 million rely on less effective traditional methods. Furthermore, when abortion is made legal, safe and accessible, women's health improves rapidly.[21] In South Africa complications resulting from unsafe abortion decreased significantly (from 16.5 % to 9.7 %) between 1994 and 2000, largely due to the legalisation of abortions in 1996.[22]

Figure 6.7 – Woman giving birth in India

© DFID

3. Preventing and treating infectious diseases

The rest of this chapter is dedicated to the challenge of preventing and treating infectious diseases. This emphasis does not reflect a view that infectious diseases are more important than other health targets in international development. However, infectious diseases are the primary focus of the MDGs and, as a result, are subject to an intensity of science innovation, particularly using new platform technologies.

Following an introduction to infectious disease theory, we will focus on four areas of innovation:

- Environmental and behavioural modification;
- The quest for vaccines;
- The role of treatment and drugs;
- Emerging infectious diseases.

The nature of infectious diseases

Infectious diseases spread by transmission between infected individuals and un-infected individuals. Survivors are often immune and not susceptible to further infection. Most infectious diseases persist at low endemic levels; the number of people infected remains fairly constant with occasional short-lived surges in particular regions. However, diseases may explode into major epidemic proportions. This may be due to the virus, bacterium or other disease agent mutating into a form that is more virulent or invasive, or because the environment or human behaviour has changed, increasing transmission or susceptibility to infection. In practice such epidemics die out naturally because the disease agent runs out of susceptible members of the population (many may be naturally immune). The disease may then disappear or return to its previous endemic level. A "pandemic" is when an epidemic of infectious disease spreads through human populations across a large region; for instance a continent, or even worldwide.

The essence of infectious disease control is to achieve a low level of R_0 (the number of secondary cases produced by a primary case during its lifetime). At $R_0 = 1.0$ the disease is at a relatively stable endemic level. If $R_0 \leq 1.0$ over a sustainable period, then the disease will ultimately disappear. So far, the latter has only happened globally for smallpox (and for the livestock disease rinderpest see Box 5.19), although polio and Guinea worm are also close to extinction. In other cases it has been possible to eliminate the disease from particular geographic regions (yellow fever from the Americas, malaria from Europe). The more complicated the disease in terms of the structure and dynamics of the disease agent, its relationship with the human immune system and with any non-human host, the more difficult it becomes to reduce to low endemic levels or to eradicate.

We can reduce R_0 in one of three ways, through:

- Changing the environment or human behaviour in ways which reduce the risk of infection;
- Using a vaccine or microbicide to kill the disease agent at infection;
- Providing drugs which cure infections early, so reducing illness and mortality, and the risk of further transmission.

These all require appropriate economic and social policies and, in particular, rely on strong political leadership. But they also depend on the use of existing or potential new technologies.

4. Environmental and behavioural modification for infectious diseases

Preventing diarrhoea

Most diarrhoeal causing infections of childhood originate in faecal material which passes through the environment, often via contaminated water, to infect more children (Figure 6.8). In the diagram below the four arrows originating from 'faeces' on the left of the figure represent the primary routes by which infectious organisms get into the environment.

- Primary barriers are the practices that stop this happening – disposal of faeces in latrines, sewers and the removal of traces of faecal material from hands after contact with excreta.

- Secondary barriers are hygiene practices that stop faecal pathogens that have entered the environment in faeces or on the hands, from multiplying and reaching new hosts. For example, washing hands before preparing food or eating, and preparing, cooking, storing and re-heating food in such a way as to avoid pathogen survival and multiplication. Also protecting water supplies from faecal contaminants by treating water through boiling or chlorination. Other secondary barriers include keeping play spaces free of faecal material, preventing children from eating earth and controlling flies.

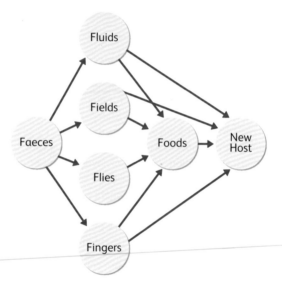

Figure 6.8 – The multiple pathways through which enteric pathogens pass from one child to another – the so-called F-diagram.[23]

The provision of improved sanitation and clean drinking water is discussed further in the next chapter. However behavioural modification is equally important. A high standard of hygiene – washing hands with soap and water (particularly after defaecation) – is key to reducing transmission (Box 6.3).[24]

Box 6.3 Hand washing with soap is the most effective intervention against diarrhoea[25]	
Intervention	**Reduction in diarrhoea risk**
Improved water quality	16 %
Improved water quantity	20 %
Sanitation	36 %
Hygiene education	35 %
Hand washing with soap	47 %

Improving hand washing

Various experiments have shown that market-based interventions to promote hand washing can result in persistent uptake of the practice even after a lapse of several years – despite the fact that soap has to be purchased.[26] This suggests that hand washing could be marketed as a consumer product – soap being sold to make hands look, feel, and smell good – rather than to prevent sickness.[25] For this to be a success soaps need to be designed specifically for hand washing in developing countries, as described in Box 6.4 below.

Box 6.4 Making hand washing easy and effective

While a wide array of hand washing products are targeted at consumers in the developed world, almost all soaps produced for the developing world market are designed for bathing, washing dishes or doing laundry. Hand washing at key times – such as after using the toilet or before eating – has failed to catch on as a widespread habit and the large soap companies, such as Unilever and Procter and Gamble, have not yet perceived the expansion into hand washing in developing country markets as a profitable opportunity. Yet, according to one estimate, if everyone in India washed their hands with soap at the appropriate moment, the soap market would grow by 40 %.[27]

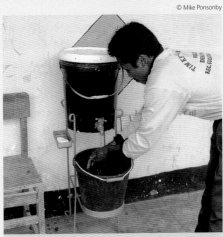
© Mike Ponsonby

Figure 6.9 – A hand washing station in Indonesia

Changing behaviour and cultural norms is extremely difficult. The niche here is unique – most households in the target group do not have running water, or any sort of 'sink' area outside their toilet. The soap needs to be conveniently placed, easy and enjoyable to use and effective at removing microbes from hands. Very little work on producing such products has been done, but according to Val Curtis, of the London School of Hygiene and Tropical Medicine (LSHTM), there is 'a big potential for technological innovation in this area.'[27]

First, there is a need to design an effective way to locate soap, and possibly water, outside a toilet. Ideas include putting bars of soap on ropes or bars, or setting up hand washing stations with water barrels fitted with taps. Second, is the formulation of the soap itself, from simple factors such as whether it is a solid or liquid, its size, price, softness or colour, to more creative ideas such as single-serving paper soap squares which dissolve in water.

There is also potential for creating soaps that are more effective at removing and/or killing the microbes that are more prevalent in particular areas. Trials of medicated soaps have been done, but so far no improvements on traditional soap have been discovered.[28] A few companies, such as Hindustan Lever in India, have started work in this area but further work is needed if hand washing is to become a universal habit and for there to be a real impact in preventing diarrhoeal disease.

The polio environment

The polio virus is also a faecal borne disease agent and spreads in a similar way to diarrhoeal agents. However, once inside the intestines it multiplies and passes into the blood stream where it invades the central nervous system destroying the muscle nerves and, in a small proportion of cases (1 %), causes muscle paralysis (poliomyelitis) in a matter of hours. 50 % of cases occur in children under three.[29]

After initial infection, the virus is shed intermittently in faeces for several weeks, irrespective of whether or not the infected person shows any symptoms. Despite a global vaccination programme to eradicate polio it remains persistent in several pockets, notably in the Indian state of Uttar Pradesh where poor sanitary conditions hinder its elimination (Box 6.5)

Box 6.5   Ghaziabad is one of the last strongholds for poliovirus.[30]

'This impoverished corner of the northern Indian state of Uttar Pradesh offers an almost perfect environment for the virus to survive – even thrive. In urban shanty towns so new they don't even have names, families live in dirt-floored huts, cobbled together out of brick or cardboard secured by grass or plastic; lucky families have a piece of wood instead of burlap for a door. There are no toilets, no running water except for a single standpipe, no electricity. Bare-bottomed kids sit quietly in the mud. Human and animal faeces commingle in drainage ditches.'

The implication is that it is going to be difficult, if not impossible, to eradicate polio unless the sanitary conditions in places like Ghaziabad are significantly improved.

Controlling mosquitoes

Environmental factors are crucial to malaria control because the infective agent – a *Plasmodium* protozoan – is transmitted from one person to another by anopheline mosquitoes (Figure 6.10). In theory, and to a considerable extent in practice, it is possible to eliminate malaria from large areas by controlling the mosquito carriers. Changing the habitat of the mosquito, in particular the water habitat in which mosquito larvae live, can be enough to bring about local elimination. This was a major factor in eliminating malaria in the UK and western Europe, but it was a slow and complicated process involving a diversity of interventions.[31,32]

In the last century attention focused on directly killing the adult mosquitoes. The rationale for this approach was elegantly presented in a mathematical model by George MacDonald in 1956. Subsequently his model was refined to take into account a wide range of factors. In essence it demonstrates the powerful consequences of reducing the mosquito survival rate. After a malaria parasite is ingested by a female mosquito feeding on human blood, it takes 9 to 10 days for the parasite to complete the cycle described in (G) in Figure 6.10 and for the sporozoites to become available in the salivary glands of the mosquito for transmission at the following feed. Mosquitoes feed every three days, and field estimates suggest that the daily survival rate of the mosquito is about 80 %. Thus only about 10 % of the mosquitoes survive long enough to transmit the disease. Reducing the survival still further will greatly reduce the probability of transmission and R_0 will drop below 1.0.[33]

This analysis was the justification for using insecticides, since they reduce both the survival rate and density of the mosquito population. It was soon realised that DDT was a cheap, highly effective mosquito insecticide. When sprayed on the walls and ceilings of dwellings it was relatively safe and persistent. In the 1950s and 1960s there were very successful malaria control campaigns: a notable example was the near elimination of malaria in Sri Lanka.[35] However, mosquitoes developed resistance to DDT and subsequently there have been resurgences in many parts of the world. DDT was also shown to damage wildlife and the environment and as a result was largely withdrawn from use.

Indoor residual spraying (IRS)

IRS has continued but with alternative insecticides such as pyrethroids. These synthetic chemicals are based on natural chemicals derived from the pyrethrum plant. Some of the alternatives are more expensive than DDT; others, such as the pyrethroids, are of comparable cost but are less persistent, requiring two to four sprays a year instead of one. In 2006 the

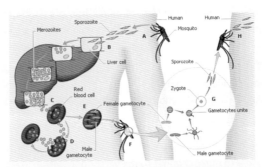

Figure 6.10 – The life cycle of the malaria parasite[34]

(A) A mosquito infected with the malaria parasite bites a human, passing cells called sporozoites into the human bloodstream.

(B) Sporozoites travel to the liver. Each sporozoite undergoes asexual reproduction, in which its nucleus splits to form two new cells, called merozoites.

(C) Merozoites enter the bloodstream and infect red blood cells.

(D) In the red blood cells, the merozoites grow and divide to produce more merozoites, eventually causing the red blood cells to rupture. Some of the newly released merozoites proceed to infect other red blood cells.

(E) Some merozoites develop into sex cells known as male and female gametocytes.

(F) Another mosquito bites the infected human, ingesting the gametocytes.

(G) The gametocytes mature in the mosquito's stomach. Male and female gametocytes undergo sexual reproduction, uniting to form a zygote. The zygote multiplies to form sporozoites, which travel to the mosquito's salivary glands.

(H) If this mosquito bites another human, the cycle begins again.[33]

policy was reviewed by WHO. It concluded that IRS using DDT was often appropriate, and more effective, in certain circumstances and its use was once again approved (this was endorsed by the Stockholm Convention on Persistent Organic Pollutants (POPs)), and updated in 2007.[36] Today some 100 million people are protected by IRS, including 70 million in India and 22 million in Africa.[35]

Insecticide treated nets (ITNs)

More recently the development of insecticide treated nets (ITNs), under which people sleep, has become an alternative to residual spraying. The nets are either dipped in insecticidal solution on a regular basis, usually at least once a year, or the insecticide is impregnated in the net fibre, during manufacture providing a long-lasting insecticidal net (LLIN) (see Chapter 1).[37] By long-lasting this means the ability to remain effective for three years or more. ITNs act in a similar way to indoor spraying in that they kill mosquitoes. However, they also provide a protective barrier, and depending on the insecticide, a degree of repellency. ITNs have been shown to avert around 50 % of malaria cases, doubling the protection afforded by untreated nets.[37] Moreover, while ITNs provide personal protection they have a significant effect on the local mosquito population, giving a community-wide reduction in malaria, even if the coverage is only about 50 % of all adults and children.[32,38,39]

The relative value of using IRS or ITNs depends on local ecological, economic and social conditions.[32] IRS is more suitable than ITNs for the rapid protection of a population, but when IRS needs to be continued for many years, there may be an attrition of people's acceptance of spraying. In contrast, ITNs are more suitable for progressive introduction and incorporation into sustainable population habits. The WHO's guidance is to rapidly scale up the use of ITNs and it recommends that national programmes should only purchase LLINs. However there is now a need for a second-generation of nets that are stronger and longer-lasting, involving more robust polymers and improved treatment technologies in order to cope with the wide range of conditions and cultural preferences encountered.

The most important downside is that IRS and ITNs share the risk of encouraging development of insecticide resistant mosquitoes. For example, pyrethroid resistance has spread very rapidly in Africa. One of the major research challenges is to mitigate this risk (Box 2.3).

Modifying mosquito behaviour

One potential solution to overcoming the limitations of control through spraying or mosquito net use is to make changes to the vector population itself. A project funded through the WHO's tropical disease research programme (TDR)[40] called MosqGuide, has been working to explore ways of modifying mosquitoes that carry dengue fever and malaria.

This can be done either through population suppression, where the goal is to reduce the size of the vector population, or population replacement, where the population is converted to a less harmful form. To achieve suppression, researchers can rear the insects in large numbers, sterilise them using irradiation or genetic sterilisation techniques, and then release them to interbreed with the wild population. The progeny of these crosses will inherit the dominant sterile mutation and not reproduce. If enough sterile insects are released, for a sufficient time, the population will decline and collapse. Open field trials, with similar species, have been carried out, as well as contained field trials and laboratory analysis of malaria-specific strains. It is anticipated that the first use of GM mosquitoes will be through a sterile-release suppression strategy.

The other approach is to modify the vector strain so that it is less able, or unable to transmit the malaria parasite. However, modified mosquitoes are likely to have reduced fitness compared to wild types, and natural selection would lead to gradual loss of the gene. Therefore, an additional factor would be required to spread the gene, a so-called 'gene drive system.' The production and release of this combination carries a range of technical challenges, and testing and implementation of this strategy is still some way off.[41]

Changing human sexual behaviour

HIV/AIDS does not have a particularly significant environmental context, but since HIV is predominantly transmitted via sexual intercourse, the simplest approach to reducing transmission is to either to stop, or reduce, the frequency of intercourse where the risk of transmission is high. In practice this means adopting safe sexual behaviour:

- Abstinence, which for young people means delaying the age of first sexual intercourse;

- Reducing the number of sexual partners;

- Using a condom correctly and consistently, especially for casual sexual activity and in high-risk situations.[42]

Surveillance indicates that the growth in the AIDS epidemic in Sub-Saharan Africa has started to stabilise or decline in many countries since the late 1990s, although it is still at high levels.[43] The question is how much of this stabilisation is due to the natural course of an epidemic and saturation of disease levels in high-risk populations, or is the result of interventions, including those aimed at changing sexual behaviour. An increasing number of countries – including Uganda, Thailand, Kenya, Cambodia, Zimbabwe, India, Rwanda, Ethiopia, Dominican Republic, and Haiti – have experienced national or sub-national declines in HIV which may be associated with the widespread adoption of prevention behaviours (Box 6.6).[44,45]

Box 6.6 Adopting safer sexual behaviour in Eastern Zimbabwe appears to be reducing HIV transmission

Recently the most convincing evidence of a decline in HIV transmission has come from a cohort study in eastern Zimbabwe. Here a decline in HIV prevalence, between 1998 and 2003, was associated with sexual behaviour change in four distinct socioeconomic strata. HIV prevalence fell most steeply at young ages – by 23% and 49%, respectively, among men aged 17 to 29 years and women aged 15 to 24 years – and in more educated groups. Sexually experienced men and women reported reductions in casual sex of 49% and 22%, respectively, whereas recent cohorts reported delayed sexual debut.[46]

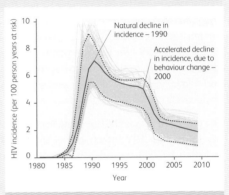

Figure 6.11 – The sharp rate of decline in HIV incidence in urban and semi-urban Zimbabwe[47]

The figure above shows that while the natural evolution of the epidemic was leading to a slow decline in incidence after 1990, a steeper than expected rate was experienced from around 2000. High mortality rates early on in the epidemic contributed to an increased fear of the disease. Word of mouth, and other informal information exchanges, as well as the large variety of formal activities launched at this time have helped to increase understanding of the disease, making it possible for Zimbabweans to make educated changes and for an overall shift in sexual norms.

Formal HIV prevention activities included: early control of sexually transmitted infections; marketing of condoms; voluntary counselling and testing services; television and radio serial dramas and the activities of the Zimbabwe National AIDS Trust Fund.

An important prevention behaviour is the use of condoms. When used correctly and consistently male condoms are *'the single, most efficient, available technology to reduce the sexual transmission of HIV… from both men to women, and also from women to men.'*[48] However, in many societies the power relations are such that it is difficult for a woman to insist that her male partner uses a condom. Even in apparently faithful partnerships transmission from man to woman of HIV (and the reverse) may be a significant risk.

Relatively recently female condoms have become available. Like the male condom, the female condom is intended to prevent HIV transmission by helping avoid exposure to semen or vaginal fluids. While in vitro studies confirm that the female condom provides an effective barrier to organisms smaller than HIV, the necessary clinical studies to confirm its effectiveness are still in progress.[49] A major drawback is that the female condom is more expensive than the male condom and not as readily available.

Male circumcision

Recent scientific research has identified another important opportunity for preventing HIV infection, through the practice of male circumcision (Box 6.7).

Box 6.7   Male circumcision for the prevention of HIV transmission

Three clinical trials in African countries have found that male circumcision can help prevent HIV transmission to HIV-negative men from vaginal intercourse by as much as 60%.[50] The practice is one of the most common surgical procedures, with an estimated 30% of men circumcised worldwide, 2/3rds of whom are Muslim.[51] In the late 1980s scientists noticed that levels of HIV infection seemed to be lower in countries with higher rates of circumcision. This prompted a series of trials between 2002 and 2006 in South Africa, Uganda and Kenya, which showed very similar results, with reduction rates of 60%, 48% and 53% respectively.

The reason for this is still not completely clear. Scientists believe that circumcision may remove key targets for HIV infections, as the foreskin contains a concentration of immune cells, including Langerhans cells that are targeted by HIV during the early stages of infection. Circumcision removes the highly susceptible inner side of the foreskin, and allows quicker drying of the area, reducing the risk of bacterial or other sexual infections. However, circumcision is a surgical operation and also comes with risks, which increase greatly in situations with less-trained medical staff, unhygienic conditions, and when the operation is performed using traditional methods.[50]

While the discovery of this new intervention has significant potential, proponents caution that it must be one of a series of methods integrated in larger prevention programmes. Funding and resources need to be injected to make sure the operation can be offered in a safe and hygienic way. Future programmes will also have to pay close attention to the cultural and religious beliefs relating to circumcision, and work with communities as well as medical staff, to design effective awareness campaigns. Further research is also needed to gain a better understanding of the intervention's effects, including its effect on women (no immediate benefit has yet been observed), and the best means of operationalising it on a larger scale. There is a great potential for the practice to have a positive impact, especially in Southern Africa where circumcision rates are low, and HIV rates high.[50]

---

5. The quest for vaccines for infectious diseases

Vaccines represent a highly efficient and targeted approach to preventing infection. They consist of pharmaceutical products of various forms that establish or improve immunity to one or more diseases. Over time they have had a major impact on the incidence of infectious diseases in both the developed and developing world.

Commonly vaccines stimulate the immune system to kill the infecting organism, usually a virus or bacterium. The human immune system is a highly complex network of interacting proteins, cells, organs, and tissues. Its elements, and the vaccine trial process, are described in Box 6.8.

Box 6.8   Key elements of the human immune system exploited by vaccines[52]

White blood cells originate from the stem cells of the bone marrow and will identify and eliminate pathogens such as viruses and bacteria. The most important are:

- B cells which are programmed to produce large numbers of antibodies that attack specific antigens (pathogens or elements of pathogens);

- 'Killer' T cells which kill the body's cells that they recognise as being infected by antigens (they express the CD8 glycoprotein on the surface);

- 'Helper' T cells that coordinate the other cells, stimulating B cells and Killer T cells to act (they express the CD4 glycoprotein on the surface).

Antigens are either parts of, or whole, viruses or bacteria which are recognised by the B and T cells. In addition to the immunity that is present at birth, immunity can be acquired by exposure to the appropriate antigen contained in a vaccine. Once exposed B and T cells retain the memory of the antigen, usually for the life of the person.

If a part of a virus or bacterium is used as an antigen it is usually harmless to humans. Otherwise a weakened or killed virus or bacterium may be used as the antigen. Vaccines normally undergo a sequence of three clinical trials (Figure 6.12):

Phase I – to assess their safety;

Phase II – to assess their efficacy on a small scale;

Phase III – to assess large scale efficacy.

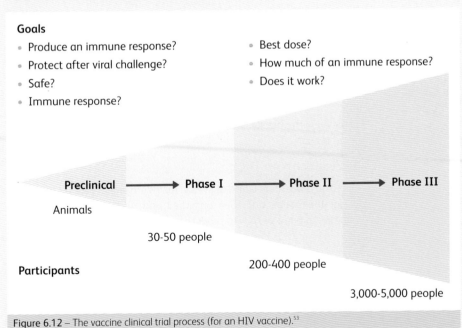

Goals
- Produce an immune response?
- Protect after viral challenge?
- Safe?
- Immune response?

- Best dose?
- How much of an immune response?
- Does it work?

Preclinical ⟶ Phase I ⟶ Phase II ⟶ Phase III

Animals

30-50 people

Participants

200-400 people

3,000-5,000 people

Figure 6.12 – The vaccine clinical trial process (for an HIV vaccine).[53]

Today there are many different forms of vaccine, the latest taking advantage of the revolution in cellular and molecular biology (Box 6.9).

Box 6.9 The main forms of vaccine[54,55]

Live, attenuated vaccines as antigens

- Consists of viruses or mycobacteria weakened (inactivated) through being repeatedly re-grown in a hostile cell culture. They are infectious but relatively benign.

- Targets: measles, mumps, polio, rubella, TB. Elicit strong cellular and antibody responses and often confer lifelong immunity with only one or two doses. Have a good safety record, but can revert to virulent form. There are risks if given to people with weakened immune systems e.g. late-stage AIDS sufferers. Also require cold storage.

Killed or inactivated vaccines as antigens

- Composed of previously virulent bacteria or viruses which have been killed with chemicals, such as formaldehyde, heat or radiation.

- Targets: flu, polio, cholera, bubonic plague and hepatitis.

- Simplest and least expensive. Can be freeze-dried and stored and carried in this form. May vary in reproducibility and require careful monitoring to ensure no live organisms are present. Cannot revert to virulent form. They stimulate a weaker immune system response than do live vaccines, so may require several additional doses, or booster shots, to maintain immunity.

Subunit vaccines as antigens

- Vaccines based on only the parts of the virus that best stimulate the immune system. They contain anywhere from one to 20 or more antigens. The virus is grown in the laboratory and chemicals are used to break it apart and gather the important antigens, or the antigen molecules are extracted from the virus using recombinant DNA technology (Recombinant Subunit Vaccines).

- Target: Hepatitis B. They are chemically defined, reproducibly prepared and assayed and relatively inexpensive to produce.

Toxoid vaccines

- Used when a bacterial toxin is the main cause of illness. Toxins are inactivated by treatment with formalin to render them safe, and then adsorbed onto a compound such as an alum which stimulates the immune system to produce antibodies that lock onto and block the toxin.

- Targets: diphtheria and tetanus.

Conjugate vaccines

- Used against bacteria that possess an outer coating of polysaccharides (sugar molecules). These disguise a bacterium's antigens so that immature immune systems of infants and

---

younger children cannot recognize or respond to them. Conjugate vaccines link antigens or toxoids to the polysaccharides so they can be recognised.

- Target: *Haemophilus influenzae* type B (Hib)

DNA vaccines

- Still largely experimental. These use the genes that code for the antigens. When introduced into the body, some cells will take up the gene DNA which then instructs those cells to make the antigen molecules. In effect the body's own cells become vaccine-making factories. Naked DNA vaccines consist of DNA that is administered directly into the body.

- Targets: influenza and herpes.

Recombinant vector vaccines

- Also experimental, they use an attenuated virus or bacterium (the vector) to introduce microbial DNA, derived from harmful microbes, to cells of the body. Since they closely mimic a natural infection they are effective in stimulating the immune system.

- Experimental targets: HIV, rabies, and measles.

Smallpox eradication

The history of smallpox eradication, perhaps the greatest vaccination achievement, illustrates that simply having an effective vaccine is only the first step in a successful programme. Edward Jenner first produced a vaccine against smallpox, inoculating patients with the related, but relatively benign, cowpox virus, in 1798. Yet smallpox was not eradicated until 1980 (Box 6.10).[9] There were a number of features of the disease that made it a suitable candidate for eradication: it had no animal host, it was transmitted through the air, usually by face-to face contact, its rash made it easy to diagnose, survivors gained lifelong immunity and the rate of transmission was relatively slow. Crucial for its success was a very heat-stable vaccine which protected with a single dose. Nevertheless *'eradication was achieved by only the narrowest of margins. Its progress in many parts of the world and at different times wavered between success and disaster, often only to be decided by quixotic circumstance or extraordinary performances by field staff.'*[56]

Box 6.10   Milestones in the long journey to smallpox eradication[56,57,58]

1798 – Jenner developed cowpox virus vaccine.

1920s – An improved vaccine was produced.

1930s – Elimination was demonstrated to be feasible in the Soviet Union and elsewhere.

1953 – World Health Assembly (WHA) rejected selecting smallpox for eradication.

1950s – A freeze-dried version of the vaccine was developed eliminating the need for refrigeration.

1958 – Soviet Union donated 25 million doses of vaccine, but the programme was continually short of vehicles, supplies and equipment.

1967 – Finally WHA approved the launch of the eventually successful Smallpox Eradication Programme.

1970s – Increasingly 'military' approach to the campaign.

1977 – Last endemic case in Somalia.

Continuing scientific research was key to the success of smallpox eradication, *'despite the opposition of senior WHO leadership who insisted that the tools were in hand and the epidemiology was sufficiently well understood and that better management was all that was necessary to eradicate smallpox.'*[56] One important contribution was the development of new innovative vaccination devices, including:

- Vaccine jet injectors – powered by compressed air or gas that deliver a high-pressure narrow jet of the injection liquid to penetrate the skin, instead of a hypodermic needle;

- Bifurcated needles – these were dipped in a vaccine vial and used to make multiple punctures. They were cheap, used less vaccine per person and could be re-used after boiling or flaming. Villagers could be trained in their use in 15 minutes.

Another contribution was field research that revealed the epidemiology of the disease to be different from that described in the textbooks and the discovery that the duration of vaccine efficacy was far longer than that normally stated – both discoveries led to important operational changes in the eradication campaign.

Childhood vaccines

The smallpox experience encouraged a belief that it might be possible to globally eradicate a wide range of infectious diseases. This was reinforced by the experience of the developed countries in eliminating (or nearly eliminating) a number of serious diseases. By the 1930s typhoid fever was almost eliminated in the UK (with deaths down from 370 per million a year in the 1870s to 5 per million by the 1930s). This was followed by near elimination of typhus, anthrax and rabies – largely by public health measures – and then diphtheria using a toxoid vaccine.[59]

More recently, the developed countries have brought about significant control over a number of the main childhood infections, using new vaccines (Box 6.11).

Although produced with the developed country market in mind, these vaccines have begun to have a significant effect in the developing countries. In Sub-Saharan Africa, a highly coordinated measles reduction strategy, led by the Measles Initiative,[60] began in 2001. This has brought the number of measles deaths down from an estimated 492,116 in 2001 to 32,278 in 2008 – a 93% reduction. The strategy involves vaccinating all children against measles before their first birthday via routine health services and providing a second opportunity through mass vaccination campaigns.[61]

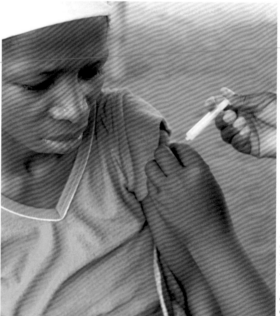

Figure 6.13 – Vaccines are an efficient and targeted approach to prevention

Box 6.11 Vaccines against childhood infections[62]

Vaccine	Type	Recommended schedule
Measles, mumps and rubella (MMR)	Live attenuated	Two doses between the ages of 12 months and 12 years.
Rotavirus A	Oral live attenuated	Two to three doses starting at two months.
Diphtheria, pertussis, tetanus (DPT)	Diphtheria and tetanus toxoids and inactivated pertussis.	Five doses between two months and 15 years.
Maternal/neonatal tetanus	Toxoid	Three dose course of tetanus toxoid (TT) given to mother, protects both mother and baby.
Hepatitis B	Subunit	A course of three injections at zero, one and six months.
Haemophilus influenza type B (Hib)	Conjugate	Three of four doses to infants, starting after six weeks.
Pneumococcal	Conjugate	Four doses, given at two, four, six and 12 months.
Inactivated Poliovirus (IPV)	Inactivated	Three doses at two, four and six to 18 months. Booster at four to six years.
Influenza	Injected inactivated or spray live attenuated	Annually, with two doses given in the first year.
Vericella (chickenpox)	Live attenuated	Can be combined with MMR (MMRV), or given as a separate vaccine in two doses.
Hepatitis A	Inactivated	Two doses, starting at one year and then at least six months after.
Meningococcal	Conjugate	One dose, after two years. Boosters as necessary.

Despite successes with vaccination, achieving the larger goal of disease elimination, especially in developing countries, is not straightforward. Campaigns require large scale, sustained funding, and a relatively sophisticated infrastructure including well-trained staff. Eradication is also much more difficult in the 21st century because of the widespread mobility of populations which encourages re-infection and renders even regional elimination difficult. This has led to a more sober assessment of the possibilities of eradication.[56] Some experts actually consider the goal to be an obstacle towards effective disease suppression and control.[59]

Polio not yet eradicated

Concerns about the feasibility of eradication are underscored by the current global attempt to eradicate polio. It has been a highly successful campaign in many parts of the world, but complete global eradication remains elusive.

The campaign began with the development, by Jonas Salk, of an inactivated (killed) polio vaccine (IPV) in 1955, but took off with the production of a live attenuated (weakened), oral polio vaccine (OPV) developed by Albert Sabin in 1961 (Box 6.12).

Immunization campaigns with OPV in Cuba and in Eastern Europe demonstrated that the poliovirus can be eliminated in large geographic areas. In 1988 when there were some 350,000 cases worldwide, the Global Polio Eradication Initiative was launched. By 1999 the number of cases had dropped to 7,000. Indigenous polio was eradicated in the Americas in 1991 and in China in 1996.[63]

Box 6.12   The poliovirus and its vaccines[59]

Poliovirus is one of the simplest of the viruses, consisting of RNA protected by a protein coat or capsid. The virus binds to a receptor on a nerve cell surface and then enters the cell; the RNA is released and instructs the cell to produce more polio viral protein (Figure 6.14).

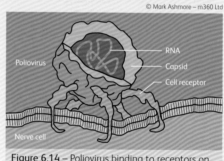

© Mark Ashmore – m360 Ltd

Figure 6.14 – Poliovirus binding to receptors on the surface of a nerve cell.[64]

Typically the virus causes paralysis in only 1 % of those infected, 5-10 % suffer a variety of relatively mild symptoms, the remainder are symptomless but shed the virus in the faeces – and may do for some time.[65] It is for this reason that surveillance is important. A single case with acute paralysis may be an indicator of the presence of a hundred or more infected and infectious children.

Polio vaccines

There are three forms of the poliovirus, serotypes 1, 2 and 3, each with a slightly different capsid protein. Type 1 is the most common, 2 was eradicated in 1999 (but see below).

The Inactivated Polio Virus (IPV) triggers an excellent response in the immune system of most recipients, producing protective antibodies in the blood – thus preventing the spread of poliovirus to the central nervous system. However, it induces only very low levels of immunity to the poliovirus inside the gut. As a result, it gives protection against polio paralysis but, when a person immunized with IPV is infected with a poliovirus, it can still multiply inside the intestines and be shed in stools – increasing the risk of continued circulation.

A further major disadvantage is that IPV has to be injected by trained health workers, which increases the costs of vaccination.

Since the **Oral Polio Virus (OPV)** is administered by mouth it does not need trained health workers. It is also much cheaper (a fifth of the cost of IPV). Like the IPV it prevents the spread of the poliovirus to the nervous system but it also produces a local immune response in the

---

lining of the intestines, so preventing the multiplication of the poliovirus in the gut. Thus mass campaigns with OPV can rapidly stop person-to-person transmission of the poliovirus. Moreover, the shedding of vaccine virus in the stools of recently immunized children means that, in areas of poor hygiene and sanitation, immunization with OPV can result in the 'passive' immunization of people in close contact. It is estimated that levels of immunity of 80-85 % are enough to provide sufficient passive immunization to protect those who are susceptible.[66] WHO aims to achieve four doses of OPV in the first year of life.

The trivalent form of OPV contains weakened forms of all three serotypes, but monovalent vaccines are also available which target just one type.

Although OPV is safe and effective, in extremely rare cases (approximately 1 in every 2.5 million doses of the vaccine) the live attenuated vaccine virus in OPV can cause paralysis – either in the vaccinated child, or to a close contact.

Resurgences and re-emergence

But in 2002 and 2003 there were severe setbacks. A resurgence occurred in India in 2002 as a result of a major decline in vaccination with OPV against type 3 polio. The following year, because of opposition by religious leaders in the northern states of Nigeria, there was a significant fall in immunisation – 30 % of children went unvaccinated in 10 states in 2005. Following the increase in cases in these two countries, there was a rapid global spread of polio to a dozen other countries (Figure 6.15)

Subsequently, the number of cases in Nigeria has declined but the upsurge in India has continued. In 2008 there were 1,600 polio cases worldwide. The task now is to bring about eradication in the two main endemic areas – in the northern parts of Nigeria and India. Reliance is being placed on OPV vaccination because of its contribution to passive immunization.

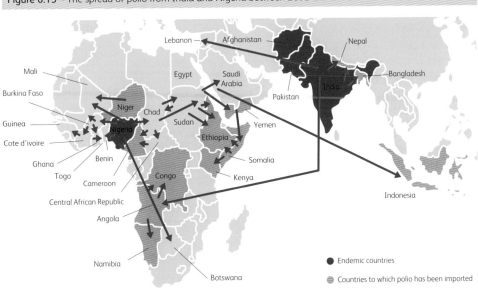

Figure 6.15 – The spread of polio from India and Nigeria between 2002 and 2006[67]

In northern India children are receiving more than 12 doses of vaccine before their second birthday. As indicated earlier (Box 6.5), places such as Ghaziabad in northern India have highly unsanitary conditions that contribute to the spread of poliovirus, but similar places elsewhere in the subcontinent are polio free, so there may be other factors at work.

Vaccine-derived polio

Full global eradication is also complicated by the existence of vaccine-derived cases of poliomyelitis. Even if human to human transmission of wild poliovirus is stopped in the endemic countries there may be a lingering problem of circulating vaccine-derived poliovirus (cVDPV) resulting from genetic mutations in the virus strains that make up the OPV. The risk in India is estimated to be 1 in 4 million doses.[64] Such mutations can produce a virulent strain of the virus and trigger an outbreak. Four such outbreaks of cVDPV have occurred since 2000 – in Hispaniola, Philippines, Madagascar and China. Because individuals with these viruses can continue to shed them in their faeces for many years, severe outbreaks in populations with little immunity may suddenly occur. The implication is that as soon as transmission has ceased, OPVs should be discontinued and replaced by IPV.

The case for this strategy is strengthened by the re-emergence of type 2 polio in Nigeria, once thought to have been eradicated.[68] It first appeared in 2005 and began to take off in early 2009. It is the result of a weakened type 2 virus that makes up the trivalent OPV, mutating and regaining its dangerous state. Because monovalent OPVs, against types 1 and 3 (which are more effective), have been used in recent years there is little or no immunity to type 2 in the population. Hopefully, a campaign with trivalent OPV in Nigeria could re-eradicate type 2, but this will not be easy. Alternatively there is a strong case for a switch to the inactivated vaccine, despite its drawbacks.

Vaccines against TB

One of the biggest obstacles to reducing the incidence of TB is the lack of an effective vaccine for prevention. The first vaccine for TB, called Bacillus Calmette-Guerin (BCG), after its creators, was discovered in France and administered to humans in 1921. It is a live attenuated form of the bovine TB pathogen. Unfortunately, its efficacy is extremely mixed, being *at most* 80% effective at preventing TB infection. Results vary greatly by geography, patient age and background, with poor protection against pulmonary TB, although it is very effective against non-pulmonary cases (also very effective against leprosy, and may be responsible for its disappearance in Africa).[69] In addition, the vaccine needs refrigeration, which is problematical in the climates of the most highly TB-infected regions. Despite these drawbacks, BCG has been relied on, as the sole form of prevention, for one of the world's most widespread diseases for over 80 years.

There are a number of reasons why decades have passed without a new vaccine. The bacteria are a difficult target. They are able to hide inside cells and avoid normal antibodies; destruction can only be accomplished through the activation of T cells. Furthermore, the bacterium can spend years dormant in the body, so an effective vaccine has to provide long-lasting protection.

A second reason has been a lack of funding, and little research priority. This situation has changed with new attention being drawn to the disease following its inclusion in the MDG targets, work by organisations like Partners in Health, and the formation of the Stop TB partnership.[70] The spotlight has also been put on TB by big funders such as the Bill and Melinda Gates Foundation.[71]

As a consequence there are at least five new types of vaccine in the pipeline, either primary vaccines, or 'boosters' to complement either BCG or a new primary vaccine. Much of the work focuses on using recombinant viruses or fusion proteins (which combine genes for two different proteins) to improve the way the body recognises TB bacteria and increases the production of T cells. Examples include:[72,73]

1. An attempt to produce an improved version of BCG, using a recombinant strain which over-expresses the most abundant protein produced by the bacterium. Phase I trials began in 2009;

2. A recombinant sub-unit booster, based on a genetically modified vaccinia virus that 'reminds' T cells of the disease and produces a high number of T 'helper' cells when given years after BCG. The most advanced of the current candidates are in Phase IIb trials in South Africa;

3. A dry powder form of the original BCG vaccine using nanotechnology. This does not require refrigeration and avoids problems with dirty needles. It should be relatively cheap and may get through trials faster. Phase I trials are imminent.

While the above vaccine candidates are not expected to be ready for the market for five to 10 years, the fact that such a large number of promising possibilities are in the pipeline after 80 years of near inactivity is good news.

No HIV vaccines yet available

We know a great deal about the human immune deficiency virus (HIV), the causative agent of the disease known as Acquired Immunodeficiency Syndrome or AIDS. We have analysed its structure, its behaviour, and how it replicates and is transmitted (Box 6.13). Yet despite over 20 years of research and development we still do not have an effective vaccine.

We know that some people never become infected, despite repeated exposure to HIV, some who are infected never seem to suffer any harm and for others the symptoms do not arise for a decade or more. So there is a form of natural immunity in the human population and the question is whether this can be exploited to provide a significant level of protection.

The challenges are considerable:

- First, HIV infects the helper T cells, the very cells whose purpose is to help combat viruses and other infectious organisms. From the start of the infection HIV directly targets and overcomes 'its enemies.' It does this within the first seven to 10 days after infection, so there is only a brief window of opportunity for a vaccine to be effective.

- Second, the viral DNA becomes hidden away in long-lived cells from where, years later, it may spawn viral particles. If a vaccine is not successful in preventing infection it has to trigger a long-lasting immune response.

- Third, is the extraordinary diversity of the virus, in particular the forms of the glycoprotein spikes. This means that a vaccine effective against one form or clade of the virus e.g. clade B which is predominant in the industrialised countries, may not be as effective against the clades of the developing countries. This diversity is increased by a high mutation rate, creating a 'hypervariability' that renders HIV a moving target (the genetic HIV variability in a single human is equivalent to the global variability in a whole year of the influenza virus A).

As a consequence HIV is one of the most formidable pathogens for which vaccine development has ever been attempted.

Box 6.13 The HIV structure and replication

The virus is a retrovirus, about 1/10,000 of a millimetre in size and is deceptively simple in structure. Embedded in the lipid envelope are numerous 'spikes' each of which has a cap made of three glycoprotein molecules.

Within the envelope are two single strands of viral RNA, each of which has a copy of the virus's nine genes. They contain the information necessary to produce proteins that control the ability of HIV to infect a cell and to produce new copies of itself.

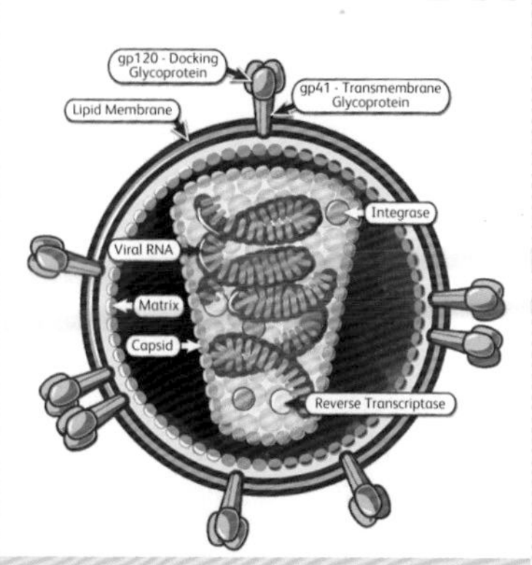

Infection typically begins when a virus encounters a 'helper T cell.' (CD4+ T cell). The glycoprotein gp120 spikes attach the virus to the cell by binding to CD4 on the cell surface and then the virus binds to a second receptor (CCR5 or CXCR4) which allows the glycoprotein gp41 to fuse with the cell membrane.

Once inside the cell, the viral RNA is converted into viral DNA using an enzyme produced by the virus known as reverse transcriptase. The viral DNA moves to the cell's nucleus, where it is spliced into the host's DNA. There it produces more viral particles.

A healthy, uninfected person usually has 800 to 1,200 helper T cells per cubic

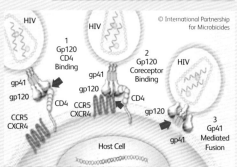

Figure 6.16 – Structure of the Human Immunodeficiency Virus (HIV).[74]

© International Partnership for Microbicides

Figure 6.17 – Stages, of the intricate process of HIV attaching and fusing with a human cell.[75]

millimetre (mm³) of blood that orchestrate the activities of the killer T cells and B cells. They may provide a level of immunity to the virus and help ensure a person remains free of the symptoms of AIDS for years.

However, after infection, the numbers of helper T cells progressively decline so reducing their capacity to detect and orchestrate a response to other pathogens. When the count falls below 200/mm³, a person becomes particularly vulnerable to opportunistic infections and cancers. The immune system collapses and full blown AIDS develops that typifies the end stage of the HIV disease.

Two approaches to produce a viral vaccine have been tried, based on stimulating production of:

- Antibodies, produced by B cells, that will destroy invading HIV before it can take hold in the body;

- Killer T cells that will destroy helper T cells in the body already infected by the virus.

The first approach used the gp120 glycoprotein spike on the surface of the virus as the antigen. The results however, were disappointing. Gp120 appears to be concealed and shielded from antibodies and also utilises 'decoys.'

The second approach, referred to as cell-mediated immunity (CMI) could, in theory, lower the peak of the viral load and maintain a much lower population of HIV over time (Figure 6.18).

Figure 6.18 – A Cell-Mediated Immunity (CMI) approach can theoretically keep the viral load below the transmission threshold.[76]

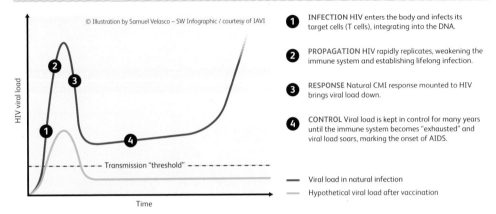

© Illustration by Samuel Velasco – SW Infographic / courtesy of IAVI

1   INFECTION HIV enters the body and infects its target cells (T cells), integrating into the DNA.

2   PROPAGATION HIV rapidly replicates, weakening the immune system and establishing lifelong infection.

3   RESPONSE Natural CMI response mounted to HIV brings viral load down.

4   CONTROL Viral load is kept in control for many years until the immune system becomes "exhausted" and viral load soars, marking the onset of AIDS.

— Viral load in natural infection
— Hypothetical viral load after vaccination

Although both approaches have been proved feasible in animal models, neither has individually produced a vaccine that is of significant human benefit. The one partial success is the RV 144, a "prime-boost" combination of two vaccines: ALVAC® HIV vaccine (the prime), and AIDSVAX® B/E vaccine (the boost). The vaccine combination was based on HIV strains that commonly circulate in Thailand and was administered in a Phase III trial involving 16,000 volunteers. The trial demonstrated that the vaccine regimen was safe and modestly effective in preventing HIV infection, reducing it by some 30 %.[77]

What is now clear is that the virus exists in both 'free' and in the helper T cells, so it can only be eliminated by the two approaches working in tandem (antibodies destroying the free viruses and killer T cells destroying the helper T cells containing the virus). Thus the aim is to find a vaccine that does both. The most promising candidates are plasmids (structures outside the chromosome that contain DNA, usually in bacteria) that encode a gene from the virus and live recombinant vaccines, again with genes from the HIV virus, but inserted into harmless viruses such as the adenovirus.[78]

What is needed is an expanded, yet coordinated, research programme aimed at virtually every element along the chain of vaccine development from basic cellular and molecular science to vaccine types and delivery systems.[76,79-81]

A malaria vaccine in sight?

An effective human malaria vaccine has been sought for over 70 years, but until recently with little success. This is largely because the infectious agent, *Plasmodium*, is a protozoan, an organism much more complex than a bacterium or virus. The *Plasmodium* has to survive in human cells until it is picked up again by a mosquito and it has developed a very good resistance to the human immune system, based in part on the great diversity of the parasite's protein coats and the variety of signals each coat provides to the antibody. In the words of Professor Kevin Marsh, Director of the KEMRI – Wellcome Collaborative Research Programme in Kenya: *"Not only do different parasites have different protein coats – like humans having different eye or hair colour – but each parasite can also vary the particular signals it displays."*[82]

The approach to a vaccine, similar in some respects to that being adopted against HIV, is to utilise (mostly) sub-unit vaccines, based on a wide range of the antigens presented by the parasite in its different forms. Hopefully this will stimulate both antibodies and cell-mediated immunity. Again, echoing the new HIV vaccine approach, there is a belief that a combination of vaccines will be critical to success.

Because the parasite's life cycle is complicated there are several different broad targets for a vaccine (Box 6.14).

Box 6.14 The cycle of targets for a malaria vaccine.[83]

After the mosquito bite transfers the parasites to a human, they first invade the liver and replicate there for two weeks, before beginning a cycle of red-blood-cell invasion. Growth, replication and red-cell destruction leads to the disease symptoms.

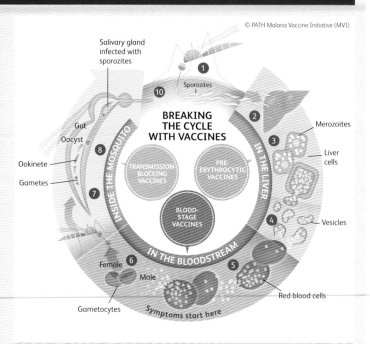

1. Pre-erythrocytic vaccine candidates – these target the stage at which the parasite enters or matures in an infected person's liver cells. They aim

Figure 6.19 – The life cycle of the *Plasmodium* parasite.[83]

to elicit an immune response that would either prevent infection or attack the infected liver cell if infection does occur. They include:

– Recombinant antigens from the surface of the parasite or from the infected liver cell that induce antibodies, for example against the sporozoite main coat protein (e.g. RTS,S);

 – DNA or viral vector vaccines that encode pre-erythrocytic antigens recognised by T cells;

 – Live, attenuated vaccines that consist of a weakened form of the sporozoite.

2. Blood-stage vaccine candidates – that target the rapid replication of the organism in human red blood cells. These do not aim to block all infection, but to decrease the parasite load, hence reducing the severity of the disease. A vaccine that contains antigens or proteins from the surface of the merozoite could allow the body to develop natural immunity with much less risk of getting ill.

3. **Transmission-blocking vaccine candidates** – these seek to interrupt the parasite's life cycle by inducing antibodies that prevent the parasite from maturing in the mosquito after it takes a blood meal from a vaccinated person. The aim would be to limit the spread of infection by preventing mosquitoes that feed on an infected person from spreading malaria to new hosts.

The most successful candidate to date is the pre-erythrocyte vaccine RTS,S. The latest field trials on children aged five to 17 months have shown promising protection.[84] The vaccine is now recommended to go into Phase III trials and could be submitted to regulatory authorities by 2011.

6. The role of treatment for infectious diseases

Treatment of people with infectious diseases serves at least three purposes:

1. To reduce the probability of mortality;

2. To reduce morbidity and help people live normal, productive lives;

3. To prevent further spread of the infection.

Advancing the treatment of TB

Once infected, a person's immune system if strong will fight to contain the TB bacteria. But, if the immune system is weakened in any way the bacteria will

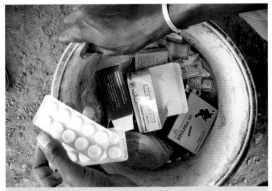

© Jessie Luna

Figure 6.20 – The range of treatments on offer in the small village of M'PeDougou in Mali

escape, multiply and develop into the active tuberculosis disease. The bacteria then attack the lungs and other organs such as the kidneys, liver, vertebra and brain. They destroy tissue and cartilage, leading to a variety of symptoms including fever, weight loss and a chronic cough producing blood. The disease kills around 60% of those who are not treated, most commonly through respiratory failure.

No treatment was available for TB for thousands of years and the disease, commonly known as 'consumption', was still killing up to one out of every seven people in the US and Europe in the early 1900s. From the 1850s through to the 1950s, the primary way of dealing with TB patients was to collapse the infected lung or to send patients to 'sanatoriums', where they could get better 'air,' nutrition – and be kept away from the general population.[85] Progress was made in the developed countries largely as a result of the improved social, economic and nutritional status of the population.

In the 1940s medical advances made TB chemotherapy possible. Streptomycin, the first effective antibiotic was discovered in 1944, but it was soon found that it produced resistant mutants within a few months. In the 1950s and 60s other antibiotics were developed, including isoniazid, ethambutol and rifampin, the primary drugs used to treat the disease today. It was also demonstrated that resistance could be overcome by treating the patient with a combination of two or three drugs. Combination therapy has been used to treat TB ever since.[86]

The drugs must be taken over an extended period of time, six to 12 months, in order to completely eliminate the bacteria from the body.[87] Initially, the first patients to be treated in this way were hospitalized for the full course of treatment to ensure compliance. However, in the 1950s, researchers from the British Medical Research Council in Madras, India found that results from those who were treated with TB drugs at home, and monitored by family members, compared equally well with those treated at a sanitarium. While this idea quickly spread, and long-term hospitalization of TB patients ceased, the need for continuing directly supervised care was not widely translated.[85] TB rates in Europe and the US began to dramatically decline, but success has not been seen on the same scale in resource-poor settings with poor health-systems, unreliable transport and unaffordable drugs.

In 1974 Dr Karel Styblo, working in Tanzania, developed a relatively successful model of short-course chemotherapy under direct supervision. It was exported to six other African countries and to Nicaragua.[85] But this was not at first taken up as a large-scale approach. In fact, TB control measures were relaxed, and often neglected.

Resurgence and the adoption of DOTS

The emergence of HIV in the 1980s changed everything. The huge increase in the number of immuno-compromised individuals led to a reversal in trends and a steady increase in TB incidence. An increase in migration, urbanization and overcrowding in cities, and the ongoing problems of poverty, malnutrition and poor public health infrastructure served to add to the problem.[88,89]

By 1993, there were seven to eight million new cases occurring each year, and TB was declared a global emergency.[90] In 1994, the WHO, seeking to respond to the problem, adopted a programme based on the work of Dr Styblo, which was renamed DOTS (Directly Observed Therapy, Short-course).[91] DOTS was gradually expanded around the world, and quickly became the standard method of TB control. The five components of DOTS are:

- Government commitment;

- Case detection by sputum smear microscopy;

- Standardized treatment regimen with directly observed treatment for at least the first two months;

- Regular drug supply;

- Standardized recording and reporting system that allows assessment of treatment results.[90]

TB prevalence worldwide has declined steadily since 1990, from about 300 cases per 100,000 people, to around 200[92] – and in 1997, the Director General of the WHO termed DOTS the health breakthrough of the 1990s.[85] The strategy has now been adopted by 187 out of 193 WHO member states at high levels of population coverage,[93] and with the 2006 Stop TB strategy continuing to focus on the use of DOTS; it remains 'one of the most widely-implemented and longest-running global health interventions in history.'[91]

Remaining challenges

Despite its widespread uptake, and success in some areas, a large number of challenges remain. Whilst the prevalence of TB has been gradually decreasing globally, it is increasing quite dramatically in both Sub-Saharan Africa and Eastern Europe. A number of factors are combining in these areas to make the successful control of TB through DOTS difficult. These include: poverty, late care-seeking behaviour, lack of transport for repeated treatment, weak health systems, HIV epidemics and, increasingly, the emergence of Multi-Drug Resistant TB (MDR-TB).

MDR-TB is defined as TB that is resistant to at least isoniazid and rifampicin, the two most powerful first-line anti-TB drugs. It therefore has to be treated with drugs that are more expensive, have more serious side effects, and need to be taken for a longer time – and the success rates go down.

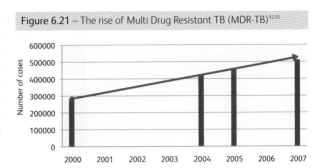

Figure 6.21 – The rise of Multi Drug Resistant TB (MDR-TB)[92,95]

Resistant strains of TB develop through the incorrect treatment of normal TB, either as a result of patients missing doses, doctors prescribing inappropriate drugs, or patients failing to complete the full six plus months treatment programme. While the majority of cases arise in these ways, MDR-TB can also be passed onto new individuals, especially to those with weak immune systems.

The first incidences of MDR-TB were reported in the 1990s, and while exact numbers are difficult to determine[94] and estimates are likely to be low, it is generally agreed to be on the rise. Figure 6.21 above shows global estimates of infected individuals from 2000. The spread of the problem is not evenly distributed. It is estimated that nearly two thirds of the global MDR-TB burden occurs in just three countries – Russia, India and China.[95]

Health officials have tried to respond to the problem, but change has been slow. In the first years of the growing epidemic, there was debate as to whether to use the limited resources of very expensive drugs to treat what was a minority of patients. The WHO only agreed to treat MDR-TB in 2002,[96] but have subsequently put in place extensive guidelines for MDR treatment in their new strategy.

Unfortunately, in the meantime, the TB bacterium has built up further resistance, leading to the evolution of extensively drug-resistant TB, or XDR-TB (TB resistant to three or more of the six classes of second-line drugs). It was first reported in August 2006, out of 52 reported cases, 51 died within a month of being tested. As of 2007 it was estimated that 27,000 new cases were emerging per year, with 80 to 100 % mortality rates being reported.[97]

Future – new drugs

New treatment options are urgently needed. Today's first-line anti-TB medicines are *more than 40 years old*. New medications could shorten the treatment time, thus greatly alleviating some of the problems with patient adherence which have led to drug resistance. In addition, drugs are now needed which can attack both multi- and extensively-drug resistant strains, as well as work alongside HIV/AIDS medications.

As with vaccines for TB, there has been a recent increase in attention and funding for the development of new TB medications, and an increase of research and new drugs under trial. The Stop TB Partnership has made new drug discovery one of its key initiatives,[70] and the TB Alliance has been set-up as a public-private partnership to speed-up and facilitate drug discovery and delivery.[98] The objectives set by the 'Stop TB Partnership Task Force on Retooling' for the development of new medicines are:

- To simplify or reduce treatment duration to two months or less;

- To effectively treat multidrug resistance;

- To treat patients with latent TB infection;

- That new medicines should be compatible with antiretroviral therapy for HIV/AIDS patients.[99]

Scientists are working towards these aims by looking at both known and new targets within the bacterium, as well as using novel approaches to target the bacterium as a whole organism. Advances in genomics have proved helpful, especially the recent success in sequencing of the bacterial genome.[100]

Figure 6.22 – The development and administration of new drugs for TB will be vitally important

There are currently thousands of potential compounds being screened, synthesized, or optimized in discovery and preclinical studies, with much of the work being done through the TB Alliance and its partners, as well as the private company AstraZeneca. Some of these new drugs may be introduced as new combinations, others as single drugs.[101]

Most advanced in development is the drug Moxifloxacin, which could be substituted for one of current first-line drugs, reducing the time for treatment to four months. Using a mechanism different to existing first-line drugs, it acts by inhibiting an enzyme called DNA gyrase, which is essential for the bacterium's survival. Trials began in 2002 and have now reached the Phase III stage.[99,101]

Another promising candidate is a diarylquinoline TMC207 which provides a new mechanism of action by inhibiting the bacterial ATP synthase. In Phase II trials it has shown effectiveness in patients with multi-drug resistant bacteria.[101]

While we are still some years off from seeing significant changes in the technologies available for TB treatment, the fact that so many new possibilities are now being developed is extremely promising. As stated in a 2007 report: '*For the first time in 40 years, there is a coordinated portfolio of promising new compounds in the pipeline, some of which have the potential to become the cornerstone drugs for the control and possible eventual elimination of TB in the future.*'[99]

Antiretrovirals (ARV) against HIV

The first effective drug for the treatment of AIDS had been used to treat cancer patients. In 1985 AZT (known as zidovudine or retrovir) was found to be effective against HIV because of its ability to block the enzyme (reverse transcriptase, see Box 6.13) that translates the viral RNA into DNA. This discovery led to the development of a number of similar nucleoside reverse transcriptase inhibitors (NRTIs). More recently they have been joined by protease inhibitors (PIs) and other drugs that interfere with the replication of the virus (Box 6.15).

Because the virus is capable of rapid mutation, the modern standard of care is a combination of three or four of these drugs (Highly Active Anti-Retroviral Therapy – HAART) to reduce the risk of resistance developing. The widespread introduction of HAART in 1995 transformed the lives of those in the developed world living with AIDS. Although not providing a cure for infected individuals, HAART can greatly reduce the viral load and allow a relatively productive life and better survival prospects.

Box 6.15   Antiretroviral drugs

The antiretroviral drugs that are used to treat HIV infected patients adopt various approaches to prevent the virus from replicating:

1. **Nucleoside reverse transcriptase inhibitors** – (NRTIs) target construction of viral DNA;

2. **Protease inhibitors** – (PIs) target viral assembly;

3. **Fusion inhibitors** – block HIV from fusing with a cell's membrane;

4. **Integrase inhibitors** – inhibit the integration of viral DNA into the DNA of the infected cell;

5. **Entry inhibitors** – block HIV from the host cell by binding the co-receptor that HIV normally uses for entry.

Initially HAART was prohibitively expensive for developing countries. However, due to increasing competition, the introduction of a growing number of generic products, new pricing policies from pharmaceutical companies and successful lobbying, the cost has dropped dramatically in the last decade. The most common first treatment for a patient (known as the first line treatment) is Lamivudine plus Stavudine plus Nevirapine. This cost about US$10,000 per patient per year in 2000, but by 2007 had dropped to US$92. Second line treatments, which are needed if resistance develops or if there are serious side effects, cost around US$1,200 per year.[102,103]

Thanks in part to the increasing affordability, access and coverage of ARV therapy has grown rapidly in low-income countries. There were nearly 4 million people receiving treatment in 2008, out of the estimated 1 billion in need. A large gap still exists, with millions of new infections occurring each year and an increasing number of patients requiring second line medicines.[43]

Although more than two dozen different products are now available for the treatment of HIV infection, there is a need for new drugs that:

1   Will combat multi-resistant forms of the virus;

2   Will reduce long-term toxicity;

3   Are easier to take;

4   Are less liable to induce resistance;

5   Are curatives.

Preventing Mother to Child Transmission (pMTCT)

One of the most effective uses of anti-retrovirals has been in the treatment of pregnant mothers for their own health and to prevent transmission of HIV to infants. More than 90 % of the children living with HIV are infected through MTCT, which can take place during pregnancy, around the time of birth, or through breastfeeding. ARVs for both infected mothers and infants play a key role in reducing MTCT, along with the use of breast milk substitutes or caesarean section delivery when appropriate.

Women who have reached advanced stages of HIV disease will need a combination of ARVs for their own health. Infected pregnant women, who do not yet need treatment can also take a short course of drugs to help protect the unborn baby. Finally, newborn babies will usually be given a course of treatment for the first days or weeks of life, to further lower the risk.[104] The WHO compiled a set of guidelines for ARV use for pregnant women and infants in 2006, listed in Box 6.16 below. They are currently in the process of reviewing these recommendations based on new experience and evidence, and an update is expected in early 2010.[105]

Box 6.16	WHO guidelines for pMTCT drug regimens in resource-limited settings[106]			
	Pregnancy	Labour	After birth: mother	After birth: infant
Recommended	Azidothymidine (AZT) after 28 weeks	Single dose nevirapine; AZT+ lamivudine (3TC)	AZT+3TC for seven days	Single dose nevirapine; AZT for seven days
Alternative (higher risk of drug resistance)	AZT after 28 weeks	Single dose nevirapine	–	Single dose nevirapine; AZT for seven days
Minimum (less effective)	–	Single dose nevirapine; AZT+3TC	AZT+3TC for seven days	Single dose nevirapine
Minimum (less effective and higher risk of drug resistance)	–	Single dose nevirapine	–	Single dose nevirapine

Due to many attempts to scale-up efforts for pMTCT, from groups such as PEPFAR,[107] The Call to Action Project,[108] MTCT-Plus[109] and The Global Fund to Fight AIDS, Tuberculosis and Malaria, ARV use by pregnant women living with HIV in low and middle-income countries is now up to 45%, up from 10% in 2004.[43] In addition, experience has enabled health workers to better define the pros and cons of using a simple treatment like single dose nevirapine, versus more effective, yet more expensive and harder to administer combinations of two or three drugs. Since 2006, an increasing number of countries have moved towards combination therapy[43] but there is a clear need for a 'simple, safe and easy-to-use ARV regimen for pregnant women with HIV.'[106]

The search for a microbicide

The quest for an effective microbicide is in response to the demand by vulnerable women for protective technologies that are under their control. Microbicides, as the name implies, are chemical compounds that kill micro-organisms. But in the context of HIV a microbicide is 'a woman-controlled method applied before sex that could kill, neutralize or block HIV and other sexually transmitted infections.' While many compounds attack HIV once it has spread through the body, a topical microbicide, applied as gel, cream, film, suppository or sponge, or contained in a vaginal ring that releases the active ingredient gradually, could be effective in blocking the entry and early multiplication of the virus. To date the concept has not been clinically proven (Box 6.17).

Box 6.17   The great diversity of potential microbicides against HIV[75]

Several approaches to developing microbicides, underpinned by basic research, are being pursued (Figure 6.23).

1. Entry inhibitors – that prevent attachment or entry of the virus

Polyanions – electronically charged molecules that create an acid environment in the vagina, attracting HIV and preventing its attachment to a cell. (e.g. Carraguard, PRO2000, BufferGel).

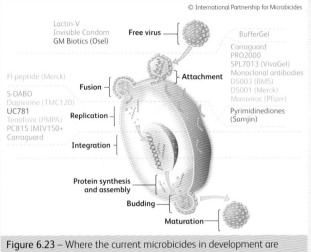

© International Partnership for Microbicides

Figure 6.23 – Where the current microbicides in development are targeted.[75]

Glycoprotein inhibitors – that bind to gp120 and gp41 preventing attachment and fusion of HIV (e.g. DS003) to the cells.

CCR5 blockers – that block the host cell receptors so preventing the virus attaching (e.g. DS001, maraviroc).

2. Reverse transcriptase inhibitors (RTI) – that interfere with replication of the virus once it is inside the cell.

Non-nucleoside reverse transcriptase inhibitors (NNRTIs) – inhibit replication by binding to the enzyme reverse transcriptase; some may bind permanently. (e.g. dapavrine, MIV 150, UC 781)

Nucleotide reverse transcriptase inhibitors (NtRTIs) – once incorporated into the viral DNA they prevent it growing further (e.g. PMPA).

3. Various combinations of the above.

Most of the compounds in clinical trials are polyanions. Carraguard, made from a substance derived from seaweed, completed Phase III trials in 2008. The trials involving 6,000 sexually active South African women, demonstrated that the microbicide was safe and acceptable but did not reduce the risk of women acquiring HIV.[110,111] BufferGel and PRO2000 are currently in Phase III trials. Even although these compounds are not specific to HIV, they are still likely to provide a worthwhile level of protection. Early modelling has shown that even with 60 % effectiveness, if just 20 % of women in the 73 lowest income countries, with access to HIV prevention services, used a microbicide 50 % of the time that a condom is not used, it could avert some 2.5 million infections over 3 years.[112] The next generation of microbicides – those based on ARVs that are specifically designed to be active against HIV – as well as combination therapies, hold the promise of a greater level of protection. But they face the same challenges as the search for a successful vaccine.

Artemisinin combination therapy against malaria

Medicines that cure malaria not only reduce illness and save lives; they can greatly reduce the rate of transmission of the disease.

In the past, chloroquine and other drugs were cheap and highly effective treatments, but growing resistance has caused them to be abandoned in many parts of Africa and Asia (Figure 6.25). The timely discovery and development of artemisinin and its derivatives (see Box 2.6 in Chapter 2) promised a new era of effective treatment.

Figure 6.25 – Drug resistance to *P. Falciparum* from studies up to 2004[113]

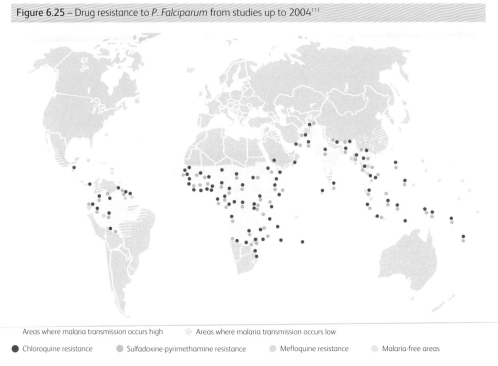

Areas where malaria transmission occurs high   Areas where malaria transmission occurs low

● Chloroquine resistance   ● Sulfadoxine-pyrimethamine resistance   ● Mefloquine resistance   ● Malaria-free areas

The mode of action of artemisinin is not fully understood, but it appears to interfere with the cell metabolism of the malaria parasite.[114] It may be less prone to resistance but recognizing the history of resistance to drugs for treatment of malaria, the artemisinin derivatives are being administered in combination with other anti-malarial drugs. The WHO recommendations are:

Artemether + lumefantrine;
Artesunate + amodiaquine;
Artesunate + mefloquine;
Artesunate + sulfadoxine/pyrimethamine.

In the treatment of uncomplicated malaria, artemisinin combination therapies (ACTs) have proven 90 % effective, with a recovery from malaria after three days, especially where the parasite is chloroquine-resistant. WHO recommends that a switch to ACT should be made in all countries where the malaria parasite has developed resistance to chloroquine. Artemisinin medicines have minimal adverse side effects.[113] However, they are costly (the most effective ACT treatment is US$2.40 – 10 to 15 times the cost of first line cures) and, because of the need to extract the compounds from annual plants, they take a long time to produce.[115] One alternative being explored is to genetically engineer yeast to synthesize a precursor called artemisinic acid. The other is to develop a range of drugs to replace artemisinin and to cope with specific situations, namely for:

1. Intermittent preventative treatment (IPT) of women during pregnancy;

2. IPT of infants;

3. Single dose treatment in emergency situations;

4. Intravenous or intramuscular treatment of severe malaria.

At present some 19 drugs or drug combinations are under development through the Medicines for Malaria Venture public-private partnership.

7. Emerging infectious diseases

Infectious diseases place an enormous burden on human health but in addition to this chronic burden, sudden outbreaks of new diseases can lead to national and global disasters that are especially devastating for developing countries.

The outbreaks may result from the emergence of a new form of disease, for instance through mutation of a less virulent strain into a more virulent one, or through a switch of a disease from a wild host species to human beings. Alternatively, outbreaks may arise from the movement of an existing disease to a new area where it did not previously occur.

New infectious diseases of these kinds appear regularly (Figure 6.26). In the past 25 years, 38 entirely new diseases have appeared in humans, about two every three years. Over 70 % of new and recently re-emerging diseases are of animal origin.[116]

Figure 6.26 – Global distribution of the relative risk of emerging infectious diseases[117]

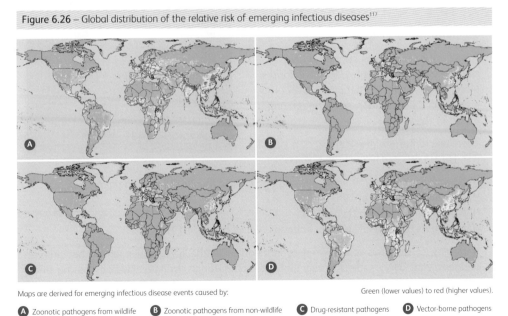

Maps are derived for emerging infectious disease events caused by: Green (lower values) to red (higher values).

A Zoonotic pathogens from wildlife   **B** Zoonotic pathogens from non-wildlife   **C** Drug-resistant pathogens   **D** Vector-borne pathogens

Some of these have evolved from similar diseases in animals, for example HIV/AIDS. The human form of HIV was derived from a Simian Immunodeficiency Virus (SIV) carried by a subspecies of chimpanzee that lives in the forests of Southern Cameroon, Gabon and the Republic of Congo.[118] SIV in chimpanzees developed from successive cross-species transmission and recombinations in the monkeys on which chimpanzees prey.[119] The virus passed to humans sometime early in the 20th century, probably as a result of humans hunting, butchering and eating wild chimpanzees.[120,121] It remained at very low levels until the 1950s and 60s when it took on epidemic form, spreading from Africa around the world.

Other emerging diseases have simply shifted from animal hosts, such as SARS and some influenza viruses. Such diseases, caused by pathogens which infect both humans and animals, are termed zoonotic. Developing countries, where there is close contact between wildlife, livestock and humans, are particularly favourable environments for the emergence of new zoonoses.

Influenza

Perhaps the most recurrent of human disease outbreaks is influenza. The influenza virus probably has its origin in wild waterfowl but long ago moved to other animals, in particular swine and domestic poultry, and to humans. *'Epidemics occur in most countries in some years, and in some countries in most years.'*[122] There are also periodic pandemics, the most serious being the so-called 'Spanish' flu of 1918 at the end of World War I when some 50 million people died.

Box 6.18   Influenza viruses

Only type A influenza viruses are capable of causing pandemics. The virus is distinguished by surface glycoprotein spikes on the viral envelope. The haemagglutinin (H) spike helps the virus attach to the host cell; the neuraminidase (N) spike facilitates the release of newly produced virus particles from the host cell.

Inside the virus are eight strands of RNA carrying a total of 11 genes that code for the glycoproteins and the other proteins that are involved in the replication, transcription and export of the virus.

There are 15 forms of the H spike (H1, H2, H3 etc) and nine of the N spike.[124]

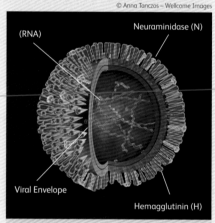

© Anna Tanczos – Wellcome Images

(RNA)

Neuraminidase (N)

Viral Envelope

Hemagglutinin (H)

Figure 6.27 – Structure of Influenza virus[123]

H1N1 caused the 1918/19 pandemic and also caused the 2009 Swine flu pandemic;
H2N2 caused Asian flu in 1957;
H3N2 caused Hong Kong flu in 1968;
H5N1 causes the current Avian flu outbreaks which began in 1996.

Immunity to the virus is conferred by antibodies to the glycoprotein and other protein antigens. Viral RNA is subject to very high rates of mutation during replication, causing small changes in the hemagglutinin and neuraminidase antigens on the surface of the virus. This so-called antigenic drift eventually results in a new strain that overcomes much of the immunity.

In addition, viral RNA may cross between different viral strains, for example between human and avian strains when both happen to occur in the cells of the same human, bird or pig host. This reassortment, also known as antigenic shift, can result in entirely new antigens (in this way H1N1 evolved into H3N2).[125] The immunity has to be recreated from scratch.

The form of the haemagglutin determines, in part, the ease of transmission between humans. Strains that are easily transmitted have hemagglutinin proteins that bind to receptors in the upper part of the respiratory tract, such as in the nose, throat and mouth. In contrast, strains such as avian flu (H5N1) bind to receptors that are mostly found deep in the lungs.[126]

The 1918-19 Spanish flu

Despite its name this flu did not originate in Spain. There is some evidence that there may have been initial small outbreaks in army barracks in France and the UK in 1916. But the first 1918 outbreaks occurred in February and March in the US, in South Carolina, in Kansas and at St Quentin Prison in California. These were followed by three pandemic waves spread, primarily, by soldiers towards the end of World War I in their barracks and during sea voyages to Europe and beyond (Figures 6.28).[128]

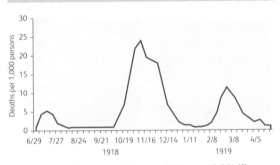

Figure 6.28 – Three pandemic waves of the 1918-1919 influenza outbreak in the UK.[127]

About 50 % of the world's population was eventually infected, half suffering a clinical infection. Fifty million or so deaths occurred, mostly in the second and third waves. The devastating nature of the pandemic has been commentated on by many writers and observers. Isaac Starr, a third year medical student, volunteered to tend the sick in Philadelphia. He commented '*the pandemic ranks with the plague of Justinian and the Black Death as one of the three most destructive human epidemics.*' He and John Barry described in graphic detail the devastation wrought by the infections: '*deaths in the hospital exceeded 25% per night during the peak.*'[129]

Although the pandemic began in the US and travelled to Europe it soon affected Africa and Asia with equal devastation. In India 7 million deaths occurred and there were 1.5 to 2.0 million in Africa. The most extreme consequences were on the Pacific island of Samoa where a quarter of the population died.

After the pandemic ceased, the virus persisted in pigs and in humans causing annual epidemics until the 1950s.[130] With the appearance of a new H2N2 pandemic strain in 1957 ('Asian' flu), the direct H1N1 descendants disappeared from human circulation, although it continued in pigs. However H1N1 're-emerged' from a laboratory in 1977 and has continued to circulate in various forms, including a reassorted H3N2 virus lineage in both pigs and humans. Fortunately none of these, so far, have been as virulent as the 1918 parent. But this could change.

The 2009 Swine Flu Pandemic

In 2009 a new lineage of H1N1 emerged, carrying genes from both bird and swine flu strains, as a result of reassortment (crossing) of North American and Eurasian H1N1 lineages.[124] Not only is it a descendant of the 1918 virus, but there is a worrying similarity in its initial progress.

The first reported case was in Veracruz, Mexico in mid-February 2009, although its origins may have been earlier either in Mexico or the US.

Subsequently it has spread rapidly round the globe driven by global human air travel and very rapid transmission among children in schools. At the time of writing it is in its second pandemic wave, occurring in 208 countries and overseas territories/communities with over 9,500 deaths (Figure 6.29).[131]

Figure 6.29 – Laboratory confirmed cases reported by WHO November 2009[131]

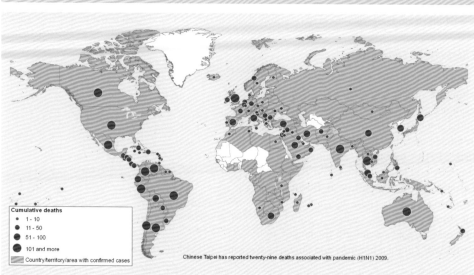

Cumulative deaths
- 1 - 10
- 11 - 50
- 51 - 100
- 101 and more

Country/territory/area with confirmed cases

Chinese Taipei has reported twenty-nine deaths associated with pandemic (H1N1) 2009.

It had an appreciable mortality in the initial phases in Mexico. Most hard hit were the very young, the very old, and young adults as happened in the 1918 pandemic. Yet in its later phases it is, so far, relatively mild in its effects and the lethality is low.[132]

Avian Flu

Coincidentally, although originating some time before the swine flu outbreak, there was an outbreak of an A strain avian flu – H5N1 – that was, from the outset, highly virulent. Research into this flu stimulated a re-examination of the 1918 pandemic and served to uncover serious gaps in our knowledge of influenza viral processes and epidemiology. Moreover, the preparations made for a possible new pandemic of this strain have provided a good basis for dealing with the new threat posed by swine flu.

Avian flu was first detected in Guangdong Province, China, in 1996, when it killed some geese, but received little attention until it spread from poultry to humans in Hong Kong in 1997. Six out of 18 infected people died but the outbreak was quickly eliminated by culling all the poultry. Nevertheless, it continued to circulate among ducks in the coastal provinces of China.[133] Subsequently there have been several distinct waves of different forms (clades) of the H5N1 virus in the current outbreak (Figure 6.30).

Today, avian flu is endemic in poultry in various parts of Asia and Africa. What is somewhat surprising is the low transmissibility to humans. Although more than 230 million domestic birds had died or been killed by 2006, only 251 people had become ill. The receptor site for the virus is deep

Figure 6.30 – Evolution of H5N1variants (clades and subclades) up until 2006.[134]

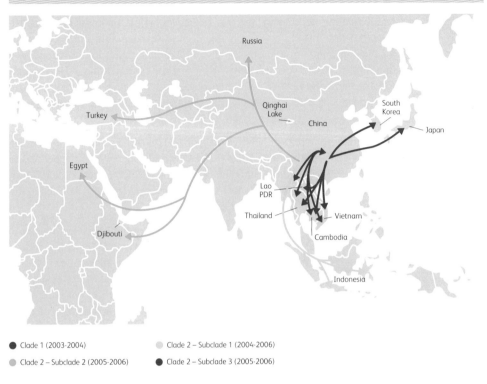

● Clade 1 (2003-2004)   ○ Clade 2 – Subclade 1 (2004-2006)

◐ Clade 2 – Subclade 2 (2005-2006)   ● Clade 2 – Subclade 3 (2005-2006)

in the human respiratory tract and it seems that only a few people have these sites in the upper part of the tract. Nevertheless the human death rate is very high; by 2009, 424 human infections have resulted in 261 deaths.[135]

So far there have only been two incidences of apparent human to human transmission – in Thailand in 2004 and Indonesia in 2006. In neither case did it go beyond a single family. However, if the virus mutates to a form where transmission is more readily achieved the consequences could be very serious. Equally worrying is the possibility of H5N1 crossing with swine flu H1N1 so combining lethality with rapid transmission. This is most likely where poultry is widely infected – e.g. in China, Indonesia or Egypt. The viral crossing may occur tomorrow or several years from now (the form of the virus that gave rise to the 1918 pandemic was probably present as early as 1900).

Influenza prevention and treatment

Influenza is transmitted among humans through the air by coughs or sneezes that create aerosols containing the virus. Standard surgical facemasks may be effective if placed on infective people, but are unlikely to offer much protection to the uninfected. The virus can also be transmitted by other human secretions. Bird to human transmission often occurs through bird droppings. Sunlight, disinfectants and detergents inactivate the virus. Frequent hand washing is very effective and this is a key public health message.

Vaccination is a well proven preventative measure, but can be defeated by viral mutation and reassortment. Commonly, vaccines are produced by cultivating one or more strains in chicken eggs and, after purification, killing them to produce an inactivated vaccine. Continued growing of the virus in the eggs can also produce a weakened live vaccine. Because these methods are logistically complicated and relatively time consuming, there is a growing effort to develop alternative vaccine methodologies.[134] These include genetically engineering vaccines that are universal for Influenza A and all its variants, either by targeting those viral proteins that do not mutate very much, or by stimulating 'killer' T cells. Vaccines effective against the current strain of H1N1, using conventional methods, are now (November 2009) available. Most industrialised countries have purchased stocks in advance, but it seems unlikely that there will be adequate supplies for the developing countries.

Vaccines have also been produced to protect poultry against H5N1. In some countries, for example Thailand, such vaccines are illegal, as they may affect the poultry trade but in China the policy is to vaccinate birds in an 8 km radius around the outbreak centre. One risk is that vaccination, which targets certain strains, may enable new more virulent strains to emerge. This may have been the reason for the rapid spread of the new subclade in 2006.[136]

Antivirals can also be effective for prevention and treatment. These target the neuraminidase spikes and reduce the release of the viruses from the host cells. Infected people then have a lower viral burden and are also less infective. Two of the commonly used drugs are oseltamivar (Tamiflu) and zanamivir (Relenza). A major downside of antiviral use is the high probability of developing resistance. Resistance in H5N1 to amantadines (which attack a different target) has occurred in humans in Vietnam, Thailand and Indonesia but there have also been a small number of cases resistant to oseltamivar.[137] H1N1 resistance to oseltamivar has already been reported in Denmark, Japan and Hong Kong.[138]

Mortality from swine flu is likely to be higher in those individuals who already have health conditions. This is evident from the recent mortality cases in the developed world. It is likely to be especially so in Africa and South Asia where many who become infected are likely to be also suffering from HIV/AIDS, malaria and TB. In the 1918 pandemic most influenza deaths resulted from bacterial pneumonia. There was then a lack of antibiotics. The situation is now very different, but it is crucial that sufficient supplies of antibiotics are available in developing countries as the swine flu pandemic progresses.

In summary it is clear that successful approaches to pandemics of both avian and swine flu must rely on a coordinated and multifactorial approach. Planning needs to be made well in advance and be based on a clear sense of priorities.

8. Non-communicable diseases

In addition to the burden of infectious diseases, there is a growing mortality from chronic non-communicable diseases (CNCDs) in the developing countries. 60% of the world's mortality is caused by these diseases. The list includes: cardiovascular conditions (mainly heart diseases and strokes), some cancers, chronic respiratory conditions and type two diabetes. People of all ages, nationalities and classes are affected. Around 80% of the deaths from chronic diseases occur in the low and middle income countries (Figure 6.31). '*The number of deaths from these diseases is double the number of deaths that result from a combination of infectious diseases (including HIV/AIDS, tuberculosis and malaria), maternal and perinatal conditions, and nutritional deficiencies*).'[139]

Fortunately, we know the underlying risk factors for CNCDs. They include:

- An unhealthy diet;

- Lack of physical activity;

- The use of tobacco.

Moreover they are largely preventable. For example, up to 80% of premature deaths from heart disease, stroke and diabetes can be prevented with known behavioural and pharmaceutical interventions.[140] What is needed now is to: raise public awareness, enhance economic, legal and environmental policies, modify the risk factors, engage business and the community, mitigate health aspects of poverty and urbanisation and reorientate health systems.[139]

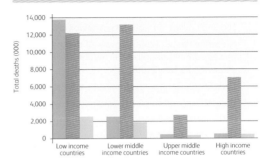

Figure 6.31 – Projected deaths by major cause and World Bank income group, all ages, 2005[140]

■ Communicable diseases, maternal and perinatal conditions, and nutritional deficiencies.

▨ Chronic diseases – including cardiovascular diseases, cancers, chronic respiratory disorders, diabetes, neuropsychiatric and sense organ disorders, musculoskeletal and oral disorders, digestive diseases, genito-urinary diseases, congenital abnormalities and skin diseases.

■ Injuries

9. Conclusion

As we concluded in Chapter 4, progress towards the health MDGs has been mixed. In some cases we have proven technologies and interventions and the challenge is largely one of implementation. In others the technologies are not yet available and progress will continue to be slow.

There are a good range of proven vaccines that can significantly help combat child mortality. They will not, of course, be sufficient on their own. There is still much to be done to improve drinking water quality and sanitation. Similarly the cause of maternal morbidity and mortality are well known as are the required interventions. But creating health systems that will deliver these interventions, where and when they are needed, is a formidable challenge.

The major scientific and technological challenges lie with the 'killer' infectious diseases. Malaria control has seen significant advances. The combination of insecticide treated nets, indoor residual spraying and artemisinin combination therapies are proven interventions which have been shown to work on a large scale. A vaccine, which appears to be just around the corner, could add significantly to this armoury.

The other major diseases – polio, TB, HIV/AIDS and influenza are much more problematic. The situation with polio is very worrying. Even though eradication is tantalisingly close there is a real danger of a breakdown of vaccine control, leading to resurgences which we know can spread globally in a matter of weeks. The current strategies need urgent rethinking. For TB, despite recent efforts, the prospects for improved treatments and vaccines are still disappointing. Even more worrying is the lack of a major step change in the hunt for vaccines and microbicides for HIV. The virus is a fiendish adversary, as trials of new products have revealed. An enormous amount has been learnt and the focus of innovation is now much clearer, but it will be some years before effective compounds are available. By contrast influenza is an easier target for vaccines, but the current pandemic has revealed the dangers of a lack of investment in research into emerging infectious diseases. There are other, as yet unknown, pandemics around the corner.

Chapter 6 references and further reading

1 World Bank Statistics. (2006) Key Development Data and Statistics.

2 Leading Causes of Death (US) Available at: www.cdc.gov/nchs/FASTATS/lcod.htm [Accessed 25 Nov 2009].

3 Niederlaender, E., (2006) Causes of death in the EU. EuroStat: Luxembourg. Available at: epp.eurostat.ec.europa.eu/cache/ITY_OFFPUB/KS-NK-06-010/EN/KS-NK-06-010-EN.PDF [Accessed 25 Nov 2009].

4 UNICEF. (2007) *Progress for Children: A world fit for children. Statistical review no 6*. UNICEF, New York, NY.

5 HarvestPlus. (nd) *Nutrients*. Available at: www.harvestplus.org/content/nutrients [Accessed 25 Nov 2009].

6 FAO. (2008) *The State of Food Insecurity in 2008*, FAO, Rome.

7 HarvestPlus (nd) *Crops*. Available at: www.harvestplus.org/content/crops [Accessed 25 Nov 2009].

8 UNDP. (2008) *Global Progress – Are we on track to meet the MDGs by 2015?* Available at: www.undp.org/mdg/basics_ontrack.shtml [Accessed 25 Nov 2009].

9 Levine, R., (2004) *Millions Saved: proven successes in global health*. Center for Global Development, Washington, DC.

10 Mahalanabis, D. et al., (1973) Oral fluid therapy of cholera among Bangladesh refugees. *The John Hopkins Medical Journal* **132**, 197-205.

11 Fontaine, O. & Newton, C., (2001) A revolution in the management of diarrhoea. *Bul. WHO*. **79**, 471-471.

12 Editorial. "Water with sugar and salt". Lancet 2, 5 August 1978, 300–301.

13 Pierce, N.F., (nd) *How Much Has ORT Reduced Child Mortality?* Available at: www.icddrb.org/pub/publication.jsp?classificationID=30&pubID=355 [Accessed 25 Nov 2009].

14 Institute for OneWorld Health. *Diarrheal Disease*. Available at: www.oneworldhealth.org/diarrheal_disease [Accessed 25 Nov 2009].

15 Resources for Diarrheal Disease Control. *Proven and affordable solutions*. Available at: www.eddcontrol.org/interventions.php [Accessed 25 Nov 2009].

16 The rehydration project. Available at: rehydrate.org [Accessed 25 Nov 2009].

17 UNICEF. (2009) *Soap, toilets and taps, a foundation for healthy children*. UNICEF, New York.

18 UN. (2009) *The Millennium Development Goals Report, 2009*, United Nations, New York.

19 DFID. (2004) *Reducing maternal deaths: Evidence and action. A strategy for DFID*. Department for International Development, London.

20 DFID. (2007) *Maternal Health*, Factsheet, Department for International Development, London.

21 Singh S, et al., (2003) *Adding It Up: The Benefits of Investing in Sexual and Reproductive Health Care*. New York: The Alan Guttmacher Institute / UNFPA. Available at: www.guttmacher.org/pubs/covers/addingitup.html [Accessed 17 Dec 2009].

22 Singh S. (2006) Hospital admissions resulting from unsafe abortion: estimates from 13 developing countries. *Lancet*, **368**, 1887-92.

23 Curtis, V. Cairncross, S. & Yonli, R., (2000) Domestic hygiene and diarrhoea – pinpointing the problem. *Tropical Medicine and International Health*, **5**, 22-32.

24 Curtis, V. & Cairncross, S., (2003) Effect of washing hands with soap on diarrhoea risk in the community: a systematic review. *Lancet Infect Dis*. **3**,275-81.

25 Curtis, V. & Cairncross, S., (2003) Water, sanitation, and hygiene at Kyoto. *BMJ* **327**, 3-4.

26 Cairncross, S. & Valdmanis, V., Water supply, sanitation and hygiene promotion (Chapter 41) in: Jamison, D. et al., (2006) *Disease Control Priorities in Developing Countries*. The World Bank, Washington DC.

27 Curtis, Val., [Email] (Pers. comm. 14 May 2009). [Phone interview] (Pers.comm. 27 April 2009).

28 Luby, S. et al., (2005) Effect of handwashing on child health: a randomised controlled trial. *Lancet*. **366**, (9481), 225-33.

29 The disease and the virus. Available at: www.polioeradication.org/disease.asp [Accessed 25 Nov 2009].

30 Roberts, L., (2004) Polio Endgame: Fighting Polio Block by Block, House by Shack. *Science*, **303**, 1964-1965.

31   Harrison, G., (1978) *Mosquitoes, Malaria, and Man: A History of the Hostilities Since 1880*. Dutton, New York.

32   WHO. (2006) *Malaria vector control and personal protection*. Technical Report Series 936, WHO. Geneva.

33   CDC. (2008) *Anopheles Mosquitoes*. Available at: www.cdc.gov/malaria/biology/mosquito/ [Accessed 25 Nov 2009].

34   Encarta Encylopaedia, *Life Cycle of a Malaria Parasite*.

35   WHO. (2006) *Indoor residual spraying: Use of indoor residual spraying for scaling up global malaria control and elimination*. Global Malaria Programme, WHO, Geneva.

36   WHO. (2007) *WHO recommended insecticides for indoor residual spraying against malaria vectors*. Available at: www.who.int/entity/whopes/Insecticides_IRS_Malaria_ok.pdf [Accessed 25 Nov 2009].

37   WHO. (2007) *Insecticide-treated Mosquito nets:* WHO Position Statement. WHO, Geneva.

38   Killeen, G. et al., (2007) Preventing childhood malaria in Africa by protecting adults from mosquitoes with insecticide-treated nets. *PLoS Medicine*, **4**, 229.

39   Hawley, W. et al., (2003) Community-wide effects of permethrin-treated bednets on child mortality and malaria morbidity in western Kenya. *Am J Trop Med Hyg*, **68**, 121–127.

40   TDR. Available at: www.who.int/tdr [Accessed 25 Nov 2009].

41   MosqGuide. Available at: www.mosqguide.org.uk [Accessed 25 Nov 2009].

42   USAID. (2008) *The ABC Approach: Preventing the Sexual Transmission of HIV*. Available at: www.usaid.gov/our_work/global_health/aids/TechAreas/prevention/abcfactsheet.html [Accessed 25 Nov 2009].

43   WHO/UNAIDS/UNICEF. (2009) *Towards universal access: scaling up priority HIV/AIDS interventions in the health sector:* progress report 2009. WHO, Geneva.

44   Hallett, T. et al., (2006) Declines in HIV prevalence can be associated with changing sexual behaviour in Uganda, urban Kenya, Zimbabwe, and urban Haiti. *Sex Transm Infect*. Apr, **82** Suppl 1, i1–8.

45   Shelton, J. Halperin, D. & Wilson, D.,(2006) Has global HIV incidence peaked? *Lancet*. Apr 8, **367** (9517):1120–2.

46   Gregson, S. et al., (2006) HIV Decline Associated with Behaviour Change in Eastern Zimbabwe. *Science*, 664-666.

47   Hallett, T. et al., (2009) Assessing evidence for behaviour change affecting the course of HIV epidemics: A new mathematical modelling approach and application to data from Zimbabwe. *Epidemics*, 1 (2) 108-117.

48   WHO/UNAIDS/UNFPA. (2004) *Position Statement on Condoms and HIV Prevention July 2004*. Available at: data.unaids.org/una-docs/condom-policy_jul04_en.pdf [Accessed 25 Nov 2009].

49   WHO/UNAIDS. (2000) *The Female Condom: A guide for planning and programming*. WHO, Geneva.

50   AVAC. (2007) *A New Way to Protect Against HIV? Understanding the Results of Male Circumcision Studies for HIV Prevention*. AIDS Vaccine Advocacy Coalition, New York.

51   WHO. (2007) *Male circumcision: global trends and determinants of prevalence, safety and acceptability*. WHO, Geneva.

52   NIAID. (2007) *Understanding the Immune System, How it Works*. National Institutes of Health, Bethesda. Available at: www3.niaid.nih.gov/topics/immuneSystem/PDF/theImmuneSystem.pdf [Accessed 25 Nov 2009].

53   HPTU. (nd) *The Vaccine Trials Clinical Process*. HIV Prevention Trials Network. Available at: depts.washington.edu/hptu/trials.html [Accessed 25 Nov 2009].

54   Bloom, B., (1989) Vaccines for the Third World. *Nature*, **342**, 115-120.

55   NIAID. (2009) *Vaccines, Types of Vaccines*. Available at: www3.niaid.nih.gov/topics/vaccines/understanding/typesVaccines.htm [Accessed 25 Nov 2009].

56   Henderson, D., (1999) Eradication: lessons from the past. *CDC Morbidity and Mortality Weekly Report*. **48**, (SU01), 16-22. Available at: www.cdc.gov/mmwr/preview/mmwrhtml/su48a6.htm [Accessed 25 Nov 2009].

57   CDC. (2007) *Smallpox: 30th Anniversary of Global Eradication*. Available at: www.cdc.gov/Features/SmallpoxEradication/ [Accessed 25 Nov 2009].

58   Fenner, F. et al., (1988) *Smallpox and Its Eradication.* History of International Public Health, No. 6. WHO, Geneva.

59   Fooks, T. & Harkess, G., (2008) Stamping out infectious disease; the rise and fall of a big idea. *The Magazine of the Health Protection Agency,* **10**, 16-18.

60   Measles Initiative. Available at: www.measlesinitiative.org [Accessed 25 Nov 2009].

61   CDC. (2009) Progress Toward Measles Control – Africa Region, 2001-2008. *MMWR Weekly,* **58** (37), 1036-1041. Available at: www.cdc.gov/mmwr/preview/mmwrhtml/mm5837a3.htm [Accessed 25 Nov 2009].

62   Immunization Action Coalition. (2009) *Vaccine Information for the public and health professionals.* Available at: www.vaccineinformation.org/pertuss/qandavax.asp [Accessed 25 Nov 2009].

63   Global Polio Eradication Initiative. *The History.* Available at: www.polioeradication.org/history.asp [Accessed 25 Nov 2009].

64   Ashmore, M., m360 Ltd.

65   Mukherji, S. et al., (2005) Polio Eradication in India: Myth or Reality. *MJAFI,* **61**, 364-366.

66   Fine, P., (1993) Herd immunity: history, theory, practice. *Epidemiol Rev,* **15** (2), 265–302.

67   Pallansch, M. & Sandhu, H., (2006) The Eradication of Polio — Progress and Challenges. *N Engl J Med,* **355**, 2508-2511.

68   Roberts, L., (2009) Type 2 Poliovirus back from the dead in Nigeria. *Science,* **325**, 660-661.

69   BBC. (2004) *New TB vaccine shown to be safe.* BBC News 24 Oct 2004.

70   Stop TB Partnership. Available at: www.stoptb.org/stop_tb_initiative/ [Accessed 25 Nov 2009].

71   BMGF. (2007) *New Grants to Fight Tuberculosis Epidemic* Available at: www.gatesfoundation.org/press-releases/Pages/tuberculosis-epidemic-grants-070918.aspx [Accessed 26 Nov 2009].

72   Aeras. (2009) *Our Portfolio of Vaccine candidates.* Aeras Global Vaccine Foundation. Available at: www.aeras.org/our-approach/vaccine-development.php?portfolio [Accessed 17 Dec 2009].

73   Bradt, S., (2008). *Inhaled tuberculosis vaccine may be more effective than injected vaccine, animal study very promising.* Harvard Science, March 11. Available at: www.harvardscience.harvard.edu/medicine-health/articles/inhaled-tuberculosis-vaccine-may-be-more-effective-injected-vaccine. [Accessed 14 Dec 2009].

74   NIAID. (2009) *Structure of HIV.* www3.niaid.nih.gov/topics/HIVAIDS/Understanding/Biology/structure.htm

75   IPM. (2008) *Microbicide Research and Development, Issue Brief,* International Partnership for Microbicides, Available at: www.ipmglobal.org/pdfs/english/ipm_publications/2009/ipm_ib_rd_oct2008_20090806v1.pdf [Accessed 26 Nov 2009].

76   IAVI. (2008) *AIDS Vaccine Blueprint 2008: A Challenge to the Field, A Roadmap for Progress.* IAVI, New York.

77   MHRP. (2009) *RV144 Phase III HIV Vaccine Trial.* Available at: www.hivresearch.org/phase3/factsheet.html [Accessed 26 Nov 2009].

78   Letvin, N., (2005) Progress towards an HIV vaccine. *Annu. Rev. Med.* **56**, 213–23.

79   Coordinating Committee of the Global HIV/AIDS Vaccine Enterprise. (2005) The Global HIV/AIDS Vaccine Enterprise: Scientific strategic plan. *PLoS Med* **2** (2), e25. Available at: www.plosmedicine.org/article/info:doi/10.1371/journal.pmed.0020025 [Accessed 26 Nov 2009].

80   Montefiori, D. et al., (2007) Antibody-based HIV-1 vaccines: Recent developments and future directions. *PLoS Med* **4** (12), e348. Available at: www.plosmedicine.org/article/info:doi/10.1371/journal.pmed.0040348 [Accessed 26 Nov 2009].

81   Cohen, J., (2008) HIV gets by with a lot of help from Human Host. *Science,* **319**, 143-144.

82   Giles, C., (2005) *Why don't we have a malaria vaccine?* Wellcome Trust, Malaria and People Features. Available at: malaria.wellcome.ac.uk/doc_WTX033040.html [Accessed 26 Nov 2009].

83   PATH Malaria Vaccine Initiative (MVI). Available at: www.malariavaccine.org/malvac-approaches.php [Accessed 25 Nov 2009].

84   Bejon, P. et al., (2008) Efficacy of RTS,S/AS01E Vaccine against Malaria in Children 5 to 17 Months of Age. *N Engl J Med*, **359**, 2521-2532.

85   Smith, I., (1999) Stop TB: Is DOTS the Answer? *Ind. J. Tub*, 1999, **46**, 81.

86   New Jersey Medical School Global Tuberculosis Institute. *History of TB*. Available at: www.umdnj.edu/globaltb/tbhistory.htm [Accessed 26 Nov 2009].

87   NJMS National Tuberculosis Center. (1996) *Brief History of Tuberculosis*. Available at: www.umdnj.edu/~ntbcweb/history.htm [Accessed 26 Nov 2009].

88   Oza, S., (2002) Tuberculosis, an overlooked global threat. *MURJ*. **6**.

89   Hopkins Tanne, J., (1999) Drug Resistant TB is spreading worldwide. *BMJ*, **319**.

90   TB Alert. (2006) *TB Historical Timeline*. Available at: www.tbalert.org.uk/news_press/TBHistoricalTimeline.htm [Accessed 26 Nov 2009].

91   Obermeyer, Z. Abbott-Klafter, J. & Murray, C., (2008) Has the DOTS Strategy Improved Case Finding or Treatment Success? An Empirical Assessment. *PLoS ONE*, **3** (3), e1721.

92   WHO. (2009) *Global Tuberculosis Control: epidemiology, strategy, financing*. WHO, Geneva.

93   WHO. (2007) *Global Tuberculosis Control: surveillance, planning, financing*. WHO, Geneva.

94   WHO. (2009) *Forecasting the control of MDR-TB epidemics*. A ministerial meeting of high M/XDR-TB burden countries. Beijing, China, 1–3 April 2009.

95   Lettieri, C., (2007) The Emergence and Impact of Extensively Drug-Resistant Tuberculosis. *Medscape Pulmonary Medicine*. 31 May.

96   Partners in Health. (2006) *Tuberculosis and MDR-TB*. Available at: www.pih.org/issues/tb.html [Accessed 26 Nov 2009].

97   The Lung Association. (2007) *Tuberculosis*. Available at: www.lung.ca/diseases-maladies/ tuberculosis-tuberculose/tbday-jourtb/oped_e.php [Accessed 26 Nov 2009].

98   TB Alliance. Available at: www.tballiance.org [Accessed 26 Nov 2009].

99   WHO, Geneva. (2007) *New technologies for Tuberculosis control: a framework for their, introduction and implementation*.

100 TB Alliance. (2008) *Confronting TB, What it Takes, 2008 Annual Report*. TB Alliance, New York.

101 Diacon, A. H. et al., (2009) The diarylquinoline TMC207 for multidrug-resistant tuberculosis. *New England Journal of Medicine*. **360**, 2397-2405.

102 GPRM. (2008) A Summary report from the Global Price Reporting Mechanism on Anitretroviral Medicines. February 2008.

103 Boniface Dongmo Nguimfack, WHO. [Email] (Pers. Comm. 20 April 2009).

104 Avert. (2009) *Preventing mother-to-child transmission of HIV*. Available at: www.avert.org/motherchild.htm [Accessed 26 Nov 2009].

105 WHO. (2009) *Revisions to WHO guidelines for antiretroviral treatment of pregnant women and prevention of HIV infection in infants*. Available at: www.who.int/hiv/topics/mtct/revisions/en/index.html [Accessed 26 Nov 2009].

106 Avert. (2009) *Preventing mother-to-child transmission of HIV*. [www.avert.org/motherchild.htm], Adapted from: WHO 2006, *Antiretroviral Drugs for Treating Pregnant Women and Preventing HIV Infection in Infants:* Towards Universal Access. WHO, Geneva.

107 US President's Emergency Plan for AIDS Relief Available at: www.pepfar.gov [Accessed 26 Nov 2009].

108 Elizabeth Glasier Pediatric Aids Foundation, Prevention of Mother-to-Child Transmission of HIV Program. Available at: www.pedaids.org/OurWork/International-HIV-Preventi-(1).aspx [Accessed 26 Nov 2009].

109 International Center for AIDS Care and Treatment Programs. Available at: www.columbia-icap.org/whatwedo/mtctplus/index.html [Accessed 26 Nov 2009].

110 Skoler-Karpoff, S. et al., (2008) Efficacy of Carraguard for prevention of HIV infection in women in South Africa: a randomised, double-blind, placebo-controlled trial. *The Lancet*, **372**, 1977-1987.

111 Cates, W. & Feldblum, P., (2008) HIV prevention research: the ecstasy and the agony. *The Lancet* **372**, 1932-1933.

112 Public Health Working Group, Microbicides Initiative. (2001) *The Public Health Benefits of Microbicides in Lower Income Countries: Model Projections*, Rockefeller Foundation. Available at: www.global-campaign.org/clientfiles/rep7_publichealth.pdf [Accessed 26 Nov 2009].

113 WHO. (2005) World Malaria Report 2005. WHO, Geneva.

114 Ridley, R., (2003) Malaria: to kill a parasite. *Nature* **424**, 887-889.

115 IRIN (2009) GLOBAL: *Artemisinin: the new drug that cannot afford to fail*. IRIN news, 16 December. www.irinnews.org/InDepthMain.aspx?InDepthId=10&ReportId=57923 [Accessed 14 December 2009].

116 Woolhouse, M. Gowtage-Sequeria, S. & Evans, B., (2006) Quantitative analysis of the characteristics of emerging and re-emerging human pathogens. In: *Infectious Diseases: Preparing for the Future*. Office of Science and Innovation, Foresight Programme, Department of Trade and Industry, UK.

117 Jones, K., (2007) Global trends in emerging infectious diseases. Nature, **51**, 990-993.

118 Keele, B. et al., (2006) Chimpanzee reservoirs of pandemic and nonpandemic HIV-1. *Science*, **313**, 523-526.

119 Bailes, E. et al., (2003) Hybrid origin of SIV in Chimpanzees. *Science*, **300**, 1713.

120 Hillis, D., (2000) Origins of HIV. *Science*, **288**, 1757-8.

121 Korber, B. et al., (2002) Timing the ancestor of the HIV-1 pandemic strains. *Science*, **288**, 1789-1796.

122 Potter, C., (2001) A history of influenza. *Journal of Applied Microbiology*, **91**, 572-579.

123 Molecular Expressions. (2005) *The Influenza Virus*. Available at: micro.magnet.fsu.edu/cells/viruses/influenzavirus.html [Accessed 26 Nov 2009].

124 Neumann, G. Noda, T. & Kawaoka, Y., (2009) Emergence and pandemic potential of swine-origin H1N1 influenza virus. *Nature*, **459**, 931-939.

125 Oxford, J.S., (2000) Influenza A pandemics of the 20th century with special reference to 1918: virology, pathology and epidemiology. *Review Medical Virology*, **10**, 119-133.

126 van Riel, D. et al., (2006). H5N1 Virus Attachment to Lower Respiratory Tract. *Science* **312**, 399.

127 Jordan, E., (1928) *Epidemic influenza: a survey*. American Medical Association, Chicago.

128 Barry, J., (2004) *The Great Influenza: The epic story of the deadliest plague in history*. Penguin Books, New York.

129 Starr, I., (1976) Influenza in 1918: recollections of the epidemic in Philadelphia. *Annals of Internal Medicine*, **85**, 516-518.

130 Taubenberger, J. & Morens, D., (2006) 1918 Influenza: the Mother of All Pandemics, *Emerging Infectious Diseases*, **12**, 15-22.

131 WHO. (2009) *Pandemic (H1N1) 2009 – update 78*. World Health Organisation. Available at: www.who.int/csr/don/2009_12_11a/en/index.html [Accessed 14 Dec 2009].

132 Kelland, K., (2009) *UK study confirms H1N1 far less lethal than feared*. Reuters, 10 December. Available at: www.reuters.com/article/idUSTRE5B939Z20091210 [Accessed 17 Dec 2009].

133 Webster, R. & Govorkova, E., (2006) H5N1 Influenza — Continuing Evolution and Spread. *New England Journal of Medicine*, **355**, 2174-7.

134 Kaiser, J., (2006) A One-Size-Fits-All Flu Vaccine? *Science*, **312**, 380-381.

135 Cumulative Number of Confirmed Human Cases of Avian Influenza A/(H5N1) Reported to WHO.15 May 2009. Available at : www.who.int/csr/disease/avian_influenza/country/cases_table_2009_05_15/en/index.html [Accessed 26 Nov 2009].

136 Smith, G., (2006) *Emergence and predominance of an H5N1 influenza variant in China*. PANS.

137 Department of Health and Human Services. (2007) *Avian Influenza: Current Situation* Available at: www.cdc.gov/flu/avian/outbreaks/pdf/current.pdf [Accessed 26 Nov 2009].

138 WHO. (2009) *Pandemic (H1N1) 2009 briefing note 1 - Viruses resistant to oseltamivir (Tamiflu)* identified. Available at: www.who.int/csr/disease/swineflu/notes/h1n1_antiviral_resistance_20090708/en/index.html [Accessed 26 Nov 2009].

139 Daar, A. et al., (2007) Grand challenges in chronic non-communicable diseases, The top 20 policy and research priorities for conditions such as diabetes, stroke and heart disease. *Nature*, **450**, 494-496.

140 WHO. (2005) *Preventing Chronic Diseases: A Vital Investmen*. WHO, Geneva.

Achieving Environmental Sustainability

*The Nile River and its delta taken on July 17 2009 from the
Earth-orbiting Space Shuttle Endeavour. © NASA*

The entire suite of development goals, including economic growth, improved education, gender equity and the reduction of disease and hunger, will be difficult to achieve without reversing the current degradation of the environment. An estimated 24 % of global disease burden is associated with environmental factors, and 25 % of all deaths in developing countries are linked to environmental risks, compared to 17 % in the developed world.[1]

While it is tempting to think of MDG 7 – with its broad environmental sweep – as somewhat more removed than agriculture and health from the immediate needs of the world's poor, this is actually not the case. Recent studies of global environmental change conclude that the poor suffer most as a consequence of environmental decline.[2] Research has demonstrated that poor people are most likely to be affected by disasters brought about, or exacerbated by, environmental degradation, such as landslides and flooding.[3,4]

The main reason for the close relationship between environmental sustainability and poverty reduction is that poor communities in developing countries are much more dependent on environmental services, particularly renewable natural resources, than those in developed countries. Over 1.3 billion people rely on forests, fisheries and agriculture for their livelihoods, accounting for nearly half of all jobs worldwide. Natural resources are also essential sources of food, energy, shelter and medicine. In Africa, more than seven out of every ten poor people live in rural areas, where their livelihoods are renewable resource-dependent.[5]

Besides supplying basic human necessities, natural resources in developing countries – such as export crops and minerals – underpin national economic growth and incomes. Natural capital – including land, minerals and forests – constitutes 5 % of the world's wealth but more than 40 % of the wealth of developing countries.[1]

1. Millennium Development Goal 7

A quick glance at the targets of MDG 7 reveals significant variation in the breadth and depth of targets and indicators (see Table 7.1). The diverse focus of these targets has been influenced by the recent history of international efforts to integrate environmental and development issues. Governments at the UN Conference on Environment and Development (UNCED) in Rio de Janeiro in 1992 adopted Agenda 21, the Rio Declaration on Environment and Development, and the Statement of Principles for the Sustainable Management of Forests.[6] This generated new initiatives on climate change, forestry and biodiversity, and established "sustainable development" as a shared, international objective, integrating economic growth, equity and environmental protection. Then in 2002, the World Summit on Sustainable Development in Johannesburg reaffirmed the principles of sustainable development and placed particular emphasis (linking to the Millennium Declaration), on water and sanitation, biodiversity conservation, climate change and energy.[7]

All of these different environmental initiatives became separate targets and indicators of MDG 7. Target 7C and 7D, dealing with water and sanitation, and urban slums respectively, were quite precise. Targets 7A and 7B in contrast, had a complex set of overlapping indicators (Table 7.1).[†]

† Indeed, depending on what international agency's website you consult, you will find that the five or seven indicators of Targets 7A and 7B are distributed across both targets in quite different ways. Here we use the UNSTATS interpretation, which identifies seven indicators across Targets 7A and 7B. This list of MDG indicators is available at: millenniumindicators.un.org/unsd/mdg/Host.aspx?Content=Indicators/OfficialList.htm [Accessed 16 Nov 2009].

Table 7.1 Goal 7: Ensure environmental sustainability[8]	
Target 7.A – Integrate the principles of sustainable development into country policies and programmes and reverse the loss of environmental resources. **Target 7.B** – Reduce biodiversity loss, achieving, by 2010, a significant reduction in the rate of loss.	**7.1** Proportion of land area covered by forest. **7.2** CO_2 emissions, total, per capita and per US\$1 GDP (PPP). **7.3** Consumption of ozone-depleting substances. **7.4** Proportion of fish stocks within safe biological limits. **7.5** Proportion of total water resources used. **7.6** Proportion of terrestrial and marine areas protected. **7.7** Proportion of species threatened with extinction.
Target 7.C – Halve, by 2015, the proportion of people without sustainable access to safe drinking water and basic sanitation.	**7.8** Proportion of population using an improved drinking water source. **7.9** Proportion of population using an improved sanitation facility.
Target 7.D – By 2020, to have achieved a significant improvement in the lives of at least 100 million slum dwellers.	**7.10** Proportion of urban population living in slums.

In this Chapter, we will consider the contribution that science and innovation make to acheiving the different targets of MDG 7. In Section 3 we will focus on those indicators in Targets 7A and 7B which are associated with reducing the loss of natural resources, specifically forests, fisheries and water, and the loss of biodiversity, in terms of protected areas and species extinction. In Section 4, we will consider the remaining indicator from 7A and 7B associated with climate change mitigation and CO_2 reduction, but not reduction of ozone-depleting substances, as this has largely been achieved. In Section 5 we will discuss the scientific aspects of Target 7C, which focuses on the supply of clean drinking water and sanitation. We will not consider Target 7D, on improving the lives of slum dwellers, but we note that a major indicator of this target involves urban water supply and sanitation.

First, we will start with an overview on environmental policy and the general role of science in its development.

2. The role of science in environmental policy

The principal cause of the failure to meet MDG 7s environmental targets is poor governance of natural resources both at a national and local level. Without effective national environmental policies, open access resources, such as forests, fisheries and water, are easily over-exploited. The most effective policies are those that have recognized and engaged all stakeholders, and in particular the poor, in the management of these resources. Successful development of policies requires that rights are granted to communities that are dependent on the resource.

As part of an evaluation of progress towards environmental MDGs, the World Bank has assembled and compared measures of the quality of national environmental policy and institutions.[1] One of these, the Environmental Performance Index (EPI) takes broadly accepted targets for a set of 25 environmental indicators for: environmental health; air pollution; water resources; biodiversity; productive natural resources; and climate change; and ranks countries on the basis of their performance relative to these. Using the scores from 149 countries, the 2008 EPI, illustrated in Figure 7.1, revealed that lower income countries generally lag behind higher income countries, and account for the most poorly performing cases.

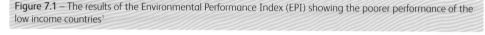

Figure 7.1 – The results of the Environmental Performance Index (EPI) showing the poorer performance of the low income countries[1]

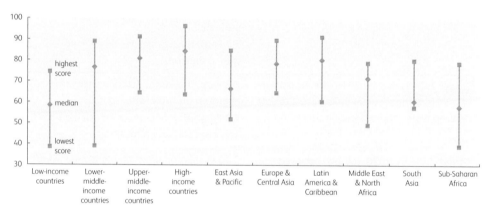

A key reason for poor progress in environmental policy has been the failure of government to regard the environment as a critical aspect of all policy development, rather than as something which needs attention only when there is an environmental crisis. The solution – called *environmental mainstreaming* – involves "the informed inclusion of relevant environmental concerns into the decisions of institutions that drive national, local and sectoral development policy, rules, plans, investment and action."[9] Environmental mainstreaming encompasses both the process by which environmental issues are brought to the attention of policy makers – including the involvement of civil society organisations, scientists and others who contribute to the policy making process – and the inclusion of environmental measures in policy itself.

Science plays an important role in mainstreaming environmental policy. In fact, many policies are based on evidence provided by scientific research. We illustrate this in Box 7.1 for the development of forest management policy around certification schemes.

More generally, science provides a means of measuring and expressing the specific value of the environment to human well being and to international development. As we will see below, ecosystem science enables us to calculate the environmental benefits and costs associated with development activities, be they a new irrigation scheme, development of a fishing industry, a disease control campaign or an action to improve the environment itself. This helps us to make policies which are more sustainable.

Finally, as we shall see, particularly for climate change, water supply and sanitation, science can play its traditional role of supplying innovative technologies which underpin environmental policy.

Box 7.1 Policy and science in sustainable forest management

The specific role that science plays in environmental policy is illustrated in the widespread development and adoption of certification schemes for sustainable forest management. Governments use these schemes to regulate the practices of forest users and to report on the status of their forests to international processes and fora. In developing countries, certification schemes recognize that the poor who live in, and around, the forests have a critical role to play in forest conservation. Poor people can also benefit substantially from commercially viable, sustainable forest management. Indeed, if not engaged in and benefiting from managing forests, they may contribute to

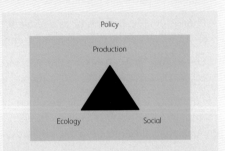

Figure 7.2 – A schematic representation of how ecological, production and social factors are linked in producing policy for sustainable forest management. The ecological component is derived directly from scientific research on forest ecosystems which identifies indicators of stable, sustainable forest systems[11]

unsustainable harvesting of forest resources. Over 47 million hectares of forest are under schemes endorsed by the Forest Stewardship Council (FSC), 18 % of which are in Asia, Africa and Latin America. While this proportion is relatively small, growth of certification schemes in more wealthy countries will affect timber markets and public opinion which should accelerate certification in poorer countries.

Certification schemes require criteria and indicators (C&I) for sustainable forest management. While forests are extremely variable, ranging from rainforest to savanna woodland, they share similar ecological features and processes that make them self-sustaining. The Centre for International Forest Research (CIFOR), developed a C&I template which has served as the basis for the development of local management schemes by governments, communities and industries worldwide.[10,11] The template is based on a set of *principles* of sustainable forest management, to which are assigned *criteria, indicators of achievement*, and *verifiers* that can be measured for these indicators. Indicators cover four areas: policy, production, social dimensions and ecology, which are inter-related. Figure 7.2 captures this relationship.

© Wikimedia commons/Semhur

Figure 7.3 – A tropical rainforest on the island of Fatu Iva, French Polynesia

Ecological indicators are built on scientific knowledge and measurement, for example:

- Landscape pattern is maintained;

- Change of habitat diversity, as a result of human interventions, is maintained within critical limits, as defined by natural variation and/or regional conservation objectives;

- Community guild[†] structures do not show significant changes in the representation of especially sensitive guilds, pollinator and disperser guilds.

For a particular ecological indicator, there will be a number of verifiers that involve scientific measurement of plant and animal diversity and abundance. For instance, with respect to the community guild structure, a few verifiers are:

- The abundance of selected avian guilds is maintained within natural variation;

- The abundance of nests of social bees is maintained within natural variation;

- The abundance of seed in key plant species does not show significant change compared to undisturbed forest.

† A guild is a group of species of organisms, not always closely related, that perform a similar ecological function, for instance, a guild of bird and bat species may consume fruits of particular forest tress and distribute their seeds.

3. Reversing the loss of natural resources

Forests, fisheries, water, biodiversity – all of these natural resources are elements of ecosystems. An ecosystem is a dynamic complex of plant, animal and microbial communities and the non-living environment, interacting as a functional unit. In order to restore depleted natural resources, we need to understand the biological and physical processes within ecosystems that generate and regulate them. This is at the core of the science of ecology. These processes are not only complex, but highly inter-linked, such that the dynamics of one kind of natural resource directly affects the dynamics of another. Through ecological research, for instance, we have come to understand the critical role of plant cover and soils in retaining and regulating water flow in landscapes, and the role of ocean turbulence in maintaining nutrient flow, food chains and fish stocks.

© Greenpeace International

Figure 7.4 – A man illegally cutting wood in the Congo to sell in Kinshasa

As we have seen in Chapter 4, critical natural resources are declining on a global scale. While deforestation and afforestation are both occurring, there is a continuing net reduction in forest cover. Fisheries are growing increasingly unsustainable, water resources are in decline, the loss of protected natural habitats continues and the rate of species extinction is rising. All of these changes have serious implications for human well-being. They are the result of over-exploitation of renewable resources, that is, going beyond the level of sustainable harvesting that would guarantee and perpetuate the supply of these resources.

The Millennium Ecosystem Assessment (MA)

The same UN initiative that set in motion the development of the MDGs (see Chapter 4) led to the development of the Millennium Ecosystem Assessment (MA). The outputs of the MA in 2005 came too late to shape the design of MDG 7, but the MA findings remain critical for achieving its targets. The MA was run under the auspices of the United Nations (UN) to *"assess the consequences of ecosystem change for human well-being and to establish the scientific basis for actions needed to enhance the conservation and sustainable use of ecosystems and their contributions to human well-being"*. It was intended to address issues arising from other international initiatives, notably the inter-governmental Convention on Biological Diversity.

The MA presents a detailed analysis of the state of each of the world's different ecosystems and the processes affecting them, with a strong geographical focus. It also relates these changes to human well-being through the concept of ecosystem services. These are the part of ecosystems, and their processes, that are of specific benefit to people. These benefits can range from the provision of water or plants and animals for food to less obvious contributions such as supporting the insects that pollinate our crops, or the geochemical cycles that remove the pollutants we put into the air and water. The MA identifies four broad categories of ecosystem services:

- Provisioning services;

- Regulating services;

- Cultural services;

- Supporting services.

Box 7.2 presents a description of the specific ecosystem services under these categories.

Box 7.2 Categories of ecosystem services[12]	
Category	**Examples of ecosystem services provided**
Provisioning services i.e. products obtained from ecosystems	• Food e.g. crops, fruit, fish. • Fibre and fuel e.g. timber, wool. • Biochemicals, natural medicines and pharmaceuticals. • Genetic resources; genes and genetic information used for animal/plant breeding and biotechnology. • Ornamental resources e.g. shells, flowers.
Regulating services i.e. benefits obtained from the regulation of ecosystem processes	• Air-quality maintenance: ecosystems contribute chemicals to and extract chemicals from the atmosphere. • Climate regulation e.g. land cover can affect local temperature and precipitation; globally, ecosystems affect greenhouse gas sequestration and emissions. • Water regulation: ecosystems affect e.g. the timing and magnitude of runoff, flooding etc.

...continued

Category	Examples of ecosystem services provided
Regulating services continued	• Erosion control: vegetative cover plays an important role in soil retention/prevention of land/asset erosion.
	• Water purification/detoxification: ecosystems can be a source of water impurities but can also help to filter out/decompose organic waste.
	• Natural hazard protection e.g. storms, floods, landslides.
	• Bioremediation of waste i.e. removal of pollutants through storage, dilution, transformation and burial.
Cultural services i.e. non-material benefits that people obtain through spiritual enrichment, cognitive development, recreation etc	• Spiritual and religious value: many religions attach spiritual and religious values to ecosystems.
	• Inspiration for art, folklore, architecture etc.
	• Social relations: ecosystems affect the types of social relations that are established e.g. fishing societies.
	• Aesthetic values; many people find beauty in various aspects of ecosystems.
	• Cultural heritage values: many societies place high value on the maintenance of important landscapes or species.
	• Recreation and ecotourism.
Supporting services, necessary for the production of all other ecosystem services	• Soil formation and retention.
	• Nutrient cycling.
	• Primary production.
	• Water cycling.
	• Production of atmospheric oxygen.
	• Provision of habitat.

In an effort to understand the consequences of declining natural resources, highlighted above, the MA examined trends in ecosystem services over the past half century. Of the ecosystem services presented in Box 7.2, 24 provisioning, regulating and cultural services could be assessed with respect to how human activity has changed them. Supporting services are not directly used by people, rather they underpin the other kinds of services, so they are not included in this analysis. Of these 24 services, 15 (60%) are undergoing degradation or are being used unsustainably. Those that have been particularly degraded over the past 50 years include: capture fisheries; water supply; waste treatment and detoxification; water purification; natural hazard protection; regulation of air quality; regulation of regional and local climate; regulation of erosion; spiritual fulfilment and aesthetic enjoyment. Two of these services, fresh water and capture fisheries, are being exploited at such levels that they cannot be sustained under current demand, much less the demand of a growing population. Only four services: food production; livestock; crops and aquaculture, have been enhanced in the past 50 years.

The MA makes a point of showing how services are inter-linked. For example, increasing services to agriculture by converting forests to crop land may contribute to reducing local poverty but at the same time this will degrade other services provided by forest watersheds and biodiversity, and make these improvements less sustainable.

The MA has provided an environmental baseline for progress against MDG 7 and has identified priority areas for attention. Perhaps more importantly, it has developed the concept of ecosystem services and their measurement for human development. While MDG 7 sets out admirable targets to reduce the loss of natural resources and biodiversity, efforts to achieve these targets will compete poorly for attention against other MDGs that have a more obvious human benefit unless these efforts can be expressed in terms of *benefits to human welfare*. This is where the concept of ecosystem services is so useful.

Figure 7.5 – A river snakes through the land in Bhutan

© Curt Carnemark – World Bank

Recent scientific advances in natural resource management

While the specified environmental targets of MDG 7, forests, fish, water and biodiversity constitute very different kinds of natural resources, their restoration and sustainable use pose more or less the same challenge: *how to understand and manage the self-renewing nature of these resources so that we can utilize them without destroying them or the ecosystems which provide them?* This requires that we have scientific tools to:

- Measure and monitor changes in natural resources over time;

- Model and predict what affects that change;

- Place a value on the resources in terms of human well-being.

These tools have a direct relevance to environmental policy development and implementation. To develop successful policies we need to understand the state of the natural resource and the risk to it, the likely consequences of our policy on its supply, and the benefits that it will bring to society. Once developed and implemented, these same three tools continue to be important in monitoring the performance of the policy and predicting whether the resource's new trajectory will realize the policy goal and demonstrate value to people.

In some cases, we have had these scientific tools for policy development for some time. Predictive, mathematical models have underpinned fisheries management for many decades. But some of the tools are new or rapidly improving, such as methods for valuing ecosystem services, and technologies for environmental monitoring. Further, scientific tools for; monitoring, modelling and valuing the environment, are coming together today with the help of advances in information technology, to generate a powerful integrated platform for developing and managing environmental policy.

Measuring and monitoring changes in natural resources

MDG 7 targets focus on measuring changes in the proportion of a resource conserved, e.g. the proportion of land which is forested or the proportion of total water resource used. But natural resources like these are often extensive and their use is therefore difficult to measure at a national, much less a global level. Some resources, because of their accessibility, are not easy to measure –

much of the water on which we rely lies below the surface of the earth, out of easy measurement. Finally, the complexity of ecological processes may make it difficult to find simple indicators that give us a measure of how complex ecosystems are changing.

A major advance in the way we measure and monitor natural resources is underway through progress in earth observation and remote sensing.[13] Satellite imagery has long provided a means of observing changes in land cover and land use. Since 1972 land cover has been routinely monitored by Landsat and similar satellites, and with higher temporal but poorer spatial resolution by sensors mounted on weather satellites. These generally measure solar reflectance at a set of narrow visible and near infrared wavebands. Reflectances can be used to distinguish vegetation types, such as agricultural and forested land. Countries such as Brazil and India have been using satellite imagery since the 1990s to measure the changes in forest cover, and these now provide a baseline for measuring change.

However, broad patterns of forest cover may not be a good indicator of forest health and degradation, as significant changes can occur underneath a forest canopy. Gathering more information from remote sensing requires greater image resolution. This can then reveal forest gaps caused by tree-felling, and evidence of logging or other activities in forested areas. The widely used SPOT and Landsat imagery has a resolution of 10-60m. Newer systems like IKONOS and QuickBird can now resolve images down to less than 5m, but are still very expensive.

Imaging radars mounted on airplanes have been used to supplement optical sensors, and have the potential to measure forest structure below the canopy. One advantage of radar is that there is no interference from clouds or smoke, and thus it is useful for mapping tropical forests where there is persistent cloud cover. Another emerging remote sensing technology is Lidar (Box 7.3).

© NASA – Visable Earth

Figure 7.6 – A Landsat image taken of the Zambezi river in April 2003, after flooding turned the normal thin blue line into a vast swamp of standing water. Tens of thousands of people were displaced

Box 7.3 The LIDAR – Light Detection and Ranging System

Lidar is an optical remote sensing technology that measures properties of scattered light to find a distant target. It relies on laser pulses and therefore uses shorter wavelengths of the electromagnetic spectrum than radar and most optical methods, making it possible to distinguish smaller objects on a landscape. Because Lidar is highly sensitive to aerosols and cloud particles it has particular environmental value in monitoring changes in atmospheric chemistry and pollution.

Figure 7.7 illustrates how Lidar, mounted in an airplane, scans a landscape. A laser scanner on the aircraft sends up to 100,000 pulses of light per second to the ground and measures how long it takes each pulse to reflect back to the unit. These times are used to compute the distance each pulse travelled from scanner to ground. The Global Positioning System (GPS) and Inertia Monitoring Unit (IMU) determine the precise location and attitude of the laser scanner as the pulses are emitted, and an exact coordinate is calculated for each point. Large areas are surveyed with a series of parallel flight lines.

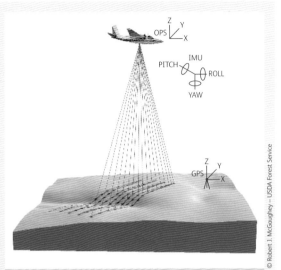

Figure 7.7 – A Lidar system scans a landscape[14]

Operating in this way, Lidar can be used to assess canopy height, biomass and leaf area, or to detect the land surface beneath a forest. In disaster situations it can detect earth movements or other landscape changes, relative to baseline scans.

Earth observation is an extremely valuable tool in monitoring, not only forest exploitation, but also the pattern and change of exploitation of other natural resources. In most cases, satellite images are "ground truthed", that is, matched to observations made on the ground, to ensure that the particular spectral image is consistently indicative of a particular ecosystem feature. This allows the calibration of spectral reflectances with the objects or activities to be measured, e.g. a certain kind of logging activity, water pollution or land degradation.

Earth observation is also of potential value in monitoring of natural disasters.[15,16] Satellites fitted with sensors, which operate over a range of wavelengths, can be used to detect recent and ongoing disasters like fire (infrared), flooding (near infrared, microwave), earthquakes (microwave), typhoons (visible, microwave).

Under the geographical knowledge provided by earth observation, we can overlay other information on this to generate an understanding of the environmental change observed and its causes. We can use successive images to provide a time series of images and identify "hot spots" where change is most rapid. To illustrate this we present two recent studies which have used earth observation to monitor changes: in the use of water resources for irrigation worldwide, and the degradation of land in Africa.

Many parts of the world, particularly arid regions, face water shortages, and it is likely that climate change will exacerbate this (see Chapter 9). Irrigation accounts for about 70% of the water that we currently use. This enables us to produce about 40% of the world's food from 17% of the cultivated area. Given our need to increase food production, there will be future pressures to increase levels of irrigation, but can we afford to do this?

An accurate measure of current global irrigation and how it could change in the future will provide important evidence for future water policy. Until recently our understanding of the extent and distribution of irrigation worldwide came from surveys. However, the accuracy of these surveys was only as good as the infrastructure which collected the data, and this was weak in many poorer countries. In 2006, scientists at the International Water Management Institute (IWMI) in Sri Lanka developed an analysis which used satellite imagery to construct an improved, global map of irrigated lands. (Box 7.4).

Box 7.4   Monitoring global trends in irrigation[17]

Production of a global map of irrigated lands was not a simple task. Areas where irrigation was unlikely to occur were masked out of the global map on the basis of remotely sensed information on altitude, temperature, rainfall and forest cover. Remaining areas were then studied using 159 layers of data, including spectral images from different satellite systems comprising reflectances at different wavelengths and different times. With the help of ground-truthing (either on the ground itself or by using high resolution pictures from Google Earth), spectra associated with different kinds of irrigation in particular regions were identified. Seasonal patterns of greening were particularly useful in identifying irrigated crops from other vegetation.

Ground truth testing showed this approach was about 90 % accurate. This was better than current methods based on national surveys, and had the added benefit of providing more precise geographical information on irrigated areas.

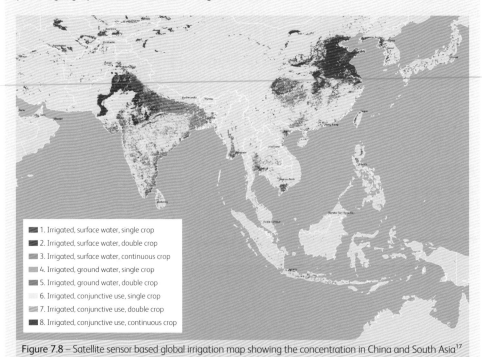

1. Irrigated, surface water, single crop
2. Irrigated, surface water, double crop
3. Irrigated, surface water, continuous crop
4. Irrigated, ground water, single crop
5. Irrigated, ground water, double crop
6. Irrigated, conjunctive use, single crop
7. Irrigated, conjunctive use, double crop
8. Irrigated, conjunctive use, continuous crop

Figure 7.8 – Satellite sensor based global irrigation map showing the concentration in China and South Asia[17]

The final map revealed the global distribution of irrigation. It is composed of images of very high resolution, in some cases down to 500m. It reveals that the total annualized irrigated areas of the world cover 480 million ha ("annualised" takes into consideration irrigated areas during different seasons). Of this irrigated land 75 % occurs in Asia, indeed 60 % occurs in just two countries, China and India, where it supports largely double cropped agriculture.

There is considerable local evidence that land degradation is a serious problem in Africa. Deforestation, overgrazing, inappropriate agriculture (particularly on poor soils) and desertification all appear to be contributing to this process. Degradation is eroding Africa's capacity to increase its food production to meet the demands of a rapidly growing population. Understanding where and why this degradation is occurring, and its extent and rate, is extremely difficult, particularly in remote areas. Yet, it is precisely this information that is needed to develop strategies and policies for land restoration. Box 7.5 illustrates how such mapping has been done using a combination of satellite-based remote sensing data and ground-based weather data.

Box 7.5 Mapping land degradation in Africa[18]

A project to map land degradation in Africa began with the assembly of a time series of satellite images and the application of these to derive the Normalized Differenced Vegetation Index (NDVI) – an algorithm for correlating spectral reflectance with vegetation cover. Annual observations over 20 years were used to identify sites in Africa where the vegetation index had changed. Then, using separate data on patterns of rainfall over that period, the study removed sites where changes in vegetation were strongly correlated with changes in rainfall. These included, for instance, large areas of the Sahel, which

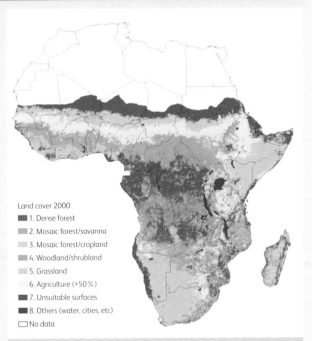

Land cover 2000
- 1. Dense forest
- 2. Mosaic forest/savanna
- 3. Mosaic forest/cropland
- 4. Woodland/shrubland
- 5. Grassland
- 6. Agriculture (>50 %)
- 7. Unsuitable surfaces
- 8. Others (water, cities, etc)
- No data

Figure 7.9 – Major land cover classes in 2000 extracted from GLC2000 data[18]

have recently been "greening" due to increased precipitation. In the areas that remained, vegetation cover had declined independent of changing rainfall implicating human activity as a cause. The distribution was then compared to another satellite-generated map of land cover and land use in Africa. This identified regions that were under agriculture, grassland, different kinds of forest and desert as seen in Figure 7.9. Figure 7.10 shows areas of declining vegetation index, presumed to be degraded. Matching these areas to the vegetation map (Figure 7.9), we can identify different kinds of degradation. These are colour coded in Figure 7.10 as follows:

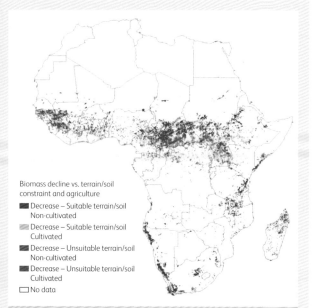

Biomass decline vs. terrain/soil constraint and agriculture

■ Decrease – Suitable terrain/soil Non-cultivated

▨ Decrease – Suitable terrain/soil Cultivated

■ Decrease – Unsuitable terrain/soil Non-cultivated

■ Decrease – Unsuitable terrain/soil Cultivated

☐ No data

- Yellow indicates areas which are suitable for agriculture and cultivated, about 0.3 million km², where degradation of agricultural land is probably occurring due to poor management;

- Blue indicates a decline in agriculturally suitable areas not in cultivation, about

Figure 7.10 – Areas with biomass decline as function of soil/terrain constraints and their agricultural use[18]

1.46 million km², which are likely to include drier grasslands being degraded by over-grazing, woodland and grassland mixtures and dense forests being degraded by deforestation;

- Red indicates regions that are considered unsuitable for agriculture but are, in fact, being cultivated and degraded. Totalling about 0.1 million km², these areas are found, for instance, on the eastern borders of Sierra Leone and Liberia as well as in Uganda.

This study is a first attempt at characterizing and mapping African land degradation, and further research needs to be done in order to make this more accurate. However it does show how technologies based on satellite-based, remote sensing systems, Geographical Information System (GIS) and Information and Communication Technologies (ICT) can be integrated to generate a better understanding of the distribution of environmental problems and how they are likely to change over time. This will be important in measuring the impact of efforts that are being made on behalf of the MDGs and other initiatives.

Future demand for improved remote sensing technology in environmental monitoring is likely to be driven by a need to monitor policy implementation and agreements. For instance, delegates at the UN Climate Change Conference in Bali in 2007 agreed to explore voluntary schemes for Reducing Emissions from Deforestation and Forest Degradation (REDD), which could involve a market-based approach whereby developing countries received carbon credits for reducing or reversing deforestation. A monitoring system would need to be established for REDD that could measure, on an annual basis, the national change in carbon stocks associated with forest management. While it was agreed that, in principle, the basic technology exists for such an accounting system, at least in developed countries, REDD raises a number of scientific challenges. For instance, forest cover is not a precise measure of forest carbon. The carbon content of forests is a function of the size of trees and other vegetation which can be difficult to measure remotely. One possibility would be to build carbon maps using a combination of remote sensing tools and field measurements to calibrate satellite images with biomass on the ground and with indicators of its change.

Earth observation by a wide range of scientific methods, from satellites to land-based surveys, provides new opportunities to constantly monitor the state of the earth and its resources. The global potential for such a system was captured in 2005 by the establishment of a plan for a Global Earth Observation System of Systems (GEOSS) to link existing earth observation systems across a wide range of regions and resources, in order to, *"increase understanding of dynamic Earth processes, to enhance prediction of the Earth system, and to further implement our international environmental treaty obligations"*. Creating GEOSS was the aim of the Group for Earth Observation (GEO),[19] a voluntary partnership of 79 governments and various international organisations. GEO is actively bringing together different earth observation systems around common formats to build this global capability.

Modelling natural resources dynamics

Because we harvest renewable resources, we are faced with the question – how much can we take and still have the resource there to use in the future? Efforts to answer this question began in the early part of the last century, when biologists began to study, in a quantitative manner, the dynamics of plant and animal populations. Many were motivated by the paradox that, while the many millions of species on earth each experience high rates of birth and death, their abundance and numbers seem strikingly constant. To understand this dynamic equilibrium, biologists turned to mathematics to understand what might regulate the numbers of single species.[20] Mathematical models of populations combined variables for birth, death, immigration and emigration to reveal, and subsequently validate, the processes which cause such systems to be stable. These single species population models, in turn, informed applied research on harvested populations and allowed prediction of the inter-generational consequences of removing individuals at different rates.

© Curt Carnemark – World Bank

Figure 7.11 – One fisherman's daily catch in Indonesia

The key role that such modelling has played in natural resource management, and its value to realizing MDG 7, is perhaps most clearly seen with fisheries. Fish play an important part in the diets of people in developing countries, who produce and consume more fish per capita than people in developed countries. Not only do they offer a great source of protein but they also provide important micronutrients. They constitute two distinct natural resources, wild fish stocks which are harvested, and cultivated fish stocks which are farmed.

MDG 7 focuses on restoring wild fish stocks that have been overexploited. At least one quarter of important commercial fish stocks are currently over-harvested. The management of commercial fisheries needs a good scientific understanding of the dynamics of fish populations.

Population models developed for single fish species populations over 50 years ago still underpin sustainable harvesting schemes around the world. Harvesting represents an additional mortality acting on a wild fish population which, above a certain rate, will cause the population to decline until no fish can be harvested. Modelling allows prediction of the maximum sustainable yield – the rate at which fish can be harvested while keeping the number of available fish constant. In practical terms, fisheries models help to identify, for any fishery, the levels of fish abundance (from the record of catches) which correspond to this optimal harvesting rate. Typically, management involves establishing levels of fish abundance which indicate sustainable supply and those lower levels which indicate that the fish population will not replace itself and will go into decline. With the help of monitoring from fish catch data, harvesting is done to approach the first level and avoid the second.

Modelling of this kind has underpinned longstanding investment by DFID to support sustainable fisheries in developing countries. From a policy perspective, models help to show that a growing number of fishers, each acting to maximize their individual catch, will drive fish populations below the optimal harvesting rate, and may cause the fishery to collapse. The solution is to regulate fishing, for instance around a total allowable catch per season. Such regulation may be achieved by shutting the fishery once this catch is realized, or moderating the catches by imposing restrictions on the number of fishers or the duration of the fishing season. Recently, the use of "individual transferable annual catch quotas" has shown advantages over traditional regulatory approaches because it allows fishers to trade quotas, reducing the number of fishers and ensuring that those remaining have a catch sufficient to maintain their livelihood.[21] Optimal regulatory strategies depend on understanding how fishing communities respond to restrictions and incentives, as well as on the modelled dynamics of fish populations. Hence, successful, sustainable fisheries depend critically on understanding the behaviour of both fish and human populations, and a scientific approach requires both natural and social science elements.[22]

Fish are, of course, not the only harvested natural resource where modelling has a value to sustainable policies. Box 7.6 gives an example of how the same approach can be used in the management of woodlands by the rural poor.

Box 7.6 Harvesting non-timber forest products[23,24]

From 2003 to 2006 the DFID Forest Research Programme funded a study to assess the sustainable harvesting of bark widely used as traditional medicine in southern Africa. The project covered miombo woodland in Malawi and Zambia and afromontane forest in South Africa and Malawi.

Bark is usually harvested by removing strips at regular intervals to allow for bark healing. Clearly, removing too much bark could kill the tree, but it is difficult to know exactly how much can be removed, and over what period of time. Researchers collected experimental data over a three year period, and developed detailed mathematical bark growth and volume models for the species in the study.

The results of this work gave the team a better understanding of optimal harvesting rates, and led to some novel recommendations. For some tree species wood exposed by bark removal is susceptible to insect attack that carries in fungal infections which can rapidly kill the tree.

It was found that for these species strip harvesting is unsustainable at any rate and a better method is to fell the tree and harvest all the bark at once and achieve sustainability by growing a new tree.

In order to clearly present results to policy makers in the region, the models were incorporated into decision-support structures like the one in Table 7.2. This table allows users to examine any species being considered for harvesting, and based on observed wound closure and pest attack, choose an appropriate harvesting method.

© Jenny Wong

Figure 7.12 – A roadside seller of herbal medicines outside a clinic in Zomba, Malawi. Most of the medicines are derived from miombo trees

	Fungal and/or insect attack		
	1 Major	2 Minor	3 None or neglible
None	Full tree harvesting	Full tree harvesting	Full tree harvesting
1 Poor	Full tree harvesting	Full tree harvesting	Marginal scope for strip harvesting[23]
2 Fair	Full tree harvesting	Marginal scope for strip harvesting[23]	Strip harvesting
3 Good	Marginal scope for strip harvesting[23]	Strip harvesting	Strip harvesting

(Wound closure)

Table 7.2 – Harvest method recommendations for tree species with different characteristics

Bark growth models were also used to make recommendations for the specific size and frequency of strip harvesting to use on species where this was determined sustainable (Table 7.3).

	Fungal and/or insect attack		
	1 Major	2 Minor	3 None or neglible
1 Poor			5cm strip 33 % of population
2 Fair		5cm strip 33 % of population	5-10cm strip 50 % of population
3 Good	5cm strip 33 % of population	5-10cm strip 50 % of population	10 cm strip 66 % of population

(Wound closure)

Table 7.3 – Strip harvesting recommendations for various tree conditions

Scientifically driven guidelines like these are now being used by the governments and NGOs in Malawi, Zambia and South Africa.

Modelling individual species, as is done for most natural resource models, is a relatively crude approach. We know that there are important interactions between species in ecosystems which are not captured in single species models. But modelling multi-species ecosystems is enormously complex. Recent advances in capturing and processing large amounts of environmental data will make this possible in the future. Scientific modellers also predict that improved modelling and computing technologies will allow us to add a more detailed, spatial dimension to modelling, and to model in "real time": measuring very recent environmental changes, feeding these data into models and generating predictions that allow us to take corrective measures immediately.

Finally, tomorrow's models will better integrate biological with economic elements, to provide powerful bio-economic tools for policy making, and to link the dynamics of resources with the economic value of the ecosystem services they deliver.

Putting a value on natural resources

A key contribution of the MA was to promote the concept of ecosystem services as a basis for putting a value on the sustainable management of natural resources. Valuing ecosystem services requires an integration of natural science and economics, and usually generates economic returns on different natural resource management options, from which the most appropriate policy can be derived. An example of this is shown in Box 7.7, for a tropical ecosystem in the Philippines.

Box 7.7   Valuing ecosystem services for forestry and fisheries[25]

On the Philippine island of Palawan in the 1980s, local communities of Bacuit Bay generated income from fishing and also tourism – as the Bay's coral reefs were popular with scuba divers. But increased erosion, and the flow of sediment into the bay from commercial logging in the surrounding highlands threatened fisheries and tourism income. Suspended sediment in the bay's water had a negative effect on the fish populations and on the survival of coral reefs. In effect, the processes which generated different ecosystem services to the community were closely inter-linked.

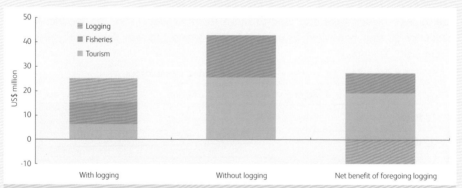

Figure 7.13 – Gross revenues over 10 years showing the benefits of foregoing logging in El Nido, Philippines[25]

As shown in Figure 7.13, an economic analysis of the value of the three ecosystem services: forestry, fisheries and tourism, estimated that the ten-year value of forestry was actually less than that of the other services combined, and that the value of fisheries and tourism without

---

logging would be even greater. Hence the net benefits of foregoing logging (third column) outweighed the benefits of logging. This analysis led the government to ban logging in the area and to declare Bacuit Bay a marine nature reserve.

It is unlikely this decision to conserve the biodiversity of Bacuit Bay would have been made without an economic analysis of ecosystem services. Fisheries recovered, but ironically their rapid growth led to over-fishing and a decline in coral reef fish, which impacted on the tourism industry. So the need to understand the ecological interactions in this ecosystem and to measure the economic value of its services has continued.

Synthesis – new platforms for policy development

The last decade has seen a dramatic increase in research on ecosystem services and the development of a range of practical tools. It has involved a convergence and synthesis of scientific approaches. The use of remote sensing has enabled geographical representations of natural resources and their monitoring in real time. This information has been incorporated into a sophisticated GIS, which can also incorporate spatial information on human populations and economic processes. As a result natural resources and their dynamics can now be mapped onto demand for the services they provide. Hot spots can be identified, where demand for ecosystem services is exceeding supply, requiring policies that reduce resource use and restore sustainable, self-renewing supply. Modelling methods can be applied to these spatially detailed data sets to predict the consequences of policies into the future for sustainable development and well-being.

So far, efforts to take this synthetic, geographical approach have been restricted largely to developed countries. One developing country example relates to an important ecosystem in Eastern Africa, comprising an arc of mountains stretching from Kenya across Tanzania, described in Box 7.8. Natural Capital Project is mapping the ecosystem services provided by these mountain ecosystems, estimating their value, and using the information to inform and finance investments in conservation and restoration of natural resources. This new approach seeks to answer previously intractable questions such as: which parts of a watershed should be preserved to provide the greatest collective benefit to carbon sequestration, biodiversity, and tourism? or where would reforestation or protection achieve the greatest downstream water quality benefits? Geographic systems for evaluating ecosystem services have policy value to both developed and developing countries. However, the need for their use is more urgent in developing countries where resource loss is most rapid and where populations are more dependent on ecosystem services for their livelihoods.

Box 7.8   "Valuing the Arc" – ecosystem service management in Tanzania[26-28]

One part of the Natural Capital Project focuses on valuing ecosystem services for the Eastern Arc Mountains in Tanzania. These mountains have an unique biology; resulting from millions of years of isolation from other African mountain systems, as well as a global conservation value. But they also constitute a development challenge. After decades of steady logging, fires and farmland conversion, the forested area on these mountains has been reduced by almost 70 %. Forests are now fragmented across 13 mountain blocks. The forests support local

© Ron Dunnington – Flickr

Figure 7.14 – African violets, *Saintpaulia* spp, one of the most popular house plants in the world, are restricted in nature to the Eastern Usumbara Mountains of Tanzania where, like many other unique species, they are threatened by deforestation

Figure 7.15 – The Eastern Arc Mountains stretch from Kenya to Western Tanzania[26]

villagers, supplying firewood, medicinal plants, lumber and meat, but they also serve as the watershed for half a dozen rivers flowing into populated regions of Tanzania. Not only do they maintain a fresh-water supply for more than three million people but they also provide more than 50 % of Tanzania's electricity through hydroelectric power.

The research project concentrates on mapping and providing economic values for a range of ecosystem services across the mountains, including: hydrological services; carbon sequestration; timber products; non-timber forest productions; ecotourism; pollination services; governance and biodiversity. Integrated in a GIS format, it will be possible to determine how future decisions, such as the creation of roads or changes in forest or water management, will affect all ecosystem services and the economic benefits to local livelihoods and other stakeholders.

Reducing biodiversity loss – a development issue?

It is relatively easy to put a value on ecosystem services that directly support human well-being by supplying essential resources like water, fuel and food, or generate income, like forestry or farming. But what about that parts of ecosystems, where there are literally millions of species that have no apparent direct benefit to human well-being? Does their conservation – by reducing biodiversity loss and species extinction – serve a development purpose or only an environmental one? Does "saving the tiger" really help to reduce poverty, hunger and disease?

MDG 7 includes reducing biodiversity loss, with specific indicators relating to increasing protected terrestrial and marine areas and reducing extinction rates, for two good reasons.

Firstly, the provision of valuable ecosystem services is closely linked to the activity of animals, plants and microbes in the ecosystem. This does not mean that every plant or bird or insect species is important to human livelihoods. The past few decades of ecological research have helped us to understand that most ecosystems contain some degree of redundancy, or overlap, between the functions of species in ecosystems that would allow a species to drop out without affecting ecosystem processes and, hence, services. But among the many thousands of species in any ecosystem, there will be some which are particularly important, often called 'keystone species', whose disappearance will change ecosystem function and services.

Box 7.9   The ecologist, Paul Ehrlich, described the phenomenon of species redundancy in ecosystems in 1981 with a now famous analogy:

"Ecosystems, like well-made airplanes, tend to have redundant subsystems and other 'design' features that permit them to continue functioning after absorbing a certain amount of abuse. A dozen rivets, or a dozen species, might never be missed. On the other hand, a thirteenth rivet popped from a wing flap, or the extinction of a key species involved in the cycling of nitrogen, could lead to a serious accident."[29]

However, we have still a poor understanding of which are the keystone species in different ecosystems. Indeed, we often discover this only after a species is eliminated and we suddenly lose an important ecosystem service, at which point a scientific 'hunting expedition' begins to discover the cause. For instance, in the 1980s when pesticide use in rice fields was initiated to protect the new, high-yielding rices of the Green Revolution, there was a region-

Figure 7.16 – A wolf spider, one of the keystone predators in Asian rice systems, devouring a brown plant hopper.

wide outbreak of a previously little known pest, the rice brown planthopper. Scientists had no idea why a pest control chemical had removed natural pest control as an ecosystem service, with such devastating results. After some years of ecological research it became apparent that the chemical pesticides were eliminating general predators in rice paddies, like spiders – keystone species in reducing pests on rice. Integrated pest management measures were then introduced which resolved this problem (see Box 5.5), but it was not until 1999 that it was fully understood why these predators were keystone species in rice, but not in other local crops.[30]

Biodiversity as a source of future innovation

Another reason why biodiversity conservation is an important influence in reducing poverty is that biodiversity has an inherent value as a source of future technologies – particularly for agriculture and health. Much of this valuable, but poorly understood, biodiversity is found in poorer regions of the world, particularly the subtropics and tropics. Understanding such useful biodiversity may benefit the poor by providing new, inexpensive and renewable crops and medicines.

Of course, the value of local species of plants and animals has often been long recognized by the indigenous population, who have fashioned them into traditional technologies such as herbal medicines. But modern science has the potential to greatly improve and extend the benefits of this biodiversity to the well-being of communities that have discovered its value and to people worldwide.

All of our crop plants and domestic animals are derived from wild species. Local races, or related wild relatives, still contain genes which have potential value to agricultural production in the future. But this biodiversity is at risk. As agricultural production intensifies, production systems select and rely on fewer and fewer species and varieties. This results in a loss of important genetic diversity that could be used to improve the nutritional value of food crops, protect them from unexpected new pests or help them adapt to changing environmental conditions.

For instance in 2007, there were a reported 7,616 breeds of livestock. Of these 20 % were classified as at risk of extinction, and since 2001, 640 breeds have become extinct.[31] For plants, we have seen over 90 % reduction in the number of different varieties of some crop species in the past century.[32] Protecting agricultural biodiversity in order to give us a variety of resources to address yet-unknown future needs is a most urgent priority. Box 7.10 illustrates an important recent response: establishing and maintaining a living collection of the world's key crop plants and their genetic diversity.

Box 7.10 The Global Crop Biodiversity Trust

In response to the disturbing trend of crop variety loss, the Global Crop Diversity Trust was established in 2004, "to ensure the conservation and availability of crop diversity for food security worldwide."[33] It supports germplasm collections around the world and established, in 2008, the Svalbard Global Seed Vault, which provides a permanent storage facility for crop biodiversity below the permafrost on Spitzbergen, an island in the Norwegian territory of Svalbard, in the Arctic Ocean. The seed collections are duplicates of national collections which can be replaced if lost.

© Gordon Conway

Figure 7.17 – The Svalbard Global Seed Vault

It is encouraging that between the 1996 and 2009 editions of the State of the World's Plant Genetic Resources reports, *ex situ* collections (e.g. those preserved as seeds in storage rather than as *in situ* living plants in the field) have increased by 20 % worldwide to reach 7.4 million accessions.

The Svalbard Global Seed Vault is a landmark undertaking in preserving future crop diversity. However, specialists agree that it is also crucial that crops, and their close relatives, which may carry beneficial traits for future breeding, are preserved *in situ*, that is, in the natural and agricultural habitats in which they have evolved and developed. The wild relatives of crops are often grown in areas that are particularly threatened by human activity. It has recently been estimated that 6 % of wild relatives of cereal crops (wheat, maize, rice, sorghum etc.) are under threat of extinction, as are 18 % of legume species (the wild relatives of beans, peas and lentils) and 13 % of species within the plant family that includes potato, tomato, eggplant, and pepper.[34]

What has just been said about the value of conserving natural biodiversity for future agricultural development applies equally to future improvements in health. Many wild plants contain chemicals of medicinal value. In many cases, their value is known locally, but is under-developed compared to their global potential for health improvement. For instance, *Artemisia annua*, a relative of the daisy found worldwide, has been used in China for over 2,000 years as a traditional herbal treatment for malaria. It was only in the 1970s that one of its chemical constituents, artemisinin, was developed as a modern drug and is now a key element of Artemisinin-based Combination Therapies (ACT) which underpin a new campaign for malaria control worldwide (see Chapter 6).

As with wild relatives of crop plants, much of this wild biodiversity of medical value is now threatened. *Catharanthus roseus* is a species of periwinkle, native to Madagascar, where habitat destruction has driven it to near extinction. Fortunately, it has been widely cultivated in other countries as an ornamental, and it is also used by some local communities for the treatment of diabetes. Some decades ago, the pharmaceutical company, Eli Lilly – while researching its medicinal properties – discovered the value of the periwinkle's constituent alkaloids, vincristine and vinblastine, in treating childhood leukemia and Hodgkin's Lymphoma. Today these are important, globally available cancer drugs.

The study of wild biodiversity and its potential global value to agriculture and medicine has involved many public and private sector organisations. Much of this work has been undertaken in developing countries, with their rich biodiversity. All too often, exploitation of this biodiversity has proceeded without benefit to the local communities where that biodiversity was found and conserved – communities which have often done much to recognise and develop its value through traditional technologies, such as herbal medicine. Exploitation of biodiversity in this way, without fair and equitable benefit sharing, is often called biopiracy. The inter-governmental Convention on Biological Diversity (CBD) came into force in 1993 with the aim of allowing developing countries to benefit from their biodiversity resources and traditional knowledge, by giving them more control over access to their local biodiversity and establishing agreed procedures for sharing benefits of its development, e.g. into new wonder drugs or super crops. However, the CBD and its member governments have made slow progress towards this goal, and "biopiracy" is still a concern.

Threats to biodiversity

The major threat to biodiversity conservation worldwide is habitat destruction. A major contributor is the extension of agriculture and commercial forestry into terrestrial natural habitats, while pollution from terrestrial habitats has a major impact on aquatic biodiversity. Habitat destruction is often associated with poverty, due to pressure that large, poor populations put on the environment, and particularly natural environments which are marginal for production. This problem is exacerbated by the strong geographical association that areas of particularly high biodiversity have with regions of high poverty. Over the past decade, scientists have identified biodiversity "hot spots", specific areas of the earth's surface which are particularly rich in biodiversity.[35]

Figure 7.18 – Pollution of a riverbed in Morocco

© Curt Carnemark – World Bank

The majority of the earth's terrestrial biodiversity is found in 34 biodiversity hot spots, comprising less than 2 % of the earth's land surface. The complete protection of these hot spots would preserve about 44 % of all plant species and about 35 % of vertebrate animal species. Figure 7.19 maps these global biodiversity hotspots. Each one is shaded according to its overlap with areas of high poverty. Darker shading means more hectares within the hotspot have high levels of undernourishment, economic poverty, poor access to clean water and high population pressure.[36,37] From this it is clear that many biodiversity hotspots are also areas of high poverty, where conservation of their rich biodiversity may bring local and global benefits.

Figure 7.19 – The 34 world biodiversity hot spots identified by Conservation International, shaded according to the area of these hotspots characterized as being under socio-economic poverty[37]

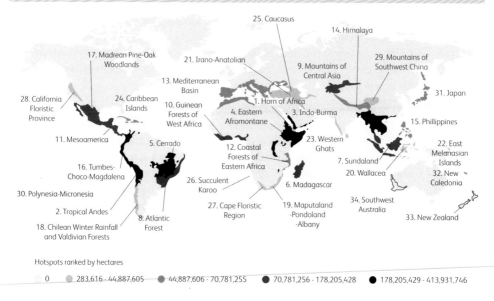

The second greatest threat to biodiversity loss, particularly in developing countries, arises paradoxically from the addition of species, not their removal. Alien plant and animal species, introduced by human activity into local ecosystems from ecosystems on other continents, will sometimes become invasive, dominating ecosystems and affecting biodiversity and ecosystem services.[38] In the Cape region of South Africa, for instance, a number of tree species, introduced for forestry, have invaded the highly sensitive native shrub vegetation, the fynbos. This highly localised flora comprises one of the world's six floristic kingdoms, comprising over 9,000 plant species, 6,400 of which are found nowhere else. In addition to threatening this unique biodiversity, invasive alien trees are drawing up water, reducing water supply for rural communities and threatening the water catchment area supplying Cape Town.

Managing alien species requires an understanding of their ecology, in order to find the best way of eliminating or containing their populations. Substantial success has been achieved, with benefits for both biodiversity conservation and poverty reduction. In South Africa, for instance, the Working for Water project has, since 1995, cleared more than one million hectares of invasive alien plants whilst at the same time providing jobs and training to approximately 20,000 people annually, from among the most marginalized sectors of society, of whom over 50 % are women.[39] Control of alien plants restores watersheds for these rural populations and nearby urban communities. Control methods range from traditional physical and chemical technologies, to innovative biological control methods that use specific natural enemies, parasites and pathogens of these plants to reduce their growth and spread.

4. Climate change mitigation

Perhaps the greatest contribution of science to the future of contemporary society has been the discovery and elucidation of the process of anthropogenic (human induced) climate change. The scientific method has been essential in establishing the convincing evidence base, without which, policy initiatives like the Kyoto Protocol would not have made progress. The scientific toolkits mentioned above for environmental measurement, monitoring, modelling and valuation, have been precisely those required to understand the problem of climate change and to evaluate measures to reduce its impact.

When the MDGs were created this scientific and policy process was only just underway. As a result climate change figures in only a handful of indicators under one target of MDG 7. Because of its importance, and particularly its relevance for international development, the next two chapters are devoted to the scientific evidence for climate change, its impacts on the poor and how developing countries can adapt.

In MDG 7 the indicator for climate change is carbon dioxide (CO_2) emissions – total, per capita, and per US$1GDP.

Over the past hundred years the bulk of emissions have been produced as a result of industrialisation and urbanisation. The developed countries have been mostly responsible for this along with, in recent decades, a growing contribution from newly emerging countries such as China and India who are undergoing rapid industrialisation. The less developed countries, on a country by country basis, have contributed relatively small amounts of GHGs to total global emissions. However, collectively they are a significant contributor, for instance through the processes of forest clearance and agricultural development.

It could be argued that mitigation measures, therefore, should be principally the responsibility of wealthy countries. Indeed, most initiatives on climate change and international development have focused on assisting less wealthy countries with adaptation to, rather than mitigation of, climate change as this is the significant challenge for poverty reduction.

Figure 7.20 – Traffic in Ho Chi Minh City

© Tran Thi Hoa – World Bank

However, mitigation will increasingly become an issue for developing countries as they industrialize. Figure 7.21 compares the per capita production of GHGs for different countries and relates this to their population size. In this figure a country's contribution is the size of its box. Therefore countries with low per capita production and large populations, such as China and India, make substantial contributions compared to highly industrialized countries with lower populations and high per capita consumption.

Figure 7.21 – Per capita production of greenhouse gases[40]

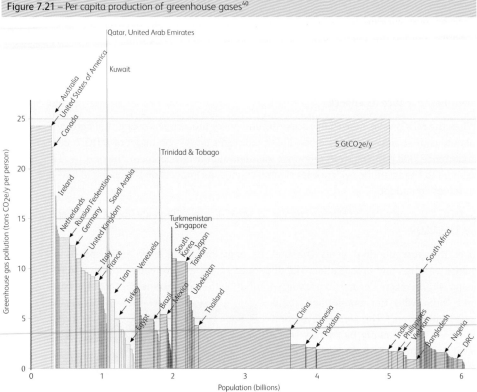

Emerging economies, such as China and India, are now responding rapidly to the challenge of climate change. The Chinese government announced in 2007 the 'Middle and Long-term Development Plan of Renewable Energies', promising to derive 10 % of national energy supply from renewables by 2010, and 15 % by 2020. While this is a large goal, they are on track to do so. For example, by doubling wind power capacity for the fifth year in a row in 2008, they have surpassed the 12GW wind target for 2010 two years early.[41]

India is also looking to increase its renewable energy capacity, under its national action plan on climate change. In August 2009 the government announced plans to boost solar energy production from the current 51 MW to 20,000 MW by 2020.[42] In both of these rapidly emerging nations, investment in this area not only helps to mitigate future environmental and climate damages, but also offers uniquely practical and efficient ways to supply electricity both to a growing number of businesses and urban consumers, and to the millions of households in remote rural areas.

For the billions of people in developing countries with no, or expensive and unreliable, electric grid connections, advances in renewable energy technologies can provide appropriate and flexible alternatives to conventional energy supplies. Scientific advances have the potential to, not only contribute to mitigating climate change and reducing fossil fuel dependence and pollution, but also to bring economic, health and broader development benefits.

Here, we look at examples of work being done on low-carbon energy production in the private, public and partnership realms, both in highly industrialized countries such as the US, Germany and Japan, as well as in China and India. We focus on science innovations which have the dual benefit of addressing greenhouse gas mitigation and potentially delivering cost effective energy alternatives to the poor. We draw on examples from solar and wind energy production, where scientists are looking at ways to harness more energy from these natural sources, and on energy production from biomass products such as wood, agricultural residues and plants where the challenge is to use the resource more effectively.

Harnessing the sun's energy

The sun is the most sustainable, plentiful and fundamental of all our energy sources. It makes sense to utilise it as an alternative to oil-based power and as a way for developing countries to 'leapfrog' existing energy options. Solar energy can be a cleaner, healthier, more flexible and cheaper technology.

Energy from the sun can be harnessed in two ways. The first is to concentrate the sun's energy using lenses or mirrors, heat up a liquid, and use the heat source to power an engine. The second, and more widely known method, is to use photovoltaic cells which directly convert solar energy to electricity. Both these applications have the potential to become important components in the global energy supply mix and new efforts to combine these two technologies are yielding even more efficient systems. Solar energy technology is now at the point where wind energy was a decade ago – poised to make big improvements.[43]

Concentrating solar thermal systems

Energy from the sun was first used to power a steam engine as early as 1866. Since then a wide variety of 'concentrating solar thermal' (CST) methods have been developed to capture and concentrate the sun's rays and use the resulting heat source to power irrigation, refrigeration, locomotion or even conventional power plants. The basic components of CST systems include: a receiving device, such as parabolic trough, dish or chimney, a tracking system to follow the sun, and a power generation system. Advances in all three areas are continually making these systems more efficient and practical (Box 7.11).

Box 7.11 New ways of concentrating the sun's energy

At the Sandia National Laboratories in New Mexico, more than a decade of steady improvements have yielded a highly productive receiver-engine configuration. Eighty two mirrors on 38 foot wide parabolic Stirling dish 'suncatchers' concentrate light onto a receiver at the dish's focal point, heating liquid which is used by a simple Stirling engine to generate power. The suncatchers produce a heat at the foci equivalent to 13,000 suns. Engineers are now looking at new ways to store the energy, incorporating thermal storage tanks to keep engines running after the sun has set.[44]

Designers have also found a way to expand mirror surface area and reduce cost, by using a series of long thin mirrors moving on a single axis instead of the more expensive parabolic shape. This type of collector, known as a Concentrating Linear Fresnel Reflector (CLFR), was used in the first large-scale CLFR plant which began commercial operations in Spain in 2009.[45,46]

Most CST systems are quite large, but the technology is modular and scalable, and can be used in a variety of situations. Groups such as Raw Solar[47] and STG International[48] have developed smaller, simple receiving systems, with the latter expanding into developing countries such as Lesotho.

© STG International

Figure 7.22 – A woman collects water next to a protype CST system installed by STG International, in Ha Teboho, Lesotho, which generates hot water from a second tap

Photovoltaics

Since the invention of the first 'solar cell' in the 1880s, made with selenium, it has been possible to directly convert solar energy to electricity, without the use of an intermediate engine. The sun's visible and UV radiation is powerful enough to knock electrons free from the atoms of particular materials, called semiconductors. This creates a useful direct electrical current, known as the photovoltaic effect. In 1954 Bell Labs in the US discovered that silicon was particularly sensitive to light, and developed the first practical solar cell, which was soon being used to power satellites in space.

© US Air Force

Figure 7.23 – 70,000 PV panels on the Nellis Air Force Base in Nevada, US generate 15MW of power

Photovoltaics (PV) are currently the fastest growing source of renewable energy, with capacity increasing at around 50 % per year.[43] The first solar cells were able to convert about 6 % of the sun's energy; new crystalline silicon cells now average around 18 % efficiency. The price of producing energy with PV has fallen but, until recently, was still a long way off from the target of 5 cents/kWh needed to compete with coal. With advances in established silicon technology, as well as the development of 'thin film' cells which use new materials, PV is set to become a viable competitor.[49] As stated in a 2008 issue of *Nature*, *'In the future, new manufacturing methods that use alternative materials should make the capture of sunlight at least an order of magnitude cheaper than it is now.'*[50]

Solar cells made from purified crystalline silicon have been the mainstay of PV technology since the 1950s, and while expensive, partly due to the competition from the high-value silicon-chip market, they have become highly efficient through years of development. SunPower in California, for example, has introduced a number of small innovations to make their single-crystal silicon cells the most efficient on the market, at about 22 %.[51] New entrants into the purified silicon production market, such as China, could also bring the price down considerably, making this established technology more competitive.[52]

Recently, a new type of photovoltaic technology has emerged in the form of *thin-film* solar cells (Box 7.12).

Box 7.12 Thin-film solar cells

Rather than using solid wafers which are generally around two tenths of a millimetre across, thin-film cells are only nanometres to a few micrometers thick, and are produced using cheaper, more flexible, although less efficient and shorter-lasting materials.

The first thin-film cells were produced by depositing vaporized silicon directly onto a glass or stainless steel substrate. New, slightly more efficient cells are now coming onto the market using materials such as cadmium telluride (CdTe), and combinations such as copper indium gallium diselenide (CIGS). New dye-sensitized and organic solar cells are also being researched, which could allow for even greater breakthroughs in customization, flexibility and cost. First Solar, currently the largest producer of thin-film cells in the US, is already producing CdTe cells on a large-scale, and there appear to be great opportunities for the new thin-film CIGS.[49]

Finally, promising work is being done in combining CST receivers with PV cells – using magnifiers to concentrate the sun's energy and focus it directly onto high-efficiency solar cells, in order to further enhance efficiency. The company SUNGRI, also based in California, has produced *'Extreme Concentrated Photovoltaic'* (XCPV) units. These systems can magnify the sun's rays 2,000 times, which when focused on a solar cell, achieve 37 % efficiency, and lower production costs to around the 5 cents/kWh target. In order to deal with the extremely high temperatures generated by the focused light, SUNGRI has incorporated a new cooling system to keep the panels operating safely. Although still in the early stages of development, advances like these are likely to succeed as research and development increase to keep up with demand.[43]

All of these new developments are making solar technologies an increasingly practical solution to providing energy to consumers in developing countries. The use of solar technologies, particularly

PV panels, has risen dramatically in the last few years, with production and use in China, for example, expanding rapidly. Many businesses and households across Africa are beginning to buy and sell PV panels and other small solar products. A number of non-profit groups are also working in this area, with the aim of fighting poverty and climate change simultaneously. The Solar Electric Light Fund (SELF)[53] began in 1990 in the US, the UK group SolarAid, was founded in 2006[54] and Lighting Africa, a joint International Finance Corporation and World Bank programme, works to support the private sector in developing off-grid lighting technologies tailored for African consumers.[55] Box 7.13 below looks at some of the projects being pursued by SolarAid.

Box 7.13 Bringing the solar business to the poor[54,56]

When the UK Solar Energy company Solarcentury was founded in 1998, the owner decided to donate 5% of its net profits to help the poorest communities access solar energy. When Solarcentury eventually netted profits in 2006, the charity SolarAid was formed.

SolarAid works by helping developing countries by-pass dirty and expensive fossil-fuelled energy options, and benefit from specially tailored solar powered technologies. The group brings the professional commercial sector knowledge from Solarcentury, emphasizing entrepreneurialism and innovation, to both its 'micro' and 'macro' solar approaches.

© Andy Bodycombe

Figure 7.24 – 'Sunnymoney' franchisee Moses Owiti demonstrates the panel he is selling in Kenya which can power a radio or LED light or charge a mobile phone

First, at the micro-level, SolarAid works with individuals to train them as entrepreneurs, teaching them about technical and business skills so that they can sell and repair products such as solar LED lights and solar chargers for radios and mobile phones. The technologies are simple – the light bulbs and chargers are powered through monocrystalline PV panels – and the products are mass produced cheaply and efficiently in China for the African market. The merchants make money, and the consumers save money which they would have spent on kerosene, disposable batteries, and travelling to access phone charging stations.

SolarAid also works at the more traditional macro-scale, working with communities to install PV panels on schools, health clinics, and community centres. By bringing electricity to these buildings many new opportunities emerge, including teaching at night and running televisions and computers, safe storage of vaccines and medicines in refrigerators, and the option for communities to run adult training classes, or just get-together in the evenings.

Energy from the wind

Humans have been harnessing the energy from wind for over 2,000 years, constructing simple windmills to grind grain and pump water. The first wind turbines built to directly convert the wind's kinetic energy into electricity were constructed as early as the late 1880's. These were used to charge batteries and run electric generators, mainly on farms and in other areas without access to

Figure 7.25 – A wind farm in Xinjiang, western China. The phrase on the tower reads "Xinjiang wind power company welcomes you"

grid power. In the last few decades, however, with a growing interest in finding alternative sources of energy, there has been renewed effort in improving turbine technology.

These efforts have resulted in great progress being made. Turbines have been developed which can achieve up to 50 % conversion efficiency, very close to the 59 % theoretical maximum.[57] Costs have been reduced to around eight cents per kilowatt-hour (kWh)[58], world wind power capacity is growing at around 30 % a year, and is predicted to reach around 3 % of world generation by 2012.[40,57] Engineers are continuously working to make turbines cheaper, more efficient, longer-lasting, more reliable and easier to produce and transport. They are tapping into new composite materials and looking at innovative designs which allow for larger, smarter blades which can flex with the wind. Advances are also being made in turbine placement – so that the wind can be used to its maximum.[57,58]

Today wind turbines are commonly built using tall steel towers (200-300ft), with three large (20-40m), light blades, made from glass-reinforced plastics, pointed into the wind by computer-controlled motors. The blades capture the wind energy and convert it to low-speed rotational energy – which is then fed into a gearbox and converted into high speed energy which can be used to power an electric generator. Average turbine capacity is now around 2MW and turbines are often grouped together on wind farms in suitable areas.

Wind power has a number of advantages. It is clean and renewable. It can also be added to on a piecemeal basis. One turbine, of any size, can be used for a small project, whilst for larger projects, turbines can be added one-by-one as time and funding allows. Designers are also developing increasingly diverse and tailored machines, using both horizontal and vertical axis turbines, and ranging from the very small (50W), to the very large (a 10MW off-shore turbine). With new technologies wind power is now becoming cheaper and more efficient – turbines can now be effective with wind speeds as low as four metres per second, making them a practical proposition in many more areas.[59]

Currently, wind turbine production is focused in a select group of countries (the top five producing countries are Denmark, the US, Germany, Spain and India). China is also rapidly developing capacity in this area, with 45% of China's 3.4GW of wind installation in 2007 being supplied by domestic producers.[60] The biggest challenge to other countries wishing to take advantage of this technology is the transportation of the large amounts of material needed to construct the turbines. Nevertheless, many developing countries are making the investment, with significant installations in India, Egypt, Morocco and Kenya – where the wind turbines help to power homes, schools, and businesses.[61]

The development of smaller turbines is also proving very promising. These are used to perform tasks such as pumping water for drinking or irrigation, or charging car batteries for use as household electric supplies. A number of small non-profit groups have started working in this area. These include the Clean Energy Initiative working in Mozambique, the German group Green Step installing turbines in Cameroon, the group Blue Energy working on solar-wind hybrid systems on the Caribbean coast of Nicaragua and Wind Aid in Peru. Practical Action, a UK charity which focuses on developing appropriate technologies, is also working on micro-turbines in both Asia and South America as one of its many energy-related programmes (Box 7.14).

Box 7.14 Small-scale wind power in developing countries[59,62,63]

Rural families in developing countries all face a similar challenge – powering their homes without access to the grid. Many use car batteries, which they pay to have charged at businesses in nearby towns or cities, to run lights, televisions and radios. Kerosene lamps are also very popular, and solar panels are slowly being introduced to the mix.

In the late 1990s the non-profit group Practical Action started working in two countries, Peru and Sri Lanka, where many households use car batteries for electricity. Here they typically spend around 8% of their income, travelling from one to two hours to reach a charging station. For those even farther away from a town, this was not even an option. With funding from DFID, Practical Action has worked with communities to design, test and pilot small-scale wind generators, which villages can use to power batteries – without the need to travel.

© Practical Action

Figure 7.26 – One of 32 100W small wind turbines being installed in 'El Alumbre' in the north Andes of Peru. Three of the individuals shown were trained to install, operate and maintain the systems.

The turbines are small, with eight to ten metre tall steel towers, and three 0.7 metre-long fibreglass blades. Outfitted with permanent magnet generators the turbines average around 100W of generating capacity which, under the five metres per second average winds of Sri Lanka, is enough to keep around ten households regularly charged. The machines have been designed so that local small enterprise groups can construct them, and they are installed and maintained by the users themselves.

The machines currently cost around US$700, about one third of the cost of an equivalent machine constructed in an industrialised country, and are estimated to last for about 20 years. They are competitive with other alternatives, with the cost per kWh being the same or cheaper than diesel or solar. They also have the added benefits of saving time on travelling, encouraging local ownership and enterprise, and of course, acting as a clean and safe source of off-grid energy.

Over the years the technology has caught on, with over 100 units installed in different parts of Peru, including 34 solar-wind hybrid systems installed by the government. The idea has also spread to both Bolivia and Ecuador, and in Asia from Sri Lanka to Nepal.

Using biomass for fuel

Biomass, or any organic material which can be used for energy production, was the first source of energy used by humans, in the form of wood for heat and cooking, and it remains an important component of global energy production today. Green plant material is a valuable source of stored chemical energy, converted by the plants from the sun, through the process of photosynthesis.

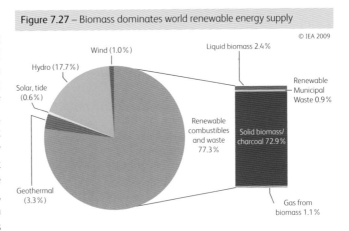

Figure 7.27 – Biomass dominates world renewable energy supply

© IEA 2009

Wind (1.0 %)

Liquid biomass 2.4 %

Hydro (17.7 %)

Solar, tide (0.6 %)

Renewable Municipal Waste 0.9 %

Renewable combustibles and waste 77.3 %

Solid biomass/ charcoal 72.9 %

Geothermal (3.3 %)

Gas from biomass 1.1 %

Biomass fuels include: woodfuels such as wood, charcoal and forestry residues, which are the most common, energy crops such as sugar and cereals, oil crops such as soya and *jatropha*, and agricultural and livestock by-products, such as stalks, straw and manure. These fuels may be produced as solids (e.g, charcoal), liquids (e.g. alcohol, biodiesel) or gases (e.g. methane). Bioenergy, then, is defined as any energy produced directly from biomass, and is considered a renewable energy source – as long as the materials are harvested sustainably, replaced, or grown for the specific purpose of energy production.

Since the industrial revolution most developed countries have used less and less biomass for energy production. However in recent years, with an increasing move to lower carbon alternatives, bioenergy – especially the growing of crops for the production of fuel for transport – has gained in popularity. Currently, bioenergy accounts for about 9 % of global primary energy supply, although there is a large variation between regions. As of 2001 developed countries obtained only about 5 % of their energy from biomass, while developing countries averaged around 22 %, with Asia at 19 % and Sub-Saharan Africa at 60 %.[64] In rural areas of developing countries, the figure is often as high as 90 % to 95 %.[65,66] This is the largest used source of renewable energy both globally and in developing countries, dwarfing the still growing hydroelectric (2.2 % of global supply), wind (0.125 %), solar and tide (0.075 %), and other renewable industries (Figure 7.27).[67]

Using more biomass for energy holds potential for billions of people without access to electricity or improved cooking fuels. The challenge, however, is to make energy production from biomass sources more sustainable and efficient: causing less GHG emissions and ideally acting as an additional source of income and enterprise. And, where crops are grown specifically for energy production, it is necessary to ensure that they do not compete with food production or distort food prices in ways which harm the poor.

A number of groups have recently formed to work towards this goal, some with a specific emphasis on developing country needs. The FAO, for example, works to support countries in strengthening their capacity to implement bioenergy programmes through assessing project potentials and reviewing policy options.[68] FAO is leading both the recently formed Bioenergy and Food Security (BEFS) project, which evaluates food security concerns relating to bioenergy,[69] and the International Bioenergy Platform (IBEP) – an attempt to bring together partners to address technical, policy and institutional questions.[70] The UN also launched the Global Bioenergy Partnership (GBEP) in 2005 to unite public, private and civil society stakeholders in promoting *'wider, cost effective, biomass and biofuels deployment, particularly in developing countries where biomass is prevalent.'*[71]

Below the issue is broken down into two areas – the household use of biomass for cooking and heating, and the larger-scale production of bioenergy for electricity or transport.

Household use of biomass

About three billion people rely on solid biomass fuels such as wood, coal and dung for cooking. Harvesting wood for stoves and for charcoal production degrades surrounding forests if it is not done sustainably. This leads not only to a decline in environmental health and an increase in soil erosion, but it also increases the time that women must spend searching for fuel.

In addition, the smoke released by these fuels, when burnt inside homes, more than doubles the risk of respiratory illnesses, such as bronchitis and pneumonia, leading to around 1.6 million deaths per year.[72] Rural women and children are the most at risk.

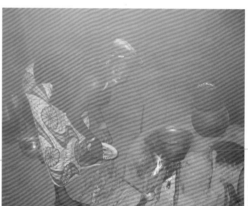

Figure 7.28 – A woman cooks dinner in her smoky kitchen in rural Mali

© Sara Delaney

There are a number of interventions that can be effective in reducing indoor air pollution, including improving fuels, reducing the time needed for heating food and technologies which improve the cooking devices themselves. Studies have shown that the health and productivity gains from these types of improvements are a good economic value.[73]

Switching from biomass to more efficient fuels, such as kerosene, Liquefied Petroleum Gas (LPG) and biogas, provides the greatest reduction in indoor smoke. While kerosene and LPG are usually expensive, biogas can be produced from cow dung mixed with water. Simple biogas units can anaerobically ferment the mixture and produce a gas which is 65 % methane, this can then be used directly for cooking or energy production.[74]

Improvements can also be made on cooking tools and stoves themselves, through simple modifications such as adding insulation, or more radical attempts to use advances in technology to create new ways of cooking altogether (Box 7.15).

Box 7.15 Improved stove designs

In many rural communities there is still limited access to alternative fuels. In these places, better stoves can reduce indoor smoke levels considerably.[72] On a simple level, cooking over open fires can be improved by constructing better insulated, mud stove structures around the pots. Practical Action in the UK has also developed a solution called the "fireless cooker." After cooking food on a traditional stove, the food is transferred to a simple basket, that is insulated with local resources such as banana leaves or old clothes and covered with dry heat-resistant polythene. The food then continues to cook over a long period of time using stored heat. This can reduce fuel use by 40 %, and save time in collecting fuel.[75]

© Bharat Pradhan – Practical Action

Figure 7.29 – A woman uses an adapted SCORE stove in Nepal

A more ambitious attempt to improve stove design is the SCORE (Stove for Cooking, Refrigeration and Electricity) project. This project uses thermoacoustic technology, to convert biomass into electrical energy to power a stove, refrigerator and generator. Heated air from the burning biomass is sent through a resonating pipe, producing sound as it cools, which can then be converted to electricity using a device similar to a 'loudspeaker working backwards'. The amount of wood or dung that is needed to cook is halved when compared with an open fire, fewer pollutants are produced, and waste energy can be used for lighting or charging batteries. The work builds on research by Los Alamos, NASA and the US military to develop engines and refrigerators for a range of applications including the cooling of satellite systems. The SCORE research team, which comprises representatives from a number of universities in London and the charity Practical Action, aims to develop stoves that are acceptable technologically, economically and socially. They also want to ensure that there is scope for communities to set up businesses around the development of the SCORE stoves. Stoves are currently being developed and tested in Kenya and Nepal.[76]

Biomass for energy production

While communities in the developing world are already using biomass for household energy, new technologies are being developed which will open up opportunities for larger-scale and more sustainable energy production. Biomass can be used as a substitute for fossil fuels to generate heat, power, or transport fuel, either for an individual village, or an entire region. While fossil fuels are expensive and difficult to transport to rural areas, biomass materials, such as non-crop plants and agricultural residues are generally readily available in communities. Both non-crop and crop plants can also be grown specifically for energy production. In addition, bioenergy projects can lead to increased opportunities for employment and income-generation within communities.

There are a large variety of established technologies for converting various sources of biomass feedstock to energy. Depending on the feedstock source available, either thermal or biochemical processes can be used and the number of options are continuously growing. For example, wood or other solid fuels, such as agricultural residues, can be converted using simple combustion to produce heat which can be captured, or through gasification, where the fuel is partially burned at a high temperature to produce a synthetic gas. Manure and other animal or vegetable waste, can be converted using the biochemical process of anaerobic digestion, where the organic materials are broken down by microbial activity in the absence of air and at slightly elevated temperatures. This produces biogas (60% methane and 40% CO_2), which can be used for cooking or lighting, fuel or electricity generation using modified gas engines or turbines.

Of growing popularity is the use of sugar and starch crops for the production of fuel called bioethanol. Sugar crops, such as sugar cane, sugar beet and sweet sorghum, and starch crops, such as maize and cassava can be grown and converted using fermentation methods. The feedstock is ground, the sugar is dissolved out and then fed to yeast in a closed, anaerobic chamber. The yeast ferments the sugar to produce ethanol which is then distilled to produce bioethanol. This can be used on its own in specialised combustion engines, or mixed with petrol. There are however drawbacks to this method, including the competition it places on land which could otherwise be used to grow food-crops, and the inefficiency of the conversion process.

Finally, oils such as animal fats, waste cooking oil, or those derived from rapeseed, sunflower, soya, palm, or coconut can all be converted through a process called transesterification. The oil is reacted with an alcohol and a base catalyst splits the oil into glycerine and methyl esters forming biodiesel. The biodiesel can then be used as fuel in a diesel engine. Engines can also be modified to run on less purified forms of oil, such as straight vegetable oil (SVO) or the oil from the seeds of plants such as *Jatropha curcas*, described in Box 7.16 below.

Box 7.16 Jatropha powered rural electrication in Mali[77]

In the Garalo commune in southern Mali, 33 villages have successfully united in a local energy production project. The area is using oil from the seeds of the shrub *Jatropha curcas* to power a hybrid power plant, which has the capacity to serve a 13km wide network of households.

Jatropha, known as *bagani* in Mali, is an inedible perennial shrub which grows widely across the country, thriving in poor soils with little water. The small tree is often planted as a 'natural fence' around crop fields, because its smell and taste repels grazing animals. The Royal Tropical Institute estimates that there are currently more than 22,000 linear kilometres of the bush in Mali.[78] Jatropha is a long-term investment – while seed production starts within six to nine months, the plant does not reach maturity for five years, and will remain in constant production for up to 25 years, and can live for up to 50 years.[79]

The seeds of jatropha can be pressed to yield a high-quality oil, due to their 32% oil content, 3kg of seed will yield about 1 litre of oil. The seeds are pressed using a locally manufactured machine, which itself is powered by jatropha oil – the energy used to press the nuts amounts to less than 10% of the oil obtained. The residues from the seeds are higher in nitrogen and phosphorous than cow dung, and so act as an excellent organic fertiliser that can be used on other food crops or sold.

Experimenters discovered in the early 1990s that jatropha oil could be used to power diesel engines, but at the time diesel prices were low, and switching over did not make economic sense. Now, with oil prices rising, and a commitment by the Malian government to increase

© Wikimedia commons/Immersia

Figure 7.30 – *Jatropha curcas*

renewable energy use, jatropha-powered energy production is gaining in popularity. The oil is being used to power small-scale generators for a wide-variety of uses, as shown in the *Energiebau* example in Chapter 3. In Garalo, however, project leaders are scaling-up this idea quite dramatically.

Initiated by the Mali Folke Centre (MFC)[80] in 2006, the Garalo project in rural electrification is funded by the FACT Foundation,[81] a Dutch group that promotes the use of biofuels for local development, and *Stichting het Groene Woudt* (SHGW), another Dutch NGO. A government-supported grant from AMADER, a parastatal company in charge of rural electrification, is also used to reduce household tariffs.

The team has worked with the local community to increase jatropha production in the region. Farmers are intercropping jatropha with their normal crops and on land previously used for increasingly less profitable cotton production. As of 2008 they had 600 hectares under production, but they are eventually hoping to be working on up to 10,000 hectares. The jatropha nuts are harvested by the farmers, processed by the local cooperative using the oil press, and the oil is then sold to the local power company ACCESS at an agreed price.

ACCESS is running a 300kW capacity vegetable oil-diesel hybrid power plant. The group is starting with a 5% jatropha oil blend and plans to slowly scale-up to 100% by 2013 as jatropha production increases. The power is then sold back to connected households in the area. As of April 2009, 283 connections had been set up, which puts the plant at about 23% capacity. Around ten new connections are being added each month, with 90% recovery of bills reported.[82] While the project is still in the beginning stages, all of the necessary institutional connections and agreements are in place for a project which will not only bring electricity, but will also generate income for the community.

© R. K. Henning – www.jatropha.org

Figure 7.31 – Extracting oil from jatropha seeds using a press

A number of challenges need to be addressed in order to move to successful and sustainable use of biomass for large-scale production. These include: competition with food production, the need for stable land ownership due to the long-term commitment needed, and technical and market support for the production process. Some of these needs are being addressed through new conversion technologies, including second-generation bioethanol and biodiesel which will enable synthesis of previously unusable plant products. This will make processing cheaper and easier. Lessons are also being learned and documented as current projects progress, which will help in the development of more appropriate institutional and policy support.

5. Water supply and sanitation

Despite its critical importance to international development, and its scarcity in many poor countries, there is no headline MDG for water. In MDG 7, the subject is split between water resource conservation, as one of a number of natural resources for conservation and restoration, and the specific target of sustainable access to safe drinking water and basic sanitation. This division reflects a long-standing split of research in this area between ecologists and hydrologists, who address the generation and distribution of water resources arising from catchments, and engineers and health specialists who have a specific interest in the supply of clean, safe water and sanitation to communities.

Needless to say, this historical division of effort on water issues is rather artificial. Watersheds must be managed to supply water sustainably to a wide range of stakeholders, not just households with their needs for safe water for drinking, washing and cooking, but to agriculture and industry as well. This challenge of sharing a limited resource across a range of societal needs cannot be achieved without good water governance, at the local, national and international level. As with other elements of MDG 7, improvements in policy are key to making progress, and science innovation can support this process by providing tools for monitoring, measuring and valuing, and in some cases by developing new enabling technologies. However, many of the technologies required for addressing the water needs of the poor, from pumps to filters, are already available and only need deployment.

Bearing in mind the overriding need for good water governance, the specific demand for clean water for drinking and sanitation enjoys a high profile because of its implications for human health. Water and sanitation are intimately linked. Poor sanitation, and particularly the spread of disease from person to person by contact with excrement, is mediated by the availability and sources of water for drinking and washing in many communities. The available data suggests that 884 million people currently lack access to safe water and 2.5 billion to basic sanitation.[83] About 1.5 million children die each year due to diarrhoea, primarily caused by unsafe drinking water and inadequate hygiene and sanitation. This is equivalent to 170 child deaths from diarrhoea per hour.[84]

Indeed, it will be virtually impossible to achieve the infant and maternal mortality targets of the MDGs without improving poor people's access to safe water and sanitation facilities. In addition, the need to collect water, and the absence of toilet and sanitary towel disposal facilities have negative impacts on girls' attendance at school, thus hampering progress towards the universal primary education and gender equality targets. Water supply and sanitation therefore represent an important point of leverage for several of the MDGs.

Figure 7.32 – A young woman pulls water from a well in Mali

In order to achieve the water and sanitation targets, as of 2005, about 175,000 people needed to gain access to safe water and 350,000 people to basic sanitation every day until 2015.[85] However, it is now clear that at current rates of progress, this water target will not be achieved in many countries in Sub-Saharan Africa and the sanitation target will be missed in both Africa and Asia by 700 million people.[83]

The reasons for this are diverse and many relate to governance and institutions. Water and sanitation are generally not given a high priority in government. Demand for sanitation is not always clearly expressed and its implementation involves infrastructure and service, as well as hygiene promotion programmes. Responsibilities for different parts of the problem may lie in different ministries, which makes progress slow, while different donors and development agencies frequently take an individual approach within a given country.[86]

Donor assistance for water and sanitation has been steadily increasing since 2001,[87] as has political support for the sector. The UN's Water Supply and Sanitation Collaborative Council (WSSCC) launched the Global Wash Campaign in 2004,[88] 2008 was designated the International Year of Sanitation[89] and the Global Sanitation Fund was opened the same year. However, aid in this sector is often poorly targeted, with only about 24% going to Sub-Saharan Africa.[90]

Supply of clean water

Infrastructure is a key constraint to water supply, particularly in rural areas, where 70% of the people live without clean water and 70% have inadequate sanitation. Extensive research in recent decades has led to a range of intermediate technologies which are relatively low cost, easy to maintain and appropriate to local, social, financial and geographical conditions in the developing world.

Figure 7.33 – Water from a community tap in Sri Lanka

Institutions like Water Aid promote a portfolio of technologies for water sourcing and provide guidance to help communities select and build the most appropriate technology for their needs, whilst encouraging and supporting the development of new technologies (Figure 7.34).[91]

Figure 7.34 – The wide range of proven technologies to increase the supply and quality of water for the rural poor. They represent largely intermediate technologies, developed by integrating innovative science and an understanding of local conditions and resources[92]

	Water source	Capital cost	Running cost	Yield	Bacteriological water quality	Situation in which technology is most applicable
	Spring protection	Low or medium if piped to community	Low	High	Good if spring catchment is adequately protected	Reliable spring flow required throughout the year
	Sand dams	Low – local labour and materials used	Low	Medium/High – depending on method used to abstract water. Water can be abstracted from the sand and gravel upstream of the sand dam via a well or tubewell	Good if area upstream of dam is protected	Can be constructed across seasonal river beds on impermeable bedrock
	Sub surface dams	Low – local labour and materials used	Low	Medium/High – depending on method used to abstract water. Water can be abstracted from the sand, gravel or soil upstream of the sub-surface dam via a well or tubewell	Good if area upstream of dam is protected	Can be constructed in sediments across seasonal river beds on impermeable bedrock
	Infiltration galleries	Low – a basic infiltration gallery can be constructed using local labour and materials	Low	Medium/High – depending on method used to abstract water	Good if filtration medium is well maintained	Should be constructed next to lake or river
	Rainwater harvesting	Low – low cost materials can be used to build storage tanks and catchment surfaces	Low	Medium – dependent on size of collection surface and frequency of rainfall	Good if collection surfaces are kept clean and storage containers are well maintained	In areas where there are one or two wet seasons per year
	Hand-dug well capped with a rope pump	Low	Medium – spare parts required for pump	Medium	Good if rope and pump mechanisms are sealed and protected from dust. Area around well must be protected	Where the water table is not lower than six metres – although certain rope pumps can lift water from depths of up to 40 metres
	Hand-dug well capped with a hand pump	Medium	Medium – spare parts required for pump	Medium	Good if area around well is protected	Where the water table is not lower than six metres
	Tube well or borehole capped with a hand pump	Medium – well drilling equipment needed. Borehole must be lined	Medium – hand pumps need spare parts	Medium	Good if area around borehole/tubewell is protected	Where a deep aquifer must be accessed
	Gravity supply	High – pipelines and storage/flow balance tanks required	Low	High	Good if protected spring used as source	Stream or spring at higher elevation – communities served via tap stands close to the home
	Borehole capped with electrical/diesel/solar pump	High – pump and storage expensive	High – fuel or power required to run pump. Fragile solar cells need to be replaced if damaged	High	Good if source is protected	In a small town with a large enough population to pay for running costs
	Direct river/lake abstraction with treatment	High – intake must be designed and constructed	High – treatment and pumping often required. Power required for operation	High	Good following treatment	Where large urban population must be served
	Reverse osmosis	High – sophisticated plant and membranes required	High – power required for operation. Replacement membranes required	High	Good	Where large urban population must be served
	Household filters	High – certain filters can be expensive to purchase/produce	Filters can be fragile. Replacement filters can be expensive or difficult to source	Low	Good as long as regular maintenance is assured	In situations where inorganic contaminants are present in groundwater sources or protected sources are not available
	SODIS (solar disinfection)	Low – although clear bottles can be difficult to source in remote areas.	Low	Low	Good	In areas where there is adequate sunlight – water needs to be filtered to remove particulate matter that may harbour pathogens before SODIS can be carried out effectively. SODIS is not appropriate for use with turbid water

☐ = most preferable   ☐ = preferable   ☐ = least preferable

While most appropriate technology for supplying clean water to poor populations is based on conventional and intermediate technologies, advances in nanotechnology may provide dramatic breakthroughs in clean water supply in the future. As discussed in Chapter 2, this new platform technology is finding application in the design of filters to remove disease causing agents and toxic chemicals from water. The technology relies on the unique properties that materials have at the extremely small, nano (one millionth of a millimetre) level. For polluted water, there are a number of approaches. Nanomembranes are manufactured with holes that allow water through, but not larger molecules of toxic chemicals, or much larger viruses or bacteria. Carbon nanotubes provide a similar barrier, trapping all but the small molecules that can pass through the tubes. Some natural attapulgite clays and zeolites have nano properties and can be used in nanofilters. Another approach is to produce nanoparticles which can be placed in water, where they bind with chemical pollutants and can then be removed. Magnetized nanoparticles, for instance, can be removed from water with a magnet, once they have bound target pollutants. Finally, nanocatalysts are materials that facilitate the breakdown of toxic substances in water. Their nano size makes them particularly active.[93]

Nanotechnology has many potential applications in water purification, from removing micro-organisms, to removing chemicals such as arsenic, which is a major problem in groundwater in South Asia and other regions, and pesticides and other chemicals from waters used in industry. A similar approach can be used to desalinate sea water for human consumption. South Africa, India and China have all invested heavily in nanotechnology research for water purification, as have many companies in wealthy countries. The cost of nanomaterials is a limiting factor in the application of these technologies but further research may reduce these.

Sanitation

While there are many challenges to realizing MDG 7 targets for water supply, the current situation for sanitation is worse because the challenge has attracted less attention than water provision. Here again, the appropriate technologies exist to build latrines which will reduce open defecation and thereby address one of the major sources of diarrhoeal diseases and other illnesses. In rural areas, various designs of pit latrine can remove both faeces, and the fly vectors of faeces-borne pathogens, from communities. In urban areas, the technical challenge is to provide latrines capable of managing high volumes of

Figure 7.35 – Toilet facilities like these do not inspire use

faeces, which would normally require a capacity for sewage removal where sewers are not available. Like water sourcing, sanitation technologies have substantial up-front costs for poor communities, to which governments in developing countries have generally not been directing sufficient resources.

While there has been more effort in recent years to improve global sanitation by increasing the number of households who have access to an adequate toilet or latrine, this is only part of the equation. People will decide where they defecate based on a wide range of factors, including distance, privacy, comfort, smell, cultural norms, and often lastly, perceived benefits to individual and community health. Having access to a latrine – particularly if it is not private or clean – does not guarantee use. In rural areas, many people find it more pleasant, and culturally acceptable, to defecate outside. In urban areas however, the problem is often lack of effective facilities.

The challenges here are broad. On the technical side it is important to ensure that facilities are being designed which not only provide the necessary health benefits, but also respond to the desires of consumers.

For millions of urban households worldwide one of the challenges of using a pit latrine which is not connected to a sewer network, is emptying the latrine. For years, families in both rural and urban areas have done this task manually – either doing it themselves or hiring others – and usually dumping the excreta in uninhabited areas or using it as compost for fields. In the developing world as a whole, around 90 % of sewage is discharged, untreated, into rivers, causing pollution, contaminating drinking water and harming aquatic life.[94]

Figure 7.36 – The slum area of 'Favela' on the outskirts of Salvador de Bahia in Brazil

© Scott Wallace – World Bank

Growing urbanisation is now confounding this problem, with millions migrating to cities, often in unplanned urban settlements, or slums, each year. They are all constructing houses and latrines which are not connected to any waste treatment facility. And, in such crowded areas, manual emptying becomes not only hygienically dangerous to those doing the job, but to all those around, and finding a place to dump the waste becomes increasingly difficult. As population density increases, it also becomes less feasible to cover a pit, dig a new one and construct a new structure, notwithstanding the cost of doing so. Urban inhabitants are therefore forced to either resort to open defecation, or use increasingly crowded shared facilities.

All of this adds up to a huge environmental and health problem. While some work has gone into the development of toilets, very little has been done to address the problems of pit emptying and waste disposal. Conventional vacuum tankers, which are used for this purpose, cannot operate in the narrow and crowded slum settlements, and thus attempts have been made to modify their design. In 1988 the Dutch NGO, WASTE, piloted a miniaturized, manually operated version of a tanker called MAPET in Dar es Salaam, Tanzania. However, it never really took-off because of the cost (£950) and a number of organisational problems. In 1995 an Irish engineer, Manus Coffey, working with UN-Habitat, developed a similar product powered by a gasoline engine, called the Vacutug. This had some success in the slums of Kibera in Kenya. However, the tanker is expensive (~£4,500) to both construct and operate, and while it has been moderately successful, the team has encountered problems with cost-recovery and manoeuvring the tanker in crowded areas.[95,96]

A researcher at the London School of Hygiene and Tropical Medicine (LSHTM), Steven Sugden, saw the need for a simple technology to fill the gap between tankers (of any size) and manual diggers. Box 7.17 describes the inexpensive hand-pump he helped to develop and pilot in Dar es Salaam, and how this has spurred further innovation in the field.

Box 7.17 The Gulper – filling a gap in urban sanitation[95,96]

Looking to introduce a new technology into the limited range of latrine-emptying machines, Sugden approached Steven Ogden, an agricultural engineer and farmer in Yorkshire. They came up with the 'Gulper,' a direct action hand pump adapted from water pump principles. The Gulper fits into the hole in the latrine slab, and with one or two operators it brings the sludge out through an outlet pipe and into a container. Importantly, the Gulper is relatively cheap (~£55 manufacturing price in Dar es Salaam), durable, small, portable, and can be constructed with local materials.

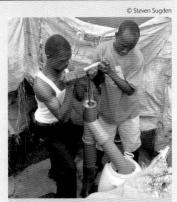
© Steven Sugden

Figure 7.37 – The Gulper in use in Dar es Salaam

Trialling of the product began in Dar Es Salaam in 2007, a city with a population of 2.8 million, only 10 % of which is served by sewers. This causes wide-spread health problems. In 2006, 60 to 80 % of the city's hospital cases, and 97 % of out-patients at health centres, were suffering from sanitation related diseases. In an attempt to reduce this huge problem, a group from WaterAid and LSHTM set up local, small-scale entrepreneurs with Gulpers, which they can use to empty customer's latrines, and then transport full containers, on the back of motorcycle based tractors, to the city's waste treatment plant.

Results have been positive, with local people saying they like using the services of the Gulper operators. And although the cost is still relatively high, (around £2 to remove 50 litres), it is cheaper than building a new latrine, and it is 'quick and clean.' The biggest limitation is the inability of the Gulper to cope with the denser, compacted sludge at the bottom of pits – as this requires more power to lift. Thus, at the moment, the Gulpers are only dealing with the top 70cm of waste.

Continued innovation is required, and Sugden and Ogden have recently developed a new model called the 'Nimbler'. This is based on the rope and washer pulling method used in the 'Elephant' water pumps.[97] The pump is able to draw up thicker sludge and is also constructed entirely from locally available materials such as bicycle parts.

Sugden says that while neither the Gulper nor the Nimbler may be the final product needed to address the issues in Dar es Salaam, or other cities, he thinks that this work may have helped to 'catalyse' work in an area which had been static for decades. International meetings on the subject are beginning to take place, with UN-Habitat, OXFAM and other NGOs increasingly recognising the importance of addressing the full cycle of sanitation management and supporting the development of the technology needed.

The final target of MDG 7 is to reduce the number of people living in urban slums. We will not discuss this target in detail here, but would note that the four key challenges for improving the lives of slum dwellers are to improve water, sanitation, living space and building tenure and durability. So far, science innovation has found particular application with the first two, water and sanitation, as discussed above.

6. Conclusion

The relationship between the environment and development has a complex and sometimes strained history, particularly with respect to economic growth. Scientific and technological advances in agricultural production, public health, and other areas, have often had negative environmental consequences. The incorporation in the MDGs of environmental targets is therefore significant. While some targets of MDG 7 lack the clarity needed to focus effective action, they make an important first step in integrating environmental targets into a framework for development.

For agriculture and health, as we have seen, recent scientific innovation has focused largely on the development of new technologies which will directly benefit the poor. For MDG 7, the contribution of science innovation is rather different. The importance of policy to environmental sustainability, and the need for environmental mainstreaming, has stimulated the development of scientific tools for policy making, specifically earth observation, modelling and GIS technologies. Perhaps most importantly, through the concept of ecosystem services, science has given policy making the tools it needs to value the environment so that it can be explicitly incorporated in development goals and programmes.

The importance of science and innovation to policy is nowhere more clear than in the understanding it has given us of the environmental and societal consequences of climate change. Written today, MDG 7 would place much more emphasis on climate change and on adaptation as a major development challenge. We devote the next two chapters to this issue. As it was written, MDG 7 focused on mitigation of climate change. While the science of climate change mitigation has its principle application in those developed and emerging economies which are contributing most to greenhouse gas generation, it has been remarkable to see how the rapid development of science for low carbon energy production has generated appropriate technology for low cost energy production for the poor.

The opportunity to better link MDG 7 with targets in other MDGs emerges clearly in opportunities to improve health through improved cooking stoves and, particularly, improved water supply and sanitation. While many of the technological tools to achieve these aims exist already, there is enormous scope to enhance these intermediate technologies through engineering innovation in materials and processes, for instance in the application of nanotechnology to water filtration systems in poor communities. This link between environment and health illustrates the kind of integration of environmental thinking into development that needs to be developed in future across the MDG portfolio.

Chapter 7 references and further reading

1   World Bank. (2008) *Global Monitoring Report 2008, MDGs & the Environment: Agenda for Inclusive and Sustainable Development*. World Bank, Washington, DC.

2   Millennium Ecosystem Assessment. (2005) *Ecosystems and Human Well-being: Synthesis*. Island Press, Washington, DC. Available at: www.millenniumassessment.org/documents/document.356.aspx.pdf [Accessed 30 Nov 2009].

3   UNEP. (2007) Chapter 7 – Vulnerability of People and the Environment: Challenges and Opportunities, *Global Environment Outlook: environment for development (GEO-4)*. United Nations Environment Programme, Nairobi.

4   Practical Action. (2009) *Climate change and poverty*. Available at: practicalaction.org/climate-change/impact [Accessed 30 Nov 2009].

5   WRI. (2005) *World Resources 2005* – The Wealth of the Poor: Managing Ecosystems to Fight Poverty. World Resources Institute, Washington DC.

6   UN. (2009) *Agenda 21*. Available at: www.un.org/esa/dsd/agenda21 [Accessed 30 Nov 2009].

7   World Summit on Sustainable Development 26 Aug to 4 Sept 2002. Available at: www.un.org/events/wssd/ [Accessed 30 Nov 2009].

8   UN Statistics Division. *Official list of MDG indicators*. Available at: millenniumindicators.un.org/unsd/mdg/Host.aspx?Content=Indicators/OfficialList.htm [Accessed 16 Nov 2009].

9   Dalal-Clayton, B. & Bass, S., (2009) *The Challenges of Environmental Mainstreaming. Experience of integrating environment into development institutions and decisions*. International Institute for Environment and Development. London. Available at: www.environmental-mainstreaming.org [Accessed 30 Nov 2009].

10 Prabhu, R. Colfer, C. & Dudley, R., (1999) *Guidelines for Developing, Testing and Selecting Criteria and Indicators for Sustainable Forest Management*. Center for International Forest Research (CIFOR), Jakarta, Indonesia.

11 CIFOR C&I team. (1999) The CIFOR Criteria and Indicators Generic Template. CIFOR, Jakarta, Indonesia.

12 Defra. (2007) *An introductory guide to the valuing of ecosystem services*. Department for Environment, Food and Rural Affairs, London.

13 DeFries, R. et al., (2007) Earth observations for estimating greenhouse gas emissions from deforestation in developing countries. *Environmental Science & Policy*, **10**, 385-394.

14 USDA Forest Service. (nd) *LIDAR overview*. Available at: forsys.cfr.washington.edu/JFSP06/lidar_technology.htm [Accessed 30 Nov 2009].

15 Lewis, S., (2009) *Spotlight on satellites for disaster management*. SciDev.net, 11 November. Available at: www.scidev.net/en/editorials/spotlight-on-satellites-for-disaster-management-1.html [Accessed 30 Nov 2009].

16 Joyce, K. et al., (2009) A review of the status of satellite remote sensing and image processing techniques for mapping natural hazards and disasters. *Progress in Physical Geography*, **33**, 183–207.

17 Thenkabail, P. et al., (2006) *An irrigated area map of the world (1999) derived from remote sensing*. Research Report 105. Colombo, Sri Lanka, International Water Management Institute. Available at: www.iwmi.cgiar.org/Publications/IWMI_Research_Reports/PDF/pub105/RR105.pdf [Accessed 30 Nov 2009].

18 Vlek, P. Bao Le, Q. & Tamene, L., (2008) *Land decline in Land-Rich Africa, A creeping disaster in the making*. CGIAR Science Council Secretariat, Rome. Available at: www.sciencecouncil.cgiar.org/fileadmin /user_upload/sciencecouncil/Reports/Land_degradation_complete.pdf [Accessed 30 Nov 2009].

19 Group on Earth Observations. Available at: www.earthobservations.org [Accessed 30 Nov 2009].

20 May, R. & McLean, A., (eds). (2007) *Theoretical Ecology. Principles and Applications*. Third Edition, Oxford University Press, Oxford.

21 Beddington, J. Agnew, D. & Clark, C., (2007) Current problems in the management of marine fisheries. *Science*, **316**, 1713-1716.

22 MRAG. (2005) *Future Research Priorities for Common Pool Resource Fisheries Management in Developing Countries*. DFID Fisheries Management Science Programme Key Sheet No 4.
Available at: www.fmsp.org.uk/Documents/keylessons/keysheet4.pdf [Accessed 30 Nov 2009].

23 Wong, J., (2006) *Developing biometric sampling systems and optimal harvesting methods for medicinal tree bark in southern Africa. Final Technical Report*. DFID Forestry Research Programme R8305. DFID, London.

24 Shackleton, C. & Clarke, J., (2007) *Research and Management of Miombo Woodlands for Products in Support of Local Livelihoods*. Genesis Analytics, Johannesburg. Available at:
www.cifor.cgiar.org/miombo/docs/SilviculturalOptions_December2007-Genesis.pdf
[Accessed 30 Nov 2009].

25 Pagiola, S. von Ritter, K. & Bishop, J., (2004). *Assessing the Economic Value of Ecosystem Conservation*. World Bank Environment Paper 101. World Bank, Washington DC. Available at:
cmsdata.iucn.org/downloads/pagiolaritterbishoplong.pdf [Accessed 30 Nov 2009].

26 Valuing the Arc. Available at: valuingthearc.org [Accessed 30 Nov 2009].

27 Eastern Arc Mountains Information Source. Available at: www.easternarc.org [Accessed 30 Nov 2009].

28 Turner, R. and Daily, G., (2008) The Ecosystem Services Framework and Natural Capital Conservation. *Environmental and Resource Economics*, **39**, 25-35.

29 Ehrlich, P. & Ehrlich, A., (1981) *Extinction: The Causes and Consequences of the Disappearance of Species*. Random House, New York.

30 Settle, W. et al., (1996) Managing tropical rice pests through conservation of generalist natural enemies and alternative prey. *Ecology*, **11**, 1975-1988.

31 FAO. (2007) T*he State of the World's Animal Genetic Resources for Food and Agriculture*. Rome, Italy.

32 FAO. (1997) *The State of the World's Plant Genetic Resources for Food and Agriculture*. Rome, Italy.

33 Global Crop Diversity Trust. Available at: www.croptrust.org [Accessed 30 Nov 2009].

34 FAO Commission on genetic resources for Food and Agriculture (2009) Draft Second Report on the State of the World's Plant Genetic Resources for Food and Agriculture. Intergovernmental Technical Working Group on Plant Genetic Resources for Food and Agriculture. Rome, Italy.

35 Myers, N. et al., (2000) Biodiversity hotspots for conservation priorities. *Nature*, **403** (6772), 853–858.

36 Sachs, J. et al., Biodiversity conservation and the Millennium Development Goals. *Science*, **325**, 1502-1503.

37 Fisher, B. & Christopher, T., (2007) Poverty and biodiversity: Measuring the overlap of human poverty and the biodiversity hotspots. *Ecological Economics*, **62**, 93-101.

38 McNeely, J. et al., (2005) *Invasive Alien Species. A New Synthesis*. Island Press, Washington.

39 DWEA. (2009) *Working for Water*. Department of Water and Environmental Affairs. Republic of South Africa. Available at: www.dwaf.gov.za/wfw/default.asp [Accessed 30 Nov 2009].

40 MacKay, D., (2008) *Sustainable Energy – without the hot air*. UIT, Cambridge.

41 Ren21. (2009) *Renewables Global Status Report, 2009 Update*. Renewable Energy Policy Network for the 21st century Secretariat, Paris.

42 Sreelata, M., (2009) *Doubts raised over India's plans for solar power*. Scidev.net, 14 August. Available at: www.scidev.net/en/news/doubts-raised-over-india-s-plans-for-solar-power-1.html.
[Accessed 30 Nov 2009].

43 The Economist. (2008) Another silicon valley? In: A special report on the future of energy.
The Economist. 21 June.

44 Hutchingson, A., (2008) Solar Thermal Power May Make Sun-Powered Grid a Reality. *Popular Mechanics*. November Issue. Available at: www.popularmechanics.com/science/research/4288743.html
[Accessed 30 Nov 2009]

45   Winnie, J., (2007) *Compact Linear Fresnel Reflector*. Available at:jcwinnie.biz/wordpress/?p=2470 [Accessed 30 Nov 2009].

46   Novatec-Biosol. (2009) *World First in Solar Power Plant Technology*. Available at: www.novatec-biosol.com/index.php?article_id=43&clang=1 [Accessed 30 Nov 2009].

47   RawSolar. Available at: raw-solar.com [Accessed 30 Nov 2009]

48   STG International. Available at: www.stginternational.org [Accessed 30 Nov 2009].

49   Nature. (2008) Special Report: Thin Films: ready for their close-up? *Nature*. **452**. 558-559.

50   Nature. (2008) A task of terawatts. *Nature*. **442**. 805.

51   Sunpower Corporation. Available at: us.sunpowercorp.com[Accessed 30 Nov 2009].

52   The Economist. (2008) Silicon rally. *The Economist*. 30 August 2008.

53   Solar Electric Light Fund. Available at: www.self.org [Accessed 30 Nov 2009].

54   SolarAid. Available at: solar-aid.org [Accessed 30 Nov 2009].

55   Lighting Africa. Available at: www.lightingafrica.org [Accessed 30 Nov 2009].

56   Katie Bliss, SolarAid, [Phone and Email] (Pers. Comm. 25 Nov 2009).

57   The Economist. (2008) Wind of change. *The Economist Technology Quarterly*. 6 December.

58   The Economist. (2008) Trade winds. In a special report on the future of energy. *The Economist*. 21 June.

59   Practical Action. (2008) *Energy from the Wind*. Practical Action Technical Brief. Available at: practicalaction.org/practicalanswers/product_info.php?cPath=21_61&products_id=371&osCsid=f60vvpkf sttct915604upbelv7&attrib=1 [Accessed 30 nov 2009].

60   Sauter, R. & Watson, J., (2008) *Technology Leapfrogging: A Review of the Evidence*. A report for DFID. Sussex Energy Group. SPRU, University of Sussex, Brighton.

61   Scidev.net. (2009) *Harnessing wind power in Africa*. 21 August. Available at: www.scidev.net/en/features/harnessing-wind-power-in-africa.html [Accessed 30 Nov 2009].

62   Practical Action. (2008) *Small-scale wind power*. Available at: practicalaction.org/energy/small_scale_wind_power [Accessed 30 Nov 2009].

63   Teodoro Sanchez from Practical Action. [Email] (Pers comm. 9 September 2009).

64   EarthTrends. (2005) Energy Consumption by Source 2005. International Energy Association. [earthtrends.wri.org/pdf_library/data_tables/ene2_2005.pdf]

65   Demirbas, A. & Demirbas, I., (2007) Importance of rural bioenergy for developing countries. *Energy Conversion and Management*. **48**, 2386–2398.

66   Kammen, D., (2006) *Bioenergy in Developing Countries: Experiences and Prospects*. 2020 Vision for Food, Agriculture and the Environment. IFPRI Brief 10 of 12.

67   IEA. (2009) *Renewables Information 2009*. IEA Statistics, International Energy Agency. Paris.

68   FAO Bioenergy. Available at: www.fao.org/bioenergy [Accessed 1 Dec 2009].

69   FAO Bioenergy and Food Security Project. Available at: www.fao.org/bioenergy/foodsecurity/befs [Accessed 1 Dec 2009].

70   SDdimensions. (2006) *Introducing the International Bioenergy Platform (IBEP)*. Available at: www.fao.org/sd/dim_en2/en2_060501_en.htm [Accessed 1 Dec 2009].

71   Global Bioenergy Partnership (GBEP). Available at: www.globalbioenergy.org [Accessed 1 Dec 2009].

72   WHO. (2006) *Indoor air pollution – Fuel for life: household energy and health*. Available at: www.who.int/indoorair/publications/fuelforlife/en/index.html [Accessed 1 Dec 2009].

73   WHO. (2009) *Indoor air pollution – Cost-benefit analysis of interventions*. Available at: www.who.int/indoorair/interventions/cost_benefit/en/index.html [Accessed 1 Dec 2009].

74   Practical Action. (2006) Biogas. Practical Action Technical Brief. Available at: practicalaction.org/practicalanswers/product_info.php?products_id=42 [Accessed 1 Dec 2009].

75   Practical Action. (2009) *Fireless cooker*. Available at: practicalaction.org/fireless-cooker [Accessed 1 Dec 2009].

76   SCORE research. Available at: www.score.uk.com/research/default.aspx [Accessed 1 Dec 2009].

77   Practical Action Consulting. (2009) *Small-Scale Bioenergy Initiatives: Brief description and preliminary lessons on livelihood impacts from case studies in Asia, Latin America and Africa*. Prepared for PISCES and FAO by Practical Action Consulting.

78   Lars., (2007) *African farmers in Mali discover Jatropha weed as biofuels crop*. Practical Environmentalist. Available at: www.practicalenvironmentalist.com/gardening/african-farmers-in-mali-discover-jatropha-weed-as-biofuel-crop.htm [Accessed 1 Dec 2009].

79   Jatropha Shop. (2008) *Jatropha curcas*. Available at: www.jatrophashop.com/index.php?option=com_content&task=view&id=65&Itemid=69 [Accessed 1 Dec 2009].

80   Mali Folke Center. Available at: www.malifolkecenter.org [Accessed 1 Dec 2009].

81   FACT Foundation. Available at: www.fact-foundation.com [Accessed 1 Dec 2009].

82   FACT Foundation. (2009) *Mali Progress Report July 2009*. Available at: www.fact-foundation.com/media_en/Progress_Report_Mali_July_2009 [Accessed 1 Dec 2009].

83   WHO/UNICEF Joint Monitoring Programme for water supply and sanitation. (2008) *Progress on Drinking water and sanitation – Special Focus on Sanitation*. UNICEF and WHO, New York.

84   UNICEF/WHO. (2009) *Diarrhoea: why children are still dying and what can be done*. UNICEF and WHO, New York.

85   WaterAid. (2005) *Getting to the Boiling Point, Turning up the heat on water and sanitation*. WaterAid, London.

86   Benn, H., (2007) *Water for Life – the UK input*. Speech for World Water Day 2005 at the Royal Geographic Society, London. Available at: www.dfid.gov.uk/Documents/speeches/hilary-water-22mar05.pdf [Accessed 1 Dec 2009].

87   OECD. (2008) *Aid activities in support of water supply and sanitation 2001-2006*.

88   Water Supply and Sanitation Collaborative Council. Available at: www.wsscc.org [Accessed 1 Dec 2009].

89   International Year of Sanitation. Available at: esa.un.org/iys/ [Accessed 1 Dec 2009].

90   Federico Properzi from the UN-Water GLASS Project. [Email] (Pers Comm. 26 November 2009).

91   Water Aid. (2008) *Technology Notes*. Available at: www.wateraid.org/documents/plugin_documents/technology_notes_2008.pdf [Accessed 1 Dec 2009].

92   WaterAid. *Water source options*. Available at: www.wateraid.org/documents/water_source_options__a_comparison.pdf [Accessed 1 Dec 2009].

93   Grimshaw, D., (2009) *Nanotechnology for clean water: Facts and figures*. Scidev.net, 6 May. Available at: www.scidev.net/en/nanotechnology/nanotechnology-for-clean-water/features/nanotechnology-for-clean-water-facts-and-figures.html [Accessed 1 Dec 2009].

94   WaterAid America. *Statistics*. Available at: www.wateraidamerica.org/what_we_do/statistics.aspx [Accessed 1 Dec 2009].

95   Sugden, S., (2007) *Excreta Management in Unplanned Areas*. Presentation. Available at: siteresources.worldbank.org/EXTWAT/Resources/4602122-1213366294492/5106220-1213649450319/1.8.1_Excreta_Management_in_Unplanned_Areas.pdf [Accessed 1 Dec 2009].

96   Sugden, S., LSHTM. [Interview] (Pers. Comm. 2009).

97   PumpAid. *The Elephant Pump*. Available at: www.pumpaid.org/The-Elephant-Pump.shtml [Accessed 1 Dec 2009].

Part 3

The Challenge of
Climate Change

The Science of
Climate Change

The receding glaciers on Mt. Kilimanjaro, Tanzania which may be caused by climate change
© Mark Garten – UN Photos

In part two we examined the role of science and innovation in addressing the challenges of the MDGs as though they constituted a set of discrete goals with their own distinct trajectories. In some cases they are on track to meet their targets; in others the prospects are gloomier. There is a justification for such a 'siloed' approach. As we have seen, the scientific issues and the technologies that are needed are themselves complicated and require the undivided attention of those who have the skills and experience to tackle them. Nevertheless, as has become increasingly apparent, the MDGs exist in a global context that is itself challenging and transforming. Globalisation, demographic changes, financial crises and a range of major global threats, including climate change, will determine whether or not we can achieve the MDGs.

In part three we begin by looking in some detail at the threat of climate change, its science, the expected impacts and then in the next chapter, we discuss how we can adapt to them. The fundamental message is that we have to become more resilient.

Global climate change has been largely driven by the activities of the industrialised countries. Yet its most severe consequences are going to be felt, and indeed are already being felt, by the developing countries. Moreover, it is the poor of those countries who, in part, because of their poverty, are most vulnerable. If left unchecked, climate change will increase hunger and mortality from infectious diseases and will cause the further deterioration of the environmental resources on which, as we have seen, the poor so often depend.

In this chapter we explore the role of science and technology in answering the following questions:

- What do we know and not know about climate change?
- What will be the most serious consequences, especially in Africa and Asia?

1. What do we know about the global impacts?

There is convincing evidence that global climate change is occurring and is the result of man-made emissions of greenhouse gases (GHG) – primarily carbon dioxide (CO_2), methane and nitrous oxide. The mechanism is relatively simple and increasingly understood: these gases form a layer over the earth's surface which traps an increasing proportion of the infrared radiation which would be otherwise radiated out to space, so warming the land and oceans beneath (Figure 8.1).

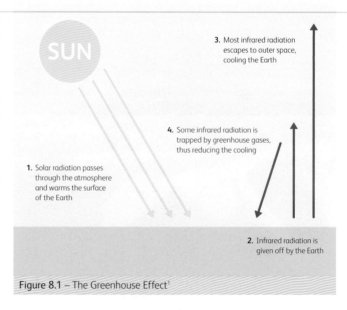

Figure 8.1 – The Greenhouse Effect[1]

As a consequence the world as a whole is warming – so far by more than 0.7°C since the industrial revolution (Figure 8.2).

Since pre-industrial times (around 1750), CO_2 concentrations have increased by just over one third from 280 parts per million (ppm) to 385 ppm in 2008 (Figure 8.3).[3] Taking the six GHGs included in the Kyoto protocol together, the total is now about 436 ppm of CO_2 equivalent and is predicted to reach 570-700ppm by the middle of the century.

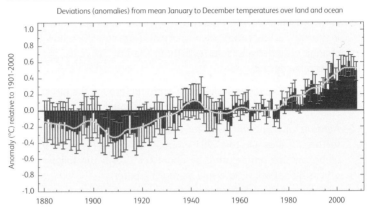

Figure 8.2 – Global warming has increased by about 0.7° C since 1900[2]

Deviations (anomalies) from mean January to December temperatures over land and ocean

There has been no comparable rise in these long lived greenhouse gases since at least the beginning of the Ice Ages, 600,000 years ago. Their cumulative radiative forcing, that is the balance of incoming and outgoing energy they cause has, over the past two decades, been about 1 Watt per metre² more than that in pre-industrial times and sufficient to explain the global warming we are now experiencing.

Alternative explanations

There have been exhaustive studies of alternative explanations for the rising temperature (Box 8.1).

Figure 8.3 – The rise in carbon dioxide (CO_2), methane (CH_4) and nitrous oxide (N_2O) over the past 2,000 years has been unprecedented. Measurements using ice cores and modern data[4]

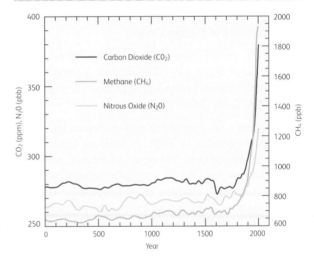

Box 8.1   Why some of the most plausible alternative explanations of recent global warming are inadequate[5-7]

1. There have been major changes in temperatures before, for example, the Younger Dryas, a cold period lasting about 1,300 years that occurred some 12,000 years ago and, more recently, the 'Warm Period' followed by the 'Little Ice Age' in Europe. But neither appears to be a global phenomenon (the Younger Dryas may be the result of significant reduction or shutdown of the North Atlantic thermohaline circulation).

2. Temperatures and CO_2 levels rose in past interglacials, but the cycles of glacial and interglacial periods were probably caused by the 'wobbles' in the Earth's orbit around the Sun (known as Milankovitch cycles) and the CO_2 rise followed the temperature rise not vice versa.

3. Sunspots can increase global temperatures. Greater sunspot activity emits more heat and light, but while there is evidence of a link between solar activity and some of the warming in the early 20th century, measurements from satellites show that there has been very little change in underlying solar activity in the last 30 years and there is even evidence of a detectable decline.

4. Galactic cosmic rays may increase warming through the effect of the tiny particles on cloud formation, but the effect is likely to be very small.

5. Aerosols and volcanic eruptions affect global warming. But they are primarily cooling factors; for example the 1991 eruption of Mount Pinatubo in the Philippines reduced the global surface temperature by about 0.3°C over the following two years. Without these effects global warming would be much greater.

The conclusion in the Stern Review, a comprehensive report by economist Sir Nicholas Stern was: *'It is now clear that, while natural factors, such as changes in solar intensity and volcanic eruptions, can explain much of the trend in global temperatures in the early nineteenth century, the rising levels of greenhouse gases provide the only plausible explanation for the observed trend for at least the past 50 years.'*[1]

The importance of feedback loops

A doubling of CO_2 levels results in an increase in temperature of 1°C, but the likely increase is going to be considerably greater because of a number of feedback loops in the global climate (Figure 8.4).

Water vapour is an example of a phenomenon that can create either positive or negative feedback loops. The greater the temperature the more evaporation and the more clouds are produced. An increase in high clouds traps outgoing long-wave radiation so warming the planet – a positive feedback. But low clouds tend to reflect incoming radiation so cooling the planet – a negative feedback.[8]

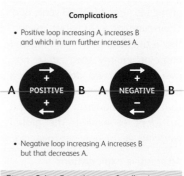

Complications

• Positive loop increasing A, increases B and which in turn further increases A.

A — POSITIVE — B   A — NEGATIVE — B

• Negative loop increasing A increases B but that decreases A.

Figure 8.4 – Complicating feedback loops in the climate system

Some of the other feedback loops are as follows:

• A major positive feedback results from the reduction of snow and ice cover. This exposes a greater area of darker land and sea, creating more heat absorbing surfaces that result in more melting;

• Rising temperatures and changes in rainfall patterns are also expected to weaken the ability of the Earth's natural land and ocean sinks to absorb CO_2, causing a larger fraction of human emissions to accumulate in the atmosphere;

• Widespread thawing of permafrost regions could release large quantities of methane, as well as CO_2, which will add to the warming;

- The most significant negative feedback is caused by the production of particles into the atmosphere, some of which have a strong cooling effect. However, the known positive feedbacks far outweigh such negative loops and will add to the direct effects of the CO_2 emissions.

Figure 8.5 – Estimates of global surface warming for different scenarios[9]

Case	Temperature Change (°C at 2090-2099 relative to 1980-1999)		Sea Level Rise (m at 2090-2099 relative to 1980-1999)
	Best estimate	Likely range	Model-based range excluding future rapid dynamical changes in ice flow
Constant Year 2000 concentrations	0.6	0.3–0.9	N/A
B1 scenario	1.8	1.1–2.9	0.18–0.38
A1T scenario	2.4	1.4–3.8	0.20–0.45
B2 scenario	2.4	1.4–3.8	0.20–0.43
A1B scenario	2.8	1.7–4.4	0.21–0.48
A2 scenario	3.4	2.0–5.4	0.23–0.51
A1FI scenario	4.0	2.4–6.4	0.26–0.59

- The A1 storyline assumes a world of very rapid economic growth, a global population that peaks in mid-century and rapid introduction of new and more efficient technologies. A1 is divided into three groups that describe alternative directions of technological change:
  - fossil intensive (A1FI);
  - non-fossil energy resources (A1T);
  - and a balance across all sources (A1B).
- B1 describes a convergent world, with the same global population as A1, but with more rapid changes in economic structures toward a service and information economy.
- B2 describes a world with intermediate population and economic growth, emphasising local solutions to economic, social, and environmental sustainability.
- A2 describes a very heterogeneous world with high population growth, slow economic development and slow technological change.

Current estimates are, that if we assume balanced energy based economic growth (the A1B scenario), the surface warming is likely be 1.7–4.4°C above 2000 levels by the end of the century (Figure 8.5).[9]

A rise in temperature of this amount may not seem significant but a *drop* of 5°C in temperature marked the coldest period of the last ice age.

Tipping points

Moreover, there are concerns that the temperature increases may result in a 'tipping point' phenomenon where the positive loops start to generate new phenomena, with consequences that are difficult, or impossible, to reverse.[10-13] In 2005 a workshop at the British Embassy in Berlin brought together a large group of experts who identified 15 so-called tipping elements:[11]

1. Arctic summer sea – ice;
2. Greenland ice sheet;
3. West Antarctic ice sheet;
4. Atlantic thermohaline circulation;
5. El Niño – southern oscillation;
6. Indian summer monsoon;
7. Sahara/Sahel and West African monsoon;
8. Amazon rainforest;
9. Boreal forest;
10. Antarctic bottom water;
11. Tundra;
12. Permafrost;
13. Marine methane hydrates;
14. Ocean anoxia;
15. Arctic ozone.

Three of these are described in more detail in Box 8.2.

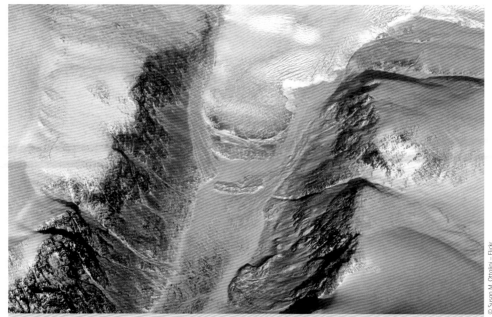

Figure 8.6 – Glacial melt on the Greenland ice sheet

Box 8.2   Possible climate tipping points

1. The disintegration of the Greenland ice sheet

The ice sheets of Greenland and Antarctica hold enough ice to raise sea level about 64 metres if fully melted.[14]

Current measurements in Greenland suggest that the ice sheet inland is growing slightly but there is significant melting and flows of ice near the coast. This is greater than predicted by the models. It appears that melt water is seeping down through the crevices of the melting ice, lubricating glaciers and accelerating their movement to the sea.[8,15-17]

Model simulations suggest that there is a critical temperature threshold beyond which the Greenland ice sheet would be committed to disappearing completely (Figure 8.7). This would result in a rise in sea level of about seven metres. Although this would take many hundreds of years, the threshold could be crossed during this century.[18]

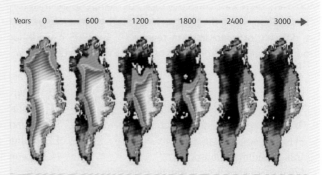

Figure 8.7 – Predicted loss of the Greenland Ice sheet with a fourfold increase in CO_2. (Red, indicates high, and black, low, elevations)[19]

2. Collapse of the West Antarctic ice sheet

Recently the western ice sheet has experienced sustained warming and significant thinning (about 20 mm/year on the Larsen-B Ice Shelf). A large section of the shelf, the size of the state of Rhode Island in the US (over 3,200 km² in area and 200 m thick), collapsed in 2002. The shelf is now only about 40 % of the size of its previous minimum stable extent.[20]

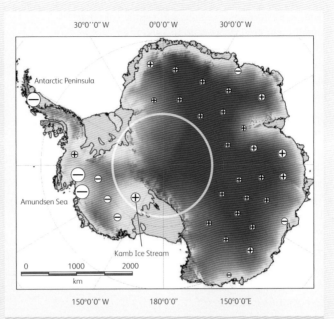

Figure 8.8 – Gains and losses of snow and ice in the Antarctic[21]

The Antarctic peninsula as a whole has warmed by 2°C over the last 40 years and this may be the cause of the spectacular collapses of the ice shelves there. However, for Antarctica as a whole there appears to be a small growth in snow and ice due to increased precipitation (Figure 8.8). For the West Antarctic ice sheet the danger is that ocean warming and the acceleration of ice flows will cause a runaway discharge into the oceans. The critical threshold is unknown but it could be as low as 2°C to 5°C. Estimates of the time for the West Antarctic Ice Sheet to totally melt range from 250 to 700 years.[22,23]

3. Release of deep sea methane hydrates

An immense quantity of methane (equivalent to 500-2,500 gigatonnes of carbon) may be trapped in marine sediments in the form of solid gas hydrates (Figure 8.9).[24] They also occur in, and under, the Arctic permafrost.[25] The amounts are prodigious – the total carbon bound in gas hydrates (mostly methane) is estimated to be twice the amount present in all known fossil fuels.

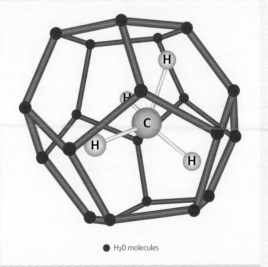

● H_2O molecules

Figure 8.9 – Methane hydrates consist of crystalline solids similar to ice in which water molecules form a cage-like structure around a methane molecule[26]

They exist in oceanic regions sufficiently cold and under enough high pressure to keep them stable. If ocean warming penetrated as far as the deep oceans it could destabilise the methane, releasing it into the atmosphere, so leading to a rapid increase in global warming (Figure 8.10).

In 2008 a British research team discovered about 250 methane plumes bubbling from the seabed in an area of about 30 square miles, in water less than 400 metres deep, off the west coast of the archipelago of Svalbard, that lies about 80°N. These releases have been occurring since the last Ice Age, but it is not yet known whether ocean warming is increasing the rate of release.[28]

There was a period of massive methane hydrate destabilisation 55 million years ago which led to rapid climate change, when the deep-sea temperature rose 5° to 6°C.[29]

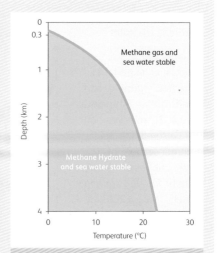

Figure 8.10 – Methane hydrates are only stable at low temperatures and high pressures. If conditions shift the hydrates can be released as methane gas[27]

It is very difficult, given our current state of knowledge, to determine when and how these tipping points are likely to occur. What is certain is that the consequences from any one of these will be devastating for many regions of the world, if not for the planet as a whole. Some believe that the risks are very low and the dangers overstated. However, the Berlin workshop concluded that *'Our synthesis of present knowledge suggests that a variety of tipping elements could reach their critical point within this century under anthropogenic climate change. The greatest threats are tipping the Arctic sea-ice and the Greenland ice sheet, and at least five other elements could surprise us by exhibiting a nearby tipping point.'* James Hansen (Head of NASA Goddard Institute for Space Studies in New York City) and his colleagues go further and conclude from their modelling that a rise of just 1°C in global temperature above the 2000 level would be 'dangerous,' and may well trigger a number of these tipping points.[30]

Global and regional consequences

Despite these longer term uncertainties there are near term consequences that are highly likely. There will be:

- Regions that are warmer or colder;

- Regions more prone to drought or flooding;

- Higher sea levels;

- More storm surges;

- Greater variation in the weather and more intensive extreme events – hurricanes, tropical cyclones, floods and droughts.

© Logan Abassi – UN Photos

Figure 8.11 – A father carries his daughter after floods caused by tropical storm 'Noel' hit Soleil, Haiti in 2007

It is striking that although the driving force is global warming the main consequences are related to water – either too much or too little in any one place.

Figure 8.12 shows the probable temperature patterns for the globe over the next 100 years. These suggest that, at least to begin with, the biggest temperature increases will occur in the upper latitudes.

Figure 8.12 – Increases in temperature over the next 100 years using the IPCC rapid growth scenario A1B[18]

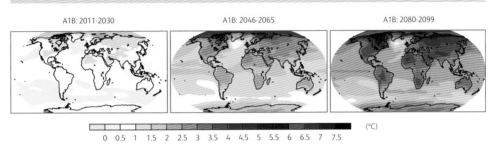

For rainfall the biggest impact is likely to be the greater incidence of drought in northern and southern Africa and in some parts of Asia (Figure 8.13).

Figure 8.13 – Changes in precipitation over the next 100 years for December to February (left) and June to August (right). (These are composites of many different models. The white areas indicate where less than 66% of the models agree; the dotted areas are where more than 90% of the models agree.)[31]

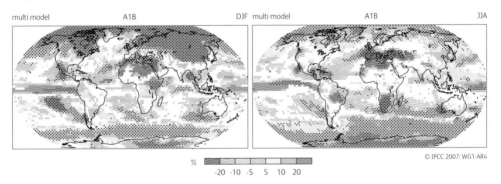

© IPCC 2007: WG1-AR4

2. What are the global drivers?

Underlying these changes are global climate phenomena that interact in complex, and still not yet fully understood, ways.[8] Most of the developing countries are located in the tropics and subtropics i.e. they lie between 0° and 30° north and south of the equator. Within this latitudinal band are three critical processes:

Two of these – tropical convection and the alternation of the monsoons – are relatively local processes that determine the regional and seasonal patterns of temperature and rainfall. A third – the El Niño-Southern Oscillation of the Pacific Ocean – is local, in one respect, but strongly influences the year to year rainfall and temperature patterns on a global scale. Although these drivers are powerful global and regional forces it is not yet clear whether their patterns are significantly altered by global warming.

What we can be sure of is that global warming – expressed, for example, through higher sea and land surface temperatures – will affect their outcomes, increasing the incidence and severity of the droughts, floods and other extreme weather events that they produce.

Tropical convection

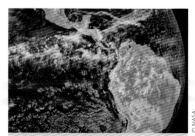

Intense solar heating near the equator leads to rising warm, moist air and heavy rainfall (Figure 8.14). As it rises the air creates a surface low-pressure area, known for centuries by sailors as the *Doldrums*, and referred to as the Intertropical Convergence Zone (ITCZ). The rising air moves north and south towards the tropics and eventually falls in the subtropics (between 20° and 30° north and south of the equator) as warm, dry air. From there it is carried back towards the equator by the trade winds.

Figure 8.14 – The thunderstorms over the Pacific along the ITCZ

Each year the ITCZ moves north and south following the seasonal tilting of the globe towards the sun. In Africa four distinct climatic zones result[9]:

1. The tropical moist climates with around 2,000mm of rain that support the equatorial rainforest;

2. Tropical climates that alternate between wet summers (brought by the ITCZ) and short dry winters, giving a total rainfall of 1,000-2,000mm;

3. Tropical semi-arid climates, with long dry seasons, at the northern-most limits of the ITCZ and rainfall of 300-800mm;

4. Arid climates located between 30° and 40° north and south, with less than 250 mm year rainfall.

In Africa and elsewhere, these are not distinct zones; their boundaries overlap and vary from year to year with both the latitudinal and longitudinal movement of the ITCZ (Figure 8.15).

Figure 8.15 – The position of the ITCZ in January and July (red lines)[32]

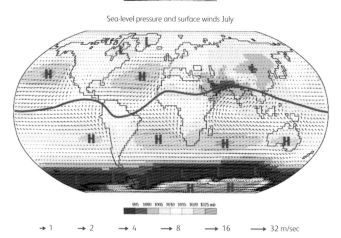

Sea-level pressure and surface winds January

Sea-level pressure and surface winds July

995 1000 1005 1010 1015 1020 1025 mb

➜ 1   ➜ 2   ➜ 4   ➜ 8   ➜ 16   ➜ 32 m/sec

Data: NCEP/NCAR Reanalysis Project, 1959-1997 Climatologies

The monsoons

Another phenomenon, closely linked to tropical convection, is the marked seasonal change in the direction of the monsoonal winds (compare the wind patterns for Jan and July in Figure 8.15) brought about by the changes in temperature gradients as the sun 'moves' north and south during the year.[9] The global monsoon system turns out to be a complicated phenomenon involving several processes (including the movement of the ITCZ) which interact in ways that are still not fully understood.[33,34] In simple terms, monsoon winds occur because land heats up

Figure 8.16 – Heavy monsoon rains in Delhi

© Micheal Foley – Flickr

and cools down more quickly than the sea. This results in changes in the surface winds and the associated precipitation. The strongest monsoons occur over the tropics of southern and eastern Asia and northern Australia, and parts of western and central Africa. In these regions the wet season migrates north and south from one hemisphere to the other following the sun.

The Indian monsoon is the most extreme form of monsoon with a 180° reversal of the wind. The south-west monsoon arises in spring and summer. As the air over north-west India and Pakistan becomes much warmer than over the Indian Ocean, it creates a low pressure area drawing in warm, moist air from over the ocean. The air moves first northward, and then because of the effects of the Earth's rotation is diverted north-eastward. It begins to rise and cool and sheds its moisture as rain. In winter the reverse occurs, the land cooling down more than the oceans, creating the north-east monsoon. These monsoon wind changes also affect lands far distant from south Asia, for example along the eastern margins of Africa.

The East Asian monsoon, while less extreme in its reversal, acts as a particularly influential climate driver, carrying moist air from the Indian and Pacific oceans to countries in East Asia such as China, Japan, North and South Korea and Taiwan, and affects up to one-third of the global population. The monsoon tends to concentrate rainfall in rain 'belts' which stretch for thousands of kilometres, acting as important, and often hard to predict, determinates of agricultural production in the affected countries. Adding to this, the East Asian summer monsoon contributes to heightened typhoon activity and increasing rainfall in the North Pacific. The monsoon also brings a cold and dry winter season, which is partly responsible for the dust deposition that created the Loess Plateau in China discussed in Chapters 1 and 2.

West Africa is affected by a south-west monsoon which arises in a similar fashion. In the summer, as the land becomes hotter than the ocean and as the air over the Sahara starts to rise, cooler, more humid air from the Atlantic Ocean is drawn in 1,000 km to the south. It brings rainfall from May to September in two phases (Figure 8.17). The first in April, May and June centres on the Gulf of Guinea (about 4°N) and appears to be influenced by sea surface temperatures. Then suddenly, usually in early to mid-July, the rainfall maximum follows the ITCZ northwards into the southern Sahel (about 10°N) over a period of a few days. So sudden is the event that it is called the "monsoon jump". The second phase is apparently influenced by easterly atmospheric waves (which are also associated with the ITCZ).

Figure 8.17 – The two phases of the West African Monsoon[35]

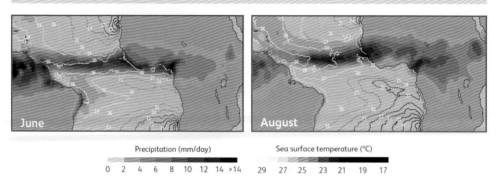

Precipitation (mm/day)

0   2   4   6   8   10   12   14   >14

Sea surface temperature (°C)

29   27   25   23   21   19   17

Monsoon activity has been affected by a transition in global atmospheric circulation which occurred in the mid-1970s.[32] Some studies have found that the most vigorous monsoonal circulations have weakened, leading to decreased long rainy spells and increased shorter spells, and in general a more erratic rainfall pattern (Figure 8.18).[36-38]

Figure 8.18 – Changes in the annual range of monsoon rainfall, comparing 1976-2003 with 1945-1975[34]

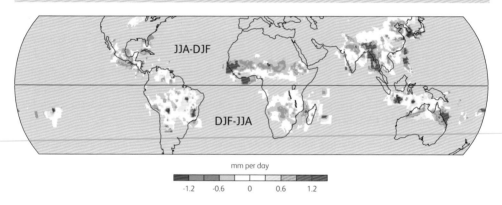

JJA-DJF

DJF-JJA

mm per day

-1.2   -0.6   0   0.6   1.2

However, there are uncertainties about the data and how it is interpreted. A study of Indian rainfall over central India reveals considerable year to year variation but no trend in daily rainfall over the past 50 years. Yet when the authors focussed on extreme

Figure 8.19 – Growth in the mean rainfall of the four highest rain events every season ($R_{1..4}$) in Central India over the past 50 years[39]

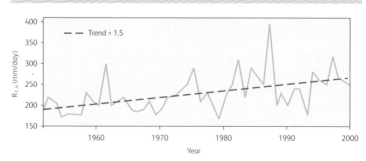

monsoon events, i.e. the four highest rain events each season they found a significant increase in the frequency and the intensity of such events over the past 50 years (Figure 8.19).[39]

At the same time, a particularly marked decline is evident in the East Asian monsoon (Figure 8.20).

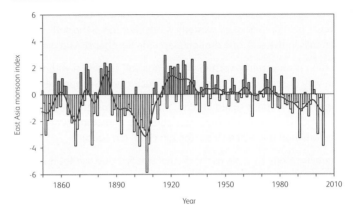

Figure 8.20 – The decline in the East Asian monsoon since the mid-1970s[34]

The West African monsoon is also in a major period of weakening, leading to droughts lasting several decades.[40,41] There was a dramatic shift from the wetter conditions of the 1950s and 60s to the much drier decades of the 70s, 80s and 90s.

The evidence suggests a number of inconsistencies. Moreover it is debatable whether these shifts in rainfall pattern are simply a natural phase, as has occurred in the past, (for example, there was a major decline in the East Asian Monsoon at the end of the 19th century – see Figure 8.20) or whether they are partly a response to a combination of recent factors including the effects of land degradation, water pollution and biomass burning, or climate change. What is certain is that these changes have made it extremely difficult for farmers and others to predict the key seasonal rains. More advanced prediction tools and modelling will hopefully provide a more nuanced understanding of monsoonal changes.

The El Niño-Southern Oscillation

The third driver, the El Niño-Southern Oscillation (ENSO) is a phenomenon of the Pacific Ocean. It is characterised by a close coupling of the ocean and the atmosphere and is referred to as an oscillation because of the characteristic switch in the Pacific between two phases, La Niña, and El Niño (Figure 8.21).

Under 'normal' conditions the Peru current brings cool water to the Central Pacific, but from there trade winds move increasingly warm water westwards from the Central Pacific's high pressure to the low pressure located over Indonesia. This results in the sea surface being about ½ metre higher on the Indonesian coast than at the Ecuadorian coast and the temperature 8-10°C warmer. Very heavy and extensive rainfall, partly fed by the trade winds, occurs over the warm water of the western Pacific, while the eastern Pacific experiences relatively dry weather.[42]

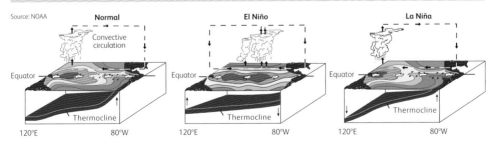

Figure 8.21 – Comparison of atmospheric and oceanic flows in the Pacific during normal, El Nino and La Niña years.[43] Water temperatures: warm: red cold: blue

Sometimes the pattern is reversed, with wide ranging consequences.[44] Every three to seven years El Niño sets in and there is a change in the prevailing pattern of ocean surface temperatures and pressures. Air pressure strengthens over Indonesia and the trade winds slacken. Sometimes they reverse, being replaced by westerly winds that move the surface waters towards the central Pacific. Rain falls in the east and droughts occur in Southeast Asia and Australia.

La Niña is an extreme version of the 'normal' condition with very cold water, strong high pressure and very dry conditions in the eastern Pacific and the opposite in the western Pacific.

The phenomenon is called El Niño, the Spanish for 'the boy child,' because the warm waters tend to arrive off the South American coast at Christmas time. The more common westward flow phenomenon is referred to as 'the girl child' (La Niña).

There are many theories as to whether this is a true oscillation and different views on the nature of the dominant mechanisms involved, but a complete theory is still lacking. It is possible to provide fairly good short term predictions of the change between La Niña and El Niño, but these rely on complex, coupled atmospheric/oceanic models.

In the Pacific, ENSO accounts for up to 40 % of the variation in temperature and rainfall.[45] Moreover, although it is primarily a Pacific Ocean process, the effects are felt as far away as Africa and, indeed, in most regions of the world. ENSO events involve large exchanges of heat between the ocean and atmosphere and hence affect the global climate. During an El Niño phase the eastward displacement of the atmospheric heat source overlaying the warmest water results in large changes in the global atmospheric circulation, which in turn force changes in weather in regions far removed from the tropical Pacific. Thus, six months after an El Niño phase the global mean surface air temperature increases. It is estimated that after the severe El Niño of 1997-98 it went up by nearly 0.2°C.[46,34]

Relatively simple statistical models predict that during an El Niño year the December to February weather is usually wetter in eastern Africa but drier to the south, while La Niña produces the reverse effect. El Niño is also associated with a drier Sahel and La Niña is correlated with a wetter Sahel and a cooler West Africa (Figure 8.22).

Figure 8.22 – The El-Niño – La Niña Oscillation has global effects[42]

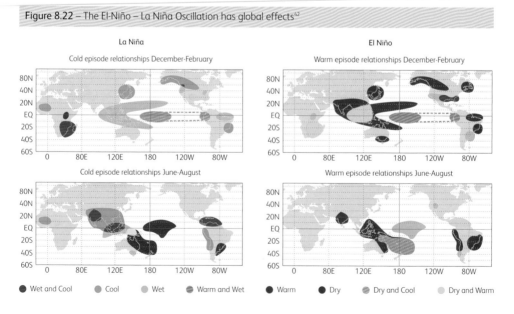

La Niña

Cold episode relationships December-February

El Niño

Warm episode relationships December-February

Cold episode relationships June-August

Warm episode relationships June-August

● Wet and Cool   ● Cool   ● Wet   ● Warm and Wet   ● Warm   ● Dry   ● Dry and Cool   ● Dry and Warm

An El Niño event with strong warming in the central Pacific can also cause the Indian monsoon to switch into a "dry mode", characterised by significant reductions in rainfall leading to severe droughts. These delicate interactions can cause abrupt shifts in rainfall patterns.

The 1997/98 El Niño was one of the strongest of the 20th century. It was associated with droughts and forest fires in Indonesia and north-east Brazil, and catastrophic floods in east Africa. Among its many other consequences was the extensive coral bleaching that occurred in the Indian Ocean and Red Sea and a massive outbreak of a *Paederus* rove beetle in Nairobi that caused severe dermatitis.[47] The following La Niña of 1998-2000 was associated with devastating floods further north in the Sudan and Sahel, and in the south in Mozambique. The floods in the south were then followed by two major cyclones.[48,49]

How is climate change affecting these drivers?

These drivers are powerful forces, yet it is still not clear to what extent they are affected by climate change. There are some observations and conjectures. As a general hypothesis each of the drivers should be influenced by the rising sea surface temperatures resulting from global warming.

We know, for example, that when the ITCZ migrates further north than usual it brings heavy rain and floods to the Sahel (as happened in 2007), and when it lies quite far south over the SW Indian Ocean it will be very dry over South Africa. The question is whether these movements are a product of changes in sea-surface temperature and hence are a consequence of climate warming.[50]

Similar questions apply to the pattern of monsoons. Simulations suggest that there is a greater intensity of monsoons with climate change.[51,52] With surface temperature increases, the land will heat up faster and there will be a greater contrast between the land and the ocean, and thus more intense monsoons. However this is the opposite of the weakening which has been observed in recent decades for all the major monsoons.[51] It is evident that monsoons are highly complex phenomena governed by a range of conflicting influences, some of which are weakening and others intensifying. What is generally agreed is that future monsoons, whether weakening or not, will be characterised by a greater frequency of extreme rainfall events. They may also become more erratic, or subject to new patterns, making them harder to predict.[51]

The ENSO phenomenon raises further complicated issues, because there is still no consensus of opinion over why the oscillation occurs in the first place. For example, it may be simply the result of a random 'trigger,' El Niño occurring very approximately at three to seven year intervals. However, this does not explain the shift in the pattern that seems to have occurred in 1976–1977. This shift was associated with marked changes in El Niño evolution with a tendency towards more prolonged El Niños, accompanied by generally above-normal sea surface temperatures (SSTs) in the eastern and central equatorial Pacific. The long run of El Niño in the early 1990s is unprecedented (Figure 8.23).[53,54]

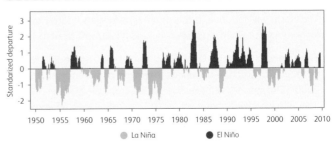

Figure 8.23 – The increase in frequency of El Niño events since the mid-1970s. (The multivariate ENSO Index is based on six variables measured across the Pacific)[55]

This has caused speculation that the shift is a consequence of global warming, but, so far, there is no evidence to substantiate the connection.[56] It is certainly plausible that the oscillation is influenced by global warming, since both phenomena involve large changes in the earth's heat balance. As the world warms, many models suggest that the East Pacific may warm more intensely than the West Pacific, mimicking the pattern of an El Niño, although significant uncertainties remain. However, current models do not agree on the nature of changes in the frequency or intensity of the El Niño.[57] Moreover, *'all models show continued El Niño-Southern Oscillation (ENSO) interannual variability in the future no matter what the change in average background conditions, but....there is no consistent indication at this time of discernible changes in projected ENSO amplitude or frequency in the 21st century.'*[18]

Tropical cyclones

One of the many consequences of these interacting drivers is the occurrence of tropical cyclones. The severity of the weather they generate can be extremely damaging to the many vulnerable populations that live in low-lying coastal areas (Box 8.3).

Box 8.3 The nature of tropical cyclones

A cyclone is an area of closed, circular fluid motion, characterised by inward spiralling winds, rotating in the same direction as the earth. Cyclones can take many forms, depending on how and where they originate. They have impacts that range from influencing trade winds and seasonal temperatures, to causing large storm surges, flooding and damage to coastal areas.

© NASA

Figure 8.24 – A south Atlantic tropical cyclone viewed from the International Space Station on March 26, 2004

Most of the highest impact storms are tropical cyclones, the more severe ones known as hurricanes or typhoons, depending on the ocean where they form. The intense solar heating near the equator leads to a large amount of evaporation, with water vapour condensing as it rises, releasing heat. The release of this latent heat of condensation then acts as the primary energy source for cyclones.

Once formed, a positive feedback loop begins, where the condensation leads to higher wind speeds, bringing about lower pressure, increased surface evaporation and more condensation. The storm will continue in this manner as long as it stays over warm water and conditions are favourable. But when it passes over land it is cut-off from its heat source and rapidly diminishes.

Thus, coastal areas receive the brunt of the damage. Heavy wind, rain and flooding can destroy infrastructure as well as take lives, as seen for example in the Orissa Super Cyclone of 2000 (Chapter 9). An average of 86 tropical cyclones of tropical storm intensity formed annually worldwide between 1970 and 1995, with 47 reaching hurricane/typhoon strength, and 20 becoming intense tropical cyclones.[58]

There is still disagreement over the effects of climate change on cyclones.[32] They are strongly influenced by sea surface temperatures and it is therefore reasonable to assume that global warming will have an effect, but other factors are also important. Experts remain divided on whether cyclones are likely to increase in frequency and / or intensity. Nevertheless, there has been a large increase in the numbers and proportion of hurricanes reaching categories four and five globally since 1970 even though the total number of cyclones and cyclone days has decreased slightly in most basins. The largest increase was in the North Pacific, Indian and Southwest Pacific Oceans.[59,60]

It seems likely that the already complex nature of cyclones could become even more unpredictable as the climate changes, and temperatures and sea levels rise. Whether or not the intensity of cyclones will increase, rising sea levels, along with increasing populations in coastal areas, will compound the damage caused by these storms.[31,61]

3. The regional changes

The uncertainties at the global level are repeated and magnified as we move to assessing regional impacts. We need better models, more fine-grained in their dynamics and also better ground data.

The need for better information

The Global Climate Models (GCMs) used to simulate the regional patterns of climate change are relatively crude: they work to a horizontal spatial resolution of several hundred kilometers: they do not take full account of the topographic, vegetation and land use diversity of the landscape. Nevertheless, their potential is still underexploited, partly because of the lack of trained climatologists in most developing countries.

A major challenge is to downscale the GCMs in some way so as to produce a finer scale of prediction. One approach is to adapt the GCM to a specific region using a smaller resolution regional climate model, e.g. a 50 km scale, by feeding in the boundary climate conditions created at the surrounding, more widely spaced, grid points. One example of such a model is PRECIS (Providing Regional Climates for Impacts Studies), a portable regional climate model, developed by the Hadley Centre of the UK Met Office, that can be run on a personal computer.[62]

Such models are valuable tools for understanding local climate dynamics (see Figure 8.25). They are more sensitive to the effects of local topographies and other phenomena. But, it must be stressed, they act by applying the coarse-resolution GCM dynamics to a regional level and, as a result, the GCM uncertainties are likely to become magnified, so reducing their usefulness. Only in a few locations is the local data sufficient in quality and quantity to provide a basis for the accuracy required at a fine scale.

Figure 8.25 – Predicted changes in annual surface run-off for Southern Africa over the next 80 years (A2 scenario). The PRECIS model on the right shows a much finer grained, and more useful, analysis than the GCM on the left[62]

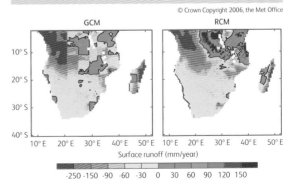

© Crown Copyright 2006, the Met Office

An alternative approach, known as empirical downscaling, works by trying to identify a statistical relationship between the observed weather (temperature or rainfall) at finer resolution grid points and the weather simulated by the GCM at the nearest large scale grid point.[63] The GCM is then run to simulate future climate and the results are 'downscaled' to finer resolutions assuming that these relationships continue to hold.

The production of regional and local models is further limited by the paucity of regular, detailed information, in particular in Africa. The global network of World Watch Weather Stations, which provide real time weather data, is very sparsely represented in Africa. There are only 1,152 stations in Africa, a density of about 1 per 26,000 km^2 which is eight times lower than the level recommended by the World Meteorological Organisation. Moreover, the location of the stations is very scattered. Vast areas are unmonitored, including Central Africa and the Horn of Africa (Figure 8.26).[64]

Figure 8.26 – The paucity of reports received by the World Meteorological Office from African World Weather Watch Stations 1998 – 2002[65]

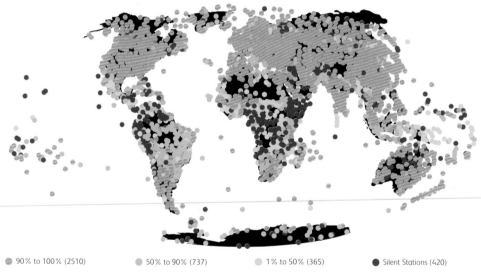

● 90% to 100% (2510)   ● 50% to 90% (737)   ● 1% to 50% (365)   ● Silent Stations (420)

One attempt to improve the availability and use of climate information in decision-making processes, the Climate for Development in Africa Programme (ClimDev-Africa), aims to strengthen Africa's response to climate variability and change. Endorsed by the African Union Commission, the United Nations Economic Commission for Africa (UNECA) and the African Development Bank (AfDB), ClimDev-Africa was developed in 2006, and is planned for an 11 year period.[66,67]

What are going to be the effects on Asia?

Despite the various complications, unknowns and the poor fits of many of the existing climate models, it is possible to detect a number of trends in Asia related to global warming.[52] Asia is very likely to warm during this century; with increases above the global mean of 3°C in East and South Asia and 4°C further north by the end of this century (Figure 8.27). Rainfall will increase over most of Asia, as much as 30% or more in the north. South and East Asia will experience increases of 5 to 15%, except for declines of 5 to 15% in the December to February period over Northeast India and the Southeast Asian mainland.

Figure 8.27 – Temperature and precipitation changes over Asia (Multi model data set for the A1B scenario see below). Top row: Annual mean, December, January, February and June, July, August temperature change between 1980 to 1999 and 2080 to 2099, averaged over 21 models. Bottom row: same as top, but for fractional change in precipitation[53]

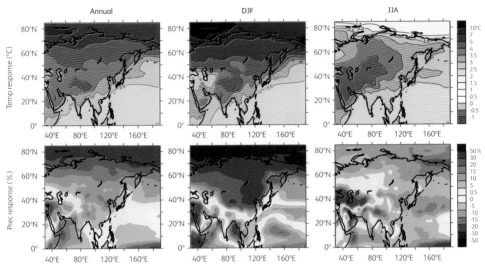

Of perhaps even greater significance is the very likely increase in the frequency of intense precipitation events in parts of South Asia, and in East Asia over this period. Extreme rainfall and winds associated with tropical cyclones are also likely to increase in East, Southeast and South Asia.[52]

China

In China there are clear differences between the expected climates in the north and west and those in the south and southeast. For example mean temperatures are expected to rise by 5° to 6°C in the north by 2080 (Figure 8.28). In effect this means considerably warmer winters.

Rainfall will also increase by up to 0.5 mm/day or more in the north and west over the same period. There will be small increases in the northeast, but reductions in the centre and southeast (Figure 8.29).

Figure 8.28 – Significantly increasing mean winter surface air temperatures by 2080 in the north of China (A2 scenario)[68]

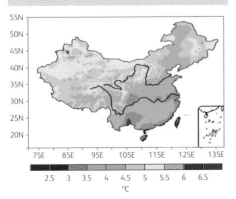

Figure 8.29 – Increased winter precipitation in the west and north of China (A2 scenario)[68]

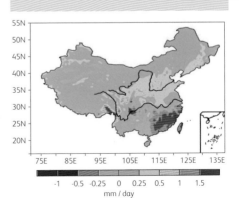

The PRECIS model, which reflects topographic features, has also been used to examine the changes in extreme events (Figure 8.30). For example, consistent with the general increases in minimum and maximum temperatures, it suggests that by 2080 China will have experienced a large reduction in the maximum consecutive number of frost days, as much as 80 % in the south of the country. It also reveals a greater incidence of extreme rainfall events (measured as days with rainfall greater than or equal to 20mm) throughout China but especially in the north and west, by 50 % to over 100 %.

Figure 8.30 – Percentage changes in (left) maximum number of consecutive frost days and (right) number of days with rainfall over 20mm[69]

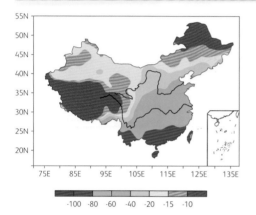
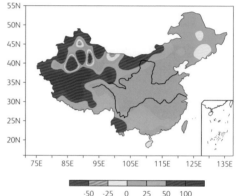

South Asia

As for China, India shows a marked north-south gradient in key predicted climatic variables over the next century. Temperatures will increase by as much as 4° to 5°C in the north. Precipitation will increase in much of the region, with up to 50 % increase along the Himalayan range, in western India and western Burma. Pakistan is predicted to experience 10 % to 15 % decline in rainfall (Figure 8.31).

Figure 8.31 – PRECIS model predictions of rising temperatures (left) and changes in precipitation (right) for South Asia by the end of the century under the A2 scenario[70]

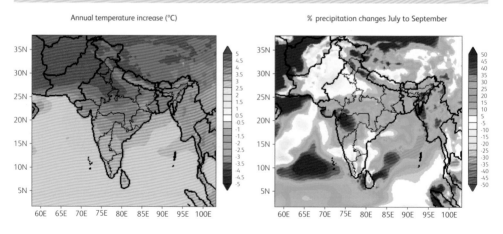

The PRECIS model also indicates future increases in extreme daily maximum and minimum temperatures throughout South Asia. Another study suggests that night temperatures will increase faster than the day temperatures, with the implication that cold extremes are very likely to be less severe in the future.[71] Such models also predict increases in the frequency, as well as intensities, of tropical cyclones in the Bay of Bengal, causing heavy precipitation during both southwest and northeast monsoon seasons.[70]

Bangladesh

One country that will experience the impacts of climate change perhaps more than most, and with increasing severity over the next decade, is Bangladesh. Most poor people in Bangladesh suffer

© Dieter Telemans – Panos Pictures

Figure 8.32 – Monsoon rains in a flooded area of Dhaka, Bangladesh. In 2004 the rains caused flooding in 40 of Bangladesh's 64 districts, displacing up to 30 million people and killing several hundred.

from severe disasters on an annual or even more frequent basis. This has been true for decades. The list of disasters includes flash floods, storm surges, tornados and cyclone winds, river bank erosion and drought. Poor Bangladeshis are used to dealing with these, as are many Bangladeshi institutions, including those of the government. But the disasters appear to becoming more frequent or intense in their actions (Box 8.4).

Box 8.4 The impacts of climate change on Bangladesh[72,73]

1. Sea levels are rising – 70% of Bangladesh is less than 10 metres above sea level. A 62 cm sea level rise would engulf 16% of the country, affecting 43 million people by 2080;

2. Increased rainfall – will cause greater frequency of flash floods and river bank erosion;

3. Increased salinity – of soil and ground water is predicted to affect two million hectares of land by 2050, as a consequence of sea level rises, rainfall and temperature changes;

4. Greater drought – particularly in the north-west which is likely to reduce agricultural production.

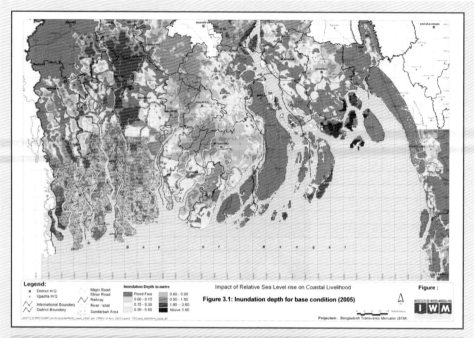

Figure 8.33 – A map showing how the coastal areas of Bangladesh are inundated during typical monsoon flooding. About 50% of land is flooded to a depth of more than 30cm.[72]

What are going to be the changes in Africa?

As in Asia, there is already evidence that Africa is warming faster than the global average and this is likely to continue (Figure 8.34). The warming occurs for all seasons of the year and, although the overall trend is geographically widespread, there are variations. In general the drier subtropical regions will warm more than the moister tropics.[52] But, for example, the tropical forests have warmed by 0.29°C per decade since 1970. In southern and western Africa there have been more warm spells and fewer extremely cold days. In eastern Africa temperatures have fallen close to the coasts and major inland lakes.[74-77]

The 21 Atmosphere-Ocean General Circulation Models (AOGCMs), analysed by the IPCC mostly agree that northern and southern Africa are likely to become much hotter (as much as 4°C or more) over the next 100 years based on the A1B scenario.

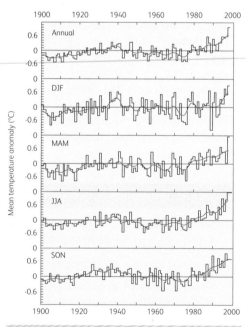

Figure 8.34 – Increasing African mean temperature anomalies over the past 100 years[78]

The warming is greater than the global annual mean warming for the continent as a whole. Northern and southern Africa will also become much drier (precipitation falling by 15 % or more) over the next century. The exceptions are in East Africa, including the Horn of Africa, where average rainfall will increase (Figure 8.35). Over much of the rest of Africa (including the Sahel) there is considerable uncertainty as to how the rainfall patterns will evolve.

Figure 8.35 – Temperature and rainfall projections for Africa, 1980 to 1999 versus 2080 to 2099 for scenario A1B[52]

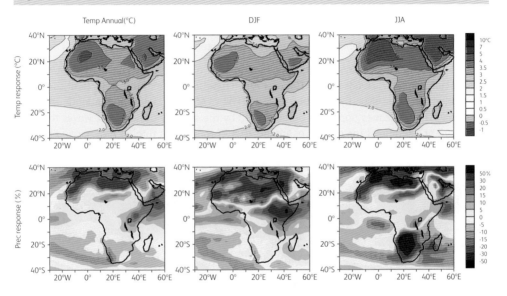

These are, it should be stressed, large scale predictions and provide a poor guide to local climates. As an illustration, an empirical downscale model for South Africa indicates increasing summer rainfall (Dec, Jan, Feb) over the central and eastern plateau and the Drakensberg Mountains, while the Western Cape will see little change, with some slight drying in summer and a slight decrease in winter rainfall (Figure 8.36).

The increasing rainfall variability is already apparent.[79] Inter-annual rainfall variability is large over most of Africa and, for some regions, multi-decadal variability is also substantial.[52] In Zimbabwe, for example, there are more cooler and hotter days, and the length and severity of the drier periods is increasing.[80] In the future, the frequency of extremely dry winters and springs in

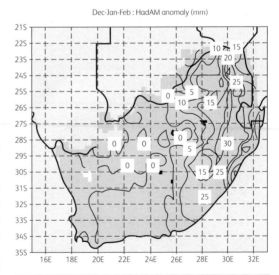

Figure 8.36 – Projected mean monthly rainfall increases for the summer period in South Africa from the downscaled Hadley model HadAM3[63]

southern Africa is likely to increase as will the frequency of extremely wet summers. As in other parts of the world, we can expect a general increase in the intensity of high-rainfall events associated, in part, with the increase in atmospheric water vapour.[81] It is not only changes in the total amount of rainfall that is important but also changes in the pattern of rainfall. For example, in regions of mean drying, there is likely to be a proportionally larger decrease in the number of rain days, but with greater intensity of rainfall.[52]

The southeast coast of Africa is subject to periodic tropical cyclones that originate over the Seychelles from October to June due to the southward displacement of the ITCZ. Rising sea surface temperatures are likely to increase cyclone intensity and there are some estimates of greater cyclone frequency, but cyclones are affected by many factors.[82,83]

It should be added that Africa's climate is also a driver at a global level. The latent heat released in deep cumulonimbus clouds in the ITCZ over Africa represents one of the major heat sources on the planet. There is also a correlation between West African rainfall and Atlantic hurricane frequency. The hurricanes appear to be generated by the easterly atmospheric waves that pass over Africa at the time of the monsoon. Around 20 % of the world's total of fires burning biomass occur in Africa's forests and sarannahs. Africa is also the world's largest source of atmospheric dust.[84] Both the fire aerosols and dust play a major role in the global climate.[85]

© Jessie Luna

Figure 8.37 – A farmer in Mali surveys the sky

4. Conclusion

There is widespread agreement in the scientific community that global warming is a reality and is a consequence of the anthropogenic release of greenhouse gases into the atmosphere. This warming, and the associated climatic changes, will have far-reaching effects throughout the developing regions. In summary, although there remain many unknowns, we do know, at least in general terms, what is likely to happen over the next 50 years.[52]

Africa and Asia are very likely to get:

- Warmer (colder in a small number of places).

Africa will get:

- Drier, but with more rainfall and floods in some regions.

Asia will get:

- Mostly wetter.

and throughout the regions there is likely to be:

- More intense tropical cyclones;
- Higher sea levels;
- More storm surges;
- More climatic variability and extreme weather events.

What is not known is how these various scenarios are affected by the three big drivers of regional climates – tropical convections, the monsoons and the El Niño – Oscillation. Nor is it yet clear how these drivers are in turn affected by global warming. Until research provides better answers it is going to be difficult to predict with any high degree of certainty how the climate of a particular region or country will unfold over the next few decades.

What is clear is that, for most regions, extreme events – heavy rainfall, prolonged hot and dry spells, and severe storms and cyclones – will be more frequent and intense. It is largely to this reality that adaptation will have to address itself, as we discuss in the next chapter.

Chapter 8 references and further reading

1   Stern, N.H., (2007) *The Economics of Climate Change: The Stern Review*.
    Cambridge University Press, Cambridge.

2   NOAA. (2009) *State of the Climate Global Analysis – Annual 2008*.
    National Oceanic and Atmospheric Administration, National Climate Data Center. Available at:
    www.ncdc.noaa.gov/sotc/index.php?report=global&year=2008&month=ann [Accessed 3 Dec 2009].

3   European Environment Agency. (2009) *CSI 013 – Atmospheric greenhouse gas concentrations*.
    Available at: themes.eea.europa.eu/IMS/ISpecs/ISpecification20041007131717/
    IAssessment1234255180259/view_content [Accessed 3 Dec 2009].

4   Foster, P. et al., (2007) *Chapter 2 – Changes in Atmospheric constituents and in radiative forcing*.
    In: Solomon, S. et al., (eds). *Climate Change 2007, The Physical Science Basis*.
    Contribution of Working Group I to the Fourth Assessment Report of the IPCC. Cambridge University
    Press, Cambridge.

5   Royal Society Climate Change Advisory Group. (2007) *Climate change controversies: a simple guide*.
    Available at: royalsociety.org/Report_WF.aspx?pageid=8030&terms=climate+change+controversies
    [Accessed 3 Dec 2009].

6   Pearce, F., (2007) Climate myths: Global warming is down to the Sun, not humans. *New Scientist*.
    16 May. Available at: www.newscientist.com/article/dn11650 [Accessed 3 Dec 2009].

7   NASA. (2003) *The 1991 Mt. Pinatubo Eruption Provides a Natural Test for the Influence of Artic
    Circulation on Climate*. 12 March. Available at:
    www.nasa.gov/centers/goddard/news/topstory/2003/0306aopin.html [Accessed 3 Dec 2009].

8   O'Hare, G. Sweeney, J. & Wilby, R., (2005) *Weather, Climate and Climate Change: Human Perspectives*,
    Prentice Hall, Harlow, England.

9   Solomon, S. et al., (2007) *Technical Summary*. In: Solomon, S. et al., (eds). *Climate Change 2007,
    The Physical Science Basis*. Contribution of Working Group I to the Fourth Assessment Report of the
    IPCC. Cambridge University Press, Cambridge.

10 Gladwell, M., (2000) *The Tipping Point: How Little Things Can Make a Big Difference*, Little Brown,
    New York.

11 National Research Council. (2002) *Abrupt Climate Change: Inevitable Surprises*, Natl Acad Press,
    Washington, DC.

12 Lenton, T. et al., (2008) Tipping elements in the Earth's climate system. *PNAS*, **105**, 1786 – 1893.

13 Hansen, J. et al., (2007) Dangerous human-made interference with climate: A GISS model E study,
    Atmos. Chem. Phys, **7**, 2287-2312.

14 Lemke, P. et al., (2007) *Ch 5 – Observations: Changes in Snow, Ice and Frozen Ground*.
    In: Solomon, S. et al., eds. *Climate Change 2007: The Physical Science Basis*. Contribution of Working
    Group I to the Fourth Assessment Report of the Intergovernmental Panel on Climate Change.
    Cambridge University Press, Cambridge.

15 Hanna, E. et al., (2005) Runoff and mass balance of the Greenland Ice Sheet: 1958-2003. *Journal of
    Geophysical Research – Atmospheres*, 110.

16 Rignot, E. et al., (2008) Mass balance of the Greenland ice sheet from 1958 to 2007, *Geophys.
    Res. Lett*, **35**, L20502.

17 Gregory, J. & Huybrechts, P., (2006) Ice-sheet contributions to future sea-level change, *Phil. Trans. Roy.
    Soc. A*, **364**, 1709.

18 Meehl, G. et al., (2007) *Ch 10 – Global Climate Projections*. In: Solomon, S. et al., (eds). *Climate Change
    2007, The Physical Science Basis*. Contribution of Working Group I to the Fourth Assessment Report of
    the IPCC. Cambridge University Press, Cambridge.

19 Lowe, J. et al., (2006) The Role of Sea-Level Rise and the Greenland Ice Sheet in Dangerous Climate Change: Implications for the Stabilisation of Climate. In: Schellnhuber, H. et al., (eds). *Avoiding Dangerous Climate Change*. Cambridge University press, Cambridge. 29-36.

20 Naranjo, L., (2002) *Fragment of its Former Shelf*. NASA Earth Observatory. Available at: Earthobservatory.nasa.gov/Features/LarsenIceShelf [Accessed 20 Dec 2009].

21 Vaughan, D., (2005) How does the Antarctic Ice Sheet affect sea level rise? *Science*, **308**, 1877-1878.

22 Oppenheimer, M., (1998) Global warming and the stability of the West Antarctic Ice Sheet. *Nature*, **393**, 325-332.

23 Lenten, T. et al., (2008) Tipping elements in the Earth's climate system. *PNAS*, **105**, 1786-1793.

24 Milkov, A., (2004) "Global estimates of hydrate-bound gas in marine sediments: how much is really out there?" *Earth-Sci Rev*, **66**, 183-197.

25 National Energy Technology Laboratory (NETL). (nd) *The National Methane Hydrates R&D Program – All Available at: About Hydrates – Arctic Regions*. www.netl.doe.gov/technologies/oil-gas/FutureSupply/MethaneHydrates/about-hydrates/arctic-regions.htm [Accessed 3 Dec 2009].

26 Earle, S., (1999) *Methane hydrates – energy source, climate control and ice worms!* Malaspina University College Geology Department – New Developments in Earth Science. Available at: records.viu.ca/~earles/m-hydrate-nov99.htm [Accessed 3 Dec 2009].

27 USGS. (2009) *Gas Hydrate: What is it?*. US Geological Survey – Woods Hole Science Center. Available at: woodshole.er.usgs.gov/project-pages/hydrates/what.html [Accessed 3 Dec 2009].

28 Conner, S., (2008) *Hundreds of methane 'plumes' discovered*. The Independent. 25 September. Available at: www.independent.co.uk/news/science/hundreds-of-methane-plumes-discovered-941456.html [Accessed 3 Dec 2009].

29 Zachos, J. et al., (2001) Trends, Rhythms, and Aberrations in Global Climate 65 Ma to Present. *Science*, **292**, 686-693.

30 Hansen, J. et al., (2007) Dangerous human-made interference with climate: A GISS model E study, *Atmos. Chem. Phys*, **7**, 2287-2312.

31 IPCC. (2007) *Summary for Policymakers*. In: Solomon, S. et al., (eds) *Climate Change 2007: The Physical Science Basis. Contribution of Working Group I to the Fourth Assessment Report of the Intergovernmental Panel on Climate Change*. Cambridge University Press, Cambridge.

32 Shinker, J., (2007) *Global Climate Animations*. Digital Library for Earth System Education Available at: www.dlese.org/library/catalog_DLESE-000-000-001-774.htm [Accessed 23 Dec 2009].

33 African Monsoon Multidisciplinary Analysis (AMMA). (2005) *The International Science Plan for AMMA*. AMMA International, Toulouse. Available at: amma-international.org/library/docs/AMMA_ISP_May2005.pdf [Accessed 3 Dec 2009].

34 Trenberth, K. et al., (2007) Ch 3 – *Observations: Surface and Atmospheric Climate Change*. In Solomon, S. et al., (eds.) *Climate Change 2007: The Physical Science Basis*. Contribution of Working Group I to the Fourth Assessment Report of the Intergovernmental Panel on Climate Change. Cambridge University Press, Cambridge.

35 NASA Goddard Space Flight Center. (2004) *Researchers seeing double on African Monsoons*. 10 June. Available at: www.nasa.gov/centers/goddard/news/topstory/2004/0510africanwaves.html [Accessed 3 Dec 2009].

36 Chase, T. et al., (2003) Changes in Global Monsoon Circulations since 1950. *Natural Hazards*, **29**, 229-254.

37 Huijun, W., (2001) The Weakening of the Asian Monsoon Circulation after the End of the 1970s. *Advances in Atmospheric Sciences*, **18**, 3.

38 Dash, S. et al., (2009), Changes in the characteristics of rain events in India, *J. Geophys. Res*, **114**.

39   Goswami, B. et al., (2006) Increasing Trend of Extreme Rain Events Over India in a Warming Environment, *Science*, **314**, 1442-1446.

40   Shanahan, T. et al., (2006) *Three millennia of variations in the West African monsoon: insights into tropical and global teleconnections from the varved sediments of Lake Bosumtwi.* American Geophysical Union, Fall Meeting. Available at: adsabs.harvard.edu/abs/2006AGUFMGC21A1321S [Accessed 3 Dec 2009].

41   Shanahan, T. et al., (2009) Atlantic Forcing of Persistent Drought in West Africa. *Science*, **17**, 324, 377-380.

42   Glantz, M., (ed.) (2002) *La Niña and its Impacts: Facts and Speculation.* United Nations University Press, New York.

43   NOAA. *Tropical Atmospheric Ocean Project – Diagrams.* Available at: www.pmel.noaa.gov/tao/proj_over/diagrams/index.html [Accessed 3 Dec 2009].

44   NOAA. (nd). *What is an El Nino?* Available at: www.pmel.noaa.gov/tao/elnino/el-nino-story.html [Accessed 3 Dec 2009].

45   Salinger, J. et al., (1996) Observed variability and change in climate and sea-level in Oceania. In: Bouma, W., Pearman, G. & Manning, M., eds. *Greenhouse: Coping with Climate Change.* CSIRO, Melbourne, 100-126.

46   Trenberth, K. et al., (2002) The evolution of ENSO and global atmospheric temperatures. *Journal of Geophysical Research*, **107**.

47   Van Shayk, I. et al.,(2005) El Niño causes dramatic outbreak of *Paederus dermatitis* in East Africa. In: Pak Sum Low (ed.) *Climate Change and Africa*, Cambridge University Press, 240-247.

48   Obasi, G., (2005) The impacts of ENSO in Africa. In: Pak Sum Low (ed.) *Climate Change and Africa*, Cambridge University Press. 218-230.

49   Vitart, F, Anderson, D. & Stockdale, T., (2003) Seasonal Forecasting of Tropical Cyclone Landfall over Mozambique. J*ournal of Climate*, **16**, 3932-3945.

50   May, W., (2004) Potential of future changes in the Indian summer monsoon due to greenhouse warming: analysis of mechanisms in a global time-slice experiment. *Clim. Dyn*, **22**, 389-414.

51   Chase, T. et al., (2003) Changes in Global Monsoon Circulations since 1950. *Natural Hazards*, **29**, 229-254.

52   Christensen, J. et al., (2007) *Ch 11 – Regional Climate Projections.* In: Solomon, S. et al., (eds.) *Climate Change 2007: The Physical Science Basis.* Contribution of Working Group I to the Fourth Assessment Report of the Intergovernmental Panel on Climate Change. Cambridge University Press, Cambridge.

53   Trenberth, K., (1990) Recent observed interdecadal climate changes in the Northern Hemisphere. *Bull. Am. Meteorol. Soc*, **71**, 988-993.

54   Trenberth, K. & Stepaniak, D., (2001) Indices of El Nino Evolution. *Journal of Climate*, **14**, 8. 1697-1701.

55   NOAA Earth System Research Laboratory. Multivariate ENSO Index. Last update: 5 October 2009. US National Oceanic and Atmospheric Administration (NOAA). Available at: www.cdc.noaa.gov/people/klaus.wolter/MEI/ [Accessed 3 Dec 2009].

56   Trenberth, K., (2002) Climate change and the ENSO cycle; are they linked? In: Glantz, M. (ed.) 2002 *La Niña and its Impacts: Facts and Speculation.* United Nations University Press, New York, 51-56.

57   Collins, M. & CMIP Modeling Groups. (2005) El Niño – or La Niña-like climate change? *Clim. Dynam*, **24**, 89-104.

58   Landsea, C., (2000) Climate Variability table – Tropical Cyclones. In: Landsea, C., (2000) climate variability of tropical cyclones: Past, Present and Future, In: Pielke, R, Sr. & Pielke, R. Jr., (eds.) *Storms*. Routledge, New York, 220-241 Available at: www.aoml.noaa.gov/hrd/Landsea/climvari/table.html [Accessed 3 Dec 2009].

59 Webster, P. et al., (2005) Changes in tropical cyclone number, duration and intensity in a warming environment. *Science*, **309**, 1844-1846.

60 Webster, P. et al., (2006) Response to comment on "Changes in tropical cyclone number, duration, and intensity in a warming environment". *Science*, **311**, 1713c.

61 McBride, J. et al., (2006) *Statement on tropical cyclones and climate change*. WMO International Workshop on Tropical Cyclones, IWTC-6, San Jose, Costa Rica, November 2006. Available at: www.wmo.int/pages/prog/arep/tmrp/documents/iwtc_statement.pdf [Accessed 3 Dec 2009].

62 Jones, R. et al., (2004) *Generating high resolution climate change scenarios using PRECIS*, Met Office Hadley Centre, Exeter. Available at: precis.metoffice.com/docs/PRECIS_Handbook.pdf [Accessed 5 Dec 2009].

63 Hewitson, B. & Crane, R., (2006) Consensus between GCM Climate Change Projections with Empirical Downscaling: Precipitation Downscaling over South Africa. *Int J Climatol*, **26**, 1315-1337.

64 Washington, R. et al., (2006) *African Climate Change: Taking the Shorter Route*. Bulletin of the American Meteorological Society 1355-1366.

65 World Meteorological Office. (2003) *Twenty-First Status Report on Implementation of the World Weather Watch: Forty years of World Weather Watch*, WMO No. **957**, 49.

66 GCOS. (2006) *Climate Information for Development Needs: An Action Plan for Africa Report and Implementation Strategy*. Addis Ababa, Ethiopia. 18-21 April.

67 UNECA. *Summary of the Climate for Development in Africa Programme*. Africa Climate Advisory Bulletin. Available at: www.uneca.org [Accessed 3 Dec 2009].

68 Xiong, W. et al., (2008) The *Impacts of Climate Change on Chinese Agriculture – Phase II, National Level Study:* The Impacts of Climate Change on Cereal Production in China, Final Report. AEA Group, UK.

69 Zhang, Y. et al., (2006) A future climate scenario of regional changes in extreme climate events over China using the PRECIS climate model. *Geophysical Research Letters*, **33**, L24702.

70 Kumar, K., (2006) High-resolution climate change scenarios for India for the 21st century, *Current Science*, **90**, 334-345.

71 Unnikrishnan, A. et al., (2006) Sea level changes along the Indian coast: Observations and projections. *Curr. Sci.India*, **90**, 362-368.

72 IWM (2007) *Investigating the Impact of Relative Sea-Level Rise on Coastal Communities and their Livelihoods in Bangladesh, Final Report*. Institute of Water Modelling, Dhaka.

73 DFID. (2007) Chapter 8 – Environment, climate change and natural resources. In: *DFID Annual Report 2007: Development on the Record*. DFID, London. Available at: www.dfid.gov.uk/Documents/publications/departmental-report/2007/DFID-AR07-Chapter8.pdf [Accessed 5 December 2009].

74 Malhi, Y. & Wright, J., (2004) Spatial patterns and recent trends in the climate of tropical forest regions. *Philosophical Transactions of the Royal Society of London Series*, B, **359** 311-329.

75 Kruger, A. & Shongwe, S., (2004) Temperature trends in South Africa: 1960-2004. *Int. J. Climatol*, **24**, 1929-1945.

76 New, M. et al., (2006) Evidence of trends in daily climate extremes over Southern and West Africa, *Journal of Geophysical Research* – Atmospheres, **111**.

77 King'uyu, S. Ogallo, L. & Anyamba, E., (2000) Recent trends of minimum and maximum surface temperatures over eastern Africa. *J. Clim*, **13**, 2876-2886.

78 Hulme, M. et al., (2001) African climate change: 1900-2100. *Climate Research*, **17**, 145-168.

79 Hulme, M. et al., (2005) Global warming and African climate change: a re-assessment. In Low, P.S. (ed.) *Climate Change and Africa*, Cambridge University Press. 29-40.

80 FAO. (2004) *Drought impact mitigation and prevention in the Limpopo River Basin: A situation analysis*. Land and Water Discussion paper 4 Natural Resources Management and Environment Department, FAO, Rome.

81   Tadross, M. Jack, C. & Hewitson, B., (2005) On RCM-based projections of change in southern Africa summer climate. *Geophysical Research Letters*, **32**, 23.

82   McDonald, R. et al., (2005) Tropical storms: representation and diagnosis in climate models and the impacts of climate change. *Climate Dynamics*, **25**, 19-36.

83   Lal, M., (2001) Tropical cyclones in a warmer world. *Current Science*, **80**, 1103-1104.

84   AMMA. (2007) *Background*. African Monsoon Multidisciplinary Analyses. Available at: www.ileaps.org/index.php?option=com_content&task=view&id=103&Itemid=1 [Accessed 3 Dec 2009].

85   Mahowald, N. & Kiehl, L., (2003) Mineral aerosol and cloud interactions, *Geophysical Research Letters*, **30**, (9), 1475.

09

Adapting to
Climate Change

Overflowing of the Seim Reap River in Cambodia after Typhoon Ketsana in early October 2009
© Ralph Combs – Flickr

The actual and potential changes to global and regional climates described in the last chapter are large and wide ranging, with the capacity to affect many aspects of people's everyday lives. Even if we succeed in mitigating climate change by keeping the average global temperature increase to just 2°C above pre-industrial levels, substantial impacts will still occur and require responses. If the temperature rise over the next few decades is significantly higher, then the impacts will be extremely damaging and significantly new and innovative adaptive approaches will be required.

In this chapter we begin by discussing the nature of vulnerability to climate change, including the likely economic and human costs. We then go on to describe the available processes of adaptation and how they may be assessed, in particular in the context of building resilience. We will also examine a range of impacts, covering sea level rise, water resources, agriculture, biodiversity and health. In each case we will demonstrate where science and innovation can help to provide means of adaptation.

1. Vulnerability

It is the developing countries who are amongst the most vulnerable to climate change (Box 9.1).

Box 9.1 Why developing countries are so vulnerable to climate change[1]

Developing countries tend to be located in regions which are already subject to climatic extremes, or where the extremes may become even worse. For example, they may be particularly vulnerable to floods, drought or sea level rise.

They tend to have a higher share of their assets and wealth tied up in natural resources and environmental assets; anything which destroys the natural resource base will bring increasing damage to these countries.

Developing countries are also highly dependent on the agricultural sector – for food, employment, incomes, tax revenue and exports. Agriculture is particularly vulnerable to climate change. In Africa and parts of South Asia, subsistence farmers rely on natural rainfall which leaves them highly vulnerable to quite small changes in rainfall patterns.

Large areas of agricultural land are already classified as "dryland", and climate change is likely to bring less rainfall and a shorter growing season in the future, expanding such drylands over a larger area (Figure 9.1). Many parts of the developing world are already experiencing water shortages and this may increase further.

In some parts of the developing world cyclones, and other extreme rainfall events, will bring flooding that can be devastating for livestock and crop production.

In addition, infrastructure that can reduce the impacts of climate hazards is often either lacking or not fit for purpose (see Box 9.4). Developing country governments and institutions are often poorly resourced and unprepared; many people will have to cope on their own. The emigration of well-qualified people further limits their capacity.

Finally, most people in developing countries operate at low income levels with limited reserves, and lack formal insurance cover.

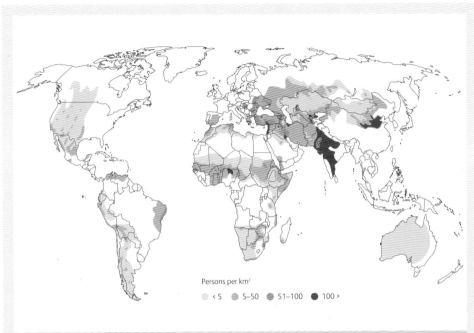

Figure 9.1 – Drylands of the world, showing the high population concentrations in South Asia, China and across the Sahel[2]

The economic costs

The economic costs of future climate change are yet unknown, but some developing countries have already started to assess the cost of climate extremes. For example, the Ningxia Autonomous Region of northern China regularly suffers from a range of major shocks, the most serious being sand storms, drought and high temperatures (Figure 9.2).

Figure 9.2 – The high incidence of major climate related disasters in Ningxia Autonomous Region, China showing the percentage of villagers who identified the disaster as important[3]

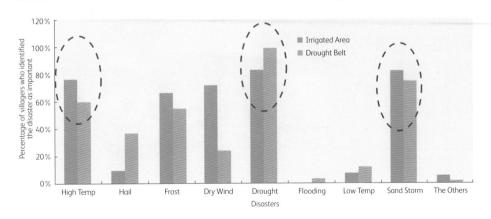

The region is prone to such disasters, but the frequency and intensity appears to be increasing as a result of climate change. The total economic cost of these disasters has risen steadily over the past ten years and was estimated to be ¥1.6 billion renminbi (RMB) (£140 million) in 2007 (Figure 9.3). Because the region has become highly industrialised the GDP has also risen, causing the percentage loss due to climatic effects to fall to 2 % – still a sizeable proportion in economic terms.

Figure 9.3 – Costs of climate related damage, Ningxia Autonomous Region, China. (Costs in 100 million RMB)[3]

It has also been estimated that without adaptation, the agricultural losses each year due to global warming will be anywhere between £1 billion and £49 billion from 2000 to 2050.[4]

Statistics like these are beginning to bring home to developing country governments that climate change is already a significant threat to their development goals. However, beneath the statistics is an even harsher reality. Climate change will affect and, indeed, is already affecting, nearly every aspect of the lives and livelihoods of the poor who live in the most vulnerable places. Not only is their health likely to suffer, they may die, directly or indirectly, as a result of climate change. And because so many of the poor, especially the rural poor, rely on natural resources to provide food, fibre and water, their livelihoods will suffer as a consequence. Even in the cities of the developing world, where the poor live in slums and squatter settlements, they too will be adversely affected by rising temperatures, increasing disease and lack of a clean water supply.

© Rafiqur Rahman Raqu – DFID

Figure 9.4 – Streets in the district of Satkhira, in southern Bangladesh, are flooded after months of heavy rain – people travel by boat to reach the local shop

Assessing vulnerability

In developed countries it has become commonplace to conduct vulnerability assessments of various kinds. These typically focus on major infrastructure projects. For example, assessments may be conducted on transportation, energy, water supply or communication systems. Of more relevance to climate change is the programme of risk and vulnerability assessments now being undertaken by the US National Oceanic and Atmospheric Administration (NOAA) for coastal communities at risk from storm damage.[5]

A number of vulnerability assessments have also been carried out by governments in developing countries (Box 9.2).

Box 9.2   An Indian vulnerability assessment[6,7]

In 2002 the Indian government initiated a large-scale assessment of the country's vulnerability to climate change. The work was funded by the Global Environment Facility under its 'enabling activities' programme, and coordinated through India's National Communication to the UNFCC (NATCOM).

Over 30 research teams throughout the country undertook modelling of climate projections using global and regional climate models which projected temperature, rainfall and extreme events. They also studied the expected impacts on, and vulnerability of, a range of key sectors. These included: water resources, agriculture/crop production, forests and natural ecosystems, coastal zones, industry, energy and infrastructure and health, particularly malaria.

The teams used a wide variety of approaches, from quantitative and economic modelling, to impact-matrices, remote sensing and Geographic Information Systems (GIS). For example, when looking at the expected impacts on biodiversity, the group predicted increased species loss, particularly due to a shift in forest boundaries, with Xeric shrubland and woodland expected to become more dominant shrubland (Figure 9.5).

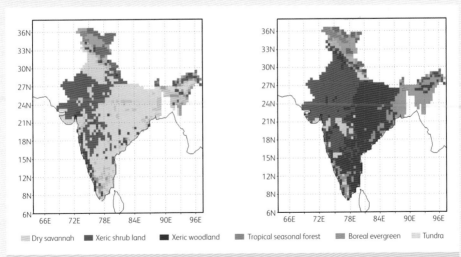

 ▨ Dry savannah   ■ Xeric shrub land   ■ Xeric woodland   ■ Tropical seasonal forest   ■ Boreal evergreen   ▨ Tundra

Figure 9.5 – The shifting forest boundaries of India, showing present biome types (left) and expected changes in 2050 (right)

The teams discovered that all sectors would experience direct climate change impacts, especially along the coastlines. The report stressed the need to factor future climate projections into current infrastructure planning and investment. In the short-term; they highlighted the need for enhanced capacity for scientific assessment, awareness among stakeholders and improved institutionalisation of the learning process.

The assessment concluded that 'the quality of development would be the prime insurance at the national level to deal with adverse impacts of climate change.'

The hazardous effects of adverse weather are nothing new, particularly for poor people in developing countries. But the scale and, in some situations, the nature of the impacts may change dramatically as the pace of climate change increases. More and more people could experience:

- Increased water and food insecurity;

- Adverse impacts on health and on social and economic services delivery;

- Outbreaks of vector borne diseases;

- Damaged and degraded infrastructure;

- Threatened human settlements and human life;

- Biodiversity destruction and damaged ecosystems.

The challenge faced by governments, communities and households is how to adapt, efficiently, fairly and sustainably to these increasingly frequent and intensive hazards.

2. Adaptation and resilience

Adapting to climate change is as complex a process as the phenomenon of climate change itself.[8] As well as understanding climatic impacts, the hazards they generate, where they occur and with what degree of certainty the prediction is made – adaptation needs to assess the various dimensions of vulnerability and the appropriateness, including costs and benefits, of a range of potential options for action.

Coping strategies

In practice, adaptation is a collection of coping strategies, with each strategy focussed on a particular threat. Some of these actions may be taken by autonomous individuals or communities reacting to climate change hazards as they occur; others may be more planned, depending for their initiation on government policies and institutions.[8]

For example; farmers faced with the threat of flooding may plant new flood resistant rice varieties. They may also build protection around the rice field, ensure the flood water is quickly drained away or develop a more diverse livelihood so that other sources of income will offset the losses from flooding. But governments may also plan for such flooding by building suitable infrastructure or developing specific policies that mitigate the effects of flooding. Some of these strategies will be technological, others social, economic or political (Box 9.3).

Box 9.3   There are a wide range of coping strategies for climate hazards

- **Institutional** – land use zoning to protect against flooding, warning systems for cyclones;

- **Economic** – weather crop insurance to compensate for climatic extremes, micro-credit schemes to develop a range of sources of income;

- **Physical** – cyclone shelters, embankments and other infrastructure to provide protection against floods;

- **Medical** – vaccines to protect against increased disease incidence;

- **Environmental** – mangrove shelterbelts and coastal forests to protect against sea level rise;

- **Agricultural** – drought and flood resistant crop varieties and cropping systems;

- **Livelihood** – income diversity, rural-urban linkages.

The construction of appropriate infrastructure is one of the key approaches used by governments to avoid or minimize serious hazards (Box 9.4).

Box 9.4   The role of infrastructure

Infrastructure plays a crucial role in avoiding or minimizing hazards. Flood defences and drainage systems can reduce the risk of flooding. Communications infrastructure can provide communities with advance warning of threats. Piped water and sanitation systems can lessen the disease burden associated with climate hazards. Adoption of relevant design standards and building codes can ensure that housing, roads, bridges and other amenities are capable of withstanding extreme weather events. Planning and land use regulations are important for discouraging building in susceptible areas. For existing infrastructure, maintenance is key to climate-proofing.

However, in poor communities essential infrastructure is either absent or inadequate, and the capacity to rectify this may also be lacking.[9] The absence of existing infrastructure can provide an opportunity to adopt good practice when building new facilities. The agreed key principle of reconstruction following disasters is to 'build back better' – but it cannot be taken for granted that this will happen.

© Nichola Krey/Austcare – Flickr

Figure 9.6 – Following events such as the tsunami in Aceh, Indonesia there is an opportunity to rebuild to withstand future climate events

Building codes are often imported and hence fail to take account of local circumstances.

- In Peru, for example, following the earthquake in 2007, it was found that there were no design standards for traditional adobe buildings.[10]

- In Afghanistan, in 2005, the reconstruction of the highway, which connects the north to the city of Kabul, used an outdated approach to the engineering design. As a result, a minor flooding event caused severe damage to the highway. This could have easily been avoided by allowing for controlled losses (sacrificial elements) in the design; any subsequent repairs would have then been less costly.[11]

© Bentley Smith – Flickr

Figure 9.7 – A stilt house on the Mekong Delta

An example of a community-based strategy using a similar principle – i.e. allowing for a degree of damage to enable the bulk of a structure to survive – is provided by the stilt houses in the Mekong delta. These have woven raffia walls that can be rolled up when a severe storm is expected, so winds blow through houses rather than blowing them away.[12]

The trend towards urbanisation in the developing world is leading to more poor people living in illegal slums, where design standards and land use regulations are of little relevance. For these people, climate vulnerability is closely coupled to their basic development needs. Infrastructure comprises not only physical structures, but also the process and institutional arrangements that facilitate the flow of goods and services between individuals, firms, and governments.[13] For the most vulnerable people, strengthening the physical and institutional elements of infrastructure is an essential step towards building climate resilience.

Usually the overall adaptation system for a household or community is a mix; infrastructure may play a key role, but institutional or livelihood responses may also be crucial. The final mix depends on the nature of the hazard and its dynamics. Hazards generally come in two forms which may require different responses:

1. Shocks – usually dramatic, largely unexpected, events such as sudden floods, cyclones, earthquakes and tsunamis, outbreaks of disease or a financial crash.

2. Stresses – gradual build-up of adverse events for example increasing temperatures, rising sea levels, greater or lesser rainfall, rising debt.

Unlike more gradual change, shocks can cause profound, sudden disruption to economies and communities. Nevertheless stresses – although more predictable – can slowly build-up to catastrophic outcomes.

The concept of resilience

A useful concept in adaptation is resilience (Box 9.5). In everyday language resilience is the ability to 'bounce back.' Implicit is the sense that the individual, community or system *can maintain its identity in the face of internal change and external shocks and disturbances*.[14]

Box 9.5   The evolution of the concept of resilience[15]

The modern scientific concept of resilience owes much to the work of ecologists, notably C.S. Holling, who in the 1970s tried to understand the circumstances which caused ecosystems to switch from one stable state to another.[16] Some of the examples involved forestry and fisheries. Typically a system threshold exists beyond which the system changes to a new state. For example, a fishery may remain relatively stable and productive up to a certain level of fishing intensity, but if the threshold is exceeded the fishery may collapse to a new, much less productive state, or disappear altogether.

The phenomenon has been popularised through the concept of 'tipping points.'[17] Several of these have already been discussed in the previous chapter in relation to climate change.

Resilience used to be a rather esoteric subject for research, but recently it has become more widely invoked in planning responses to a wide range of global threats.

In terms of poverty-reduction, resilience can be related to a desired development pathway – measured by agricultural production, household income, GDP per capita or some other statistic. This pathway is then subjected to a shock or stress. In Figure 9.8 development is illustrated as an increasing trend. Along comes a stress or shock which in some circumstances can be fully resisted; a dam or barrage may prevent a flood. More often the development path is adversely affected and growth falls, this is generally followed by recovery which may be fast or slow. In some cases the disturbance is too great and recovery may not fully occur. Development may resume along a less productive path or in extreme cases may collapse altogether. A resilient pathway is one that persists, despite the stresses and shocks, in more or less its intended form.

For each stress or shock there is an appropriate adaptation consisting of one or more countermeasures that serve to maintain the resilience.

Figure 9.8 – The patterns of resilience, showing the effects of stress (left) and shocks (right)

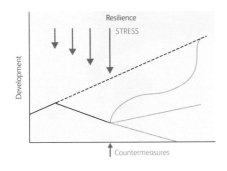
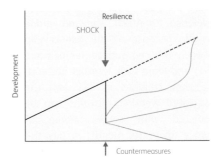

In practical terms it is useful to categorise the countermeasures on a time scale relevant to the incidence of the stress or shock (Figure 9.9).

This conceptualization follows, in some respects, the steps taken in modern disaster risk reduction to cope with hazards such as earthquakes and cyclones. Developing resilience to climate change thus builds on the various approaches to disaster risk reduction that have been successfully practiced over the years.[18]

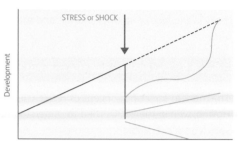

Figure 9.9 – The timescale of countermeasure interventions

Anticipate Survey Prevent Tolerate Recover Restore Learn

Anticipation

Anticipation of stresses and shocks consists of one part of a vulnerability analysis as discussed in the previous section. In essence it is a process of surveying in order to determine the likely location and probability of potential disturbances. Such inventories can be depicted as hazard maps. Some on a large scale are often produced by government agencies. These maps need to take into account:

- Physical vulnerabilities e.g. the location of sites prone to floods and droughts, infrastructure vulnerabilities – particularly in relation to sea level rises and storm surges;

- Biological vulnerabilities e.g. crops and livestock at risk, fragile ecosystems;

- Human vulnerabilities e.g. populations likely to suffer from flooding or drought, or health hazards.

Figure 9.10 depicts the spatial hazard of drought for maize growing in southern Africa.

Other smaller scale surveys can be produced by local communities for their own planning. The advantage of these is that if a flood or other hazard arises, potentially affected communities can respond rapidly.

Anticipation also involves producing long-range weather forecasts which can be used to put in place adaptive measures. Such forecasts have been developed for Africa. They are made possible because of the relationship between the sea surface temperature (SST) and large scale weather patterns. The slow changes in SST and the associated weather patterns can be predicted with some degree of ccuracy up to six months in advance (Figure 9.11).

Figure 9.10 – Risk of drought during the crucial grain filling stage of maize in southern Africa[19]

Risk of drought
- Very High
- High
- Medium
- Low
- Very Low

Figure 9.11 – Long range precipitation forecast for Africa made by the European Centre for Medium-Range Weather Forecasts in September 2009 for the following December, January and February[20]

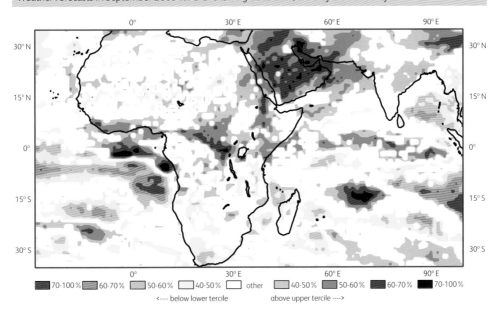

Prevention and tolerance

The subsequent steps – prevention and tolerance, recovery and restoration – involve defining objectives, identifying the various options and then appraising them in terms of their outcomes and the relevant costs and benefits. A team from the Chinese Academy of Agricultural Sciences, the University of East Anglia and other advisors in China and the UK developed a process which outlines the most appropriate options for climate change adaptation (Figure 9.12).

Figure 9.12 – An adaptation option appraisal process developed in China[21]

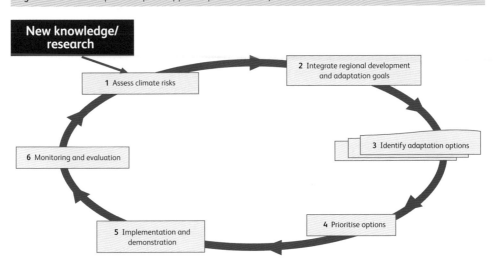

To be effective such an option appraisal process needs to be fairly sophisticated. Table 9.1 lists the multiple criteria used in appraising options in the Chinese adaptation model, using methods developed for a DFID climate screening process called ORCHID (Opportunities and Risks of Climate Change and Disasters).[3,22]

Table 9.1 Criteria for climate change option appraisals

- **Win-win options**
  Does the option address current climate variability and future climate change?

- **Existing risk management**
  Is the option consistent with existing risk management activities?

- **Cost-effectiveness**
  Can costs and benefits of the option be easily determined?

- **Adaptive flexibility**
  Does the option focus on a narrow range of future scenarios, or does it allow for flexibility of response?

- **Unintended impacts**
  Potential negative spin-off impacts beyond targeted activity?

- **Practical considerations**
  Is the option practical and feasible for the implementer?

- **Knowledge level**
  How certain are we in predicting a particular change in the hazard and its impact?

- **Policy coherence**
  Does the option reflect local and national Disaster Risk Reduction (DRR) / adaptation plans or studies?

Calculating costs and benefits is not easy. Resilience, however, has the advantage of being both a qualitative and quantitative concept. In theory, the strength of stress and shock can be measured, as can the path of resistance or recovery – or the collapse. Costs can then be assigned to the impacts of the shocks and stresses and to countermeasures, while benefits are calculated for the subsequent development pathway. Hence the different countermeasures can be assessed in terms of both costs and benefits.

In some respects it is easier in the case of climate stresses which tend to be highly targeted. For example the impact of reduced rainfall can be prevented by a variety of specific water harvesting and water saving systems. These can be devices ranging from large-scale reservoirs to village tanks with accompanying systems of delivery. The design and construction of such systems may be relatively well known; but the challenge is to ensure they are sustainable and easily accessed by the poor as well as the rich.

By contrast major shocks, such as sudden floods or outbreaks of major disease, have wide ranging consequences and require more generic responses. The costs and benefits are therefore less precise.

Finally there is the important recognition that the process of development itself is a contribution to adaption. If people have higher incomes, are better fed and educated and are in better health they are more able to cope with hazards whether in the form of shocks or stresses. As the Lancet and University of London Commission on Managing the Health Effects of Climate Change concluded, 'Investment to achieve the Millennium Development Goals will not only reduce vulnerability but also release public expenditure for climate change currently consumed by basic prevention strategies (e.g. malaria control). Health-oriented and climate-orientated investments in food security, safe water supply, improved buildings, reforestation, disaster risk assessments, community mobilisation, and essential maternal and child health and family planning services, will all produce dividends in adaptation to climate change.'[23]

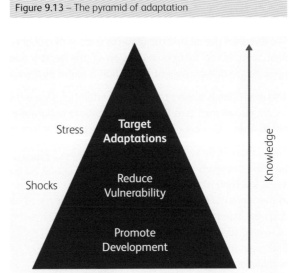

Figure 9.13 – The pyramid of adaptation

In summary it is useful to envisage a pyramid of adaptation (Figure 9.13). At the base is the process of development, above is reducing the general vulnerability of people to major shocks and at the top are the specific adaptations required for individual stresses. In effect the greater the knowledge of the likely impact the more refined the response. There will inevitably be some overlaps; a region may be subject to increasing dryness but it is also likely to suffer from unexpected major droughts. In this case the targeted adaptations – breeding for drought tolerance – may also serve when a sudden drought arises. Nevertheless, an unexpected major drought may need a range of other adaptations to reduce vulnerability generally.

This scheme does not imply that we have to wait until we know everything about the likely impacts – much will be achieved by increasing the general resilience of households, communities and institutions.

Learning

Finally, building resilience is about learning. If a number of small-scale stresses and shocks are experienced by a country, or a community, they will learn to assess how they coped and how well their planned adaptations performed in practice. This means putting learning processes into place at all levels, in the household, the community and at the district and national levels of government. It entails creating effective monitoring and development systems, together with accessible archives and the means of sharing experiences between communities. Most importantly it develops a sense of collective responsibility. In the longer term, this will help build a development process that is both resilient and self-learning, and hence sustainable.

In the rest of this chapter we examine the major classes of climate change risk and vulnerability, and describe some of the principal forms of adaptation.

3. Anticipated sea-level rise

Sea levels will rise around the globe as a result of global warming. The primary cause, at least in the near term, is the thermal expansion of the oceans due to rising oceanic temperatures. This is predicted to deliver a rise of about half a metre by the end of this century.[24]

This prediction is subject to many uncertainties. One is the speed that the Greenland and Antarctic ice sheets will melt (see Box 8.2). Current predictions are that it will take many hundreds of years before these disappear but there is some evidence that the melting could be faster.

Those most likely to be affected by rising sea levels are the many small, low lying islands, especially in the Indian and Pacific Oceans and the extensive delta regions of rivers such as the Ganges-Brahmaputra (see figure 8.34) and Mekong (Figure 9.14).

Even a modest 20cm rise in the sea level would cause contour lines of water levels in the Mekong delta to shift 25 km towards the sea during the flood season and salt water to ingress further upstream, probably altering the fish species composition.[26]

Figure 9.14 – Extensive inundation from a one metre rise in sea level at the mouth of the Mekong and elsewhere in south-east Asia[25]

1 Metre Inundation
Inundated Area

Box 9.6 Inundation of Small Island Developing States (SIDS)[27-29]

Small islands are particularly vulnerable to expected climate changes. They are often low lying and in areas prone to natural hazards, and their small size limits their ability to adapt. Most island nations have a concentration of people and infrastructure near to the coast – in the Caribbean and Pacific more than 50% of the population lives within 1.5km of the shore.[28]

Changing rainfall patterns, rising temperatures and sea level rise are expected to hit small island nations hard. The ecosystems in these areas, which include mangrove forests, coastal beach

© Stefan Lins – Flickr

Figure 9.15 – A beach on the Funafuti atoll in Tuvalu

areas and coral reefs, will be affected. This will not only impact on the local population, who depend on the resources for fishing and other natural resources, but will damage the tourist industries on which many of the SIDS's economies depend. Rising water tables also increase evaporation of fresh water, already a scarce commodity on many small islands. Finally, the impacts that are expected in other areas, such as changes in disease patterns and declines in agricultural productivity will hit these nations as well.

Many small islands may shrink considerably, or even disappear. The nation of Tuvalu, made up of nine tiny atolls near Fiji has already lost one metre of land from its largest atoll. Its widest point only spans a couple of hundred metres and the group of islands lies just 10cm above sea level; the losses are expected to be significant.[30]

Africa will be less damaged. The most extensive inundation is likely to be in the Nile delta where a one metre rise would affect some 6 million people (Box 9.7).

Box 9.7   The inundation of the Nile Delta[31]

The Nile Delta is a highly fertile flood plain, surrounded by deserts, that supports a very large population with densities as high as 1,600 people per square kilometre. Most of the 50 km wide land strip along the coast is less than two metres above sea level and is only protected from flooding by a one to ten km wide coastal sand belt, shaped by the discharge of the Rosetta and Damietta branches of the Nile. Erosion of the protective sand belt is a serious problem and has accelerated since the construction of the Aswan Dam.

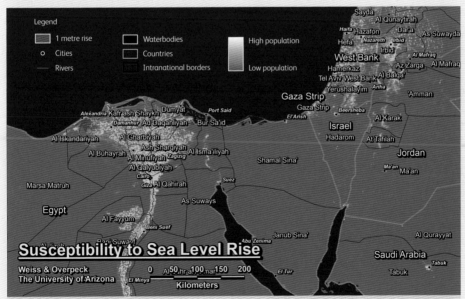

Figure 9.16 – A one metre sea level rise in the Nile Delta will result in widespread inundation around Alexandria[32]

Rising sea levels would destroy weak parts of the sand belt, which is essential for the protection of lagoons and the low-lying reclaimed lands. The impact of this would be very serious. One third of Egypt's fish catches are made in the lagoons. Sea level rise would change the water quality and affect most fresh water fish. Valuable agricultural land would be inundated. Vital, low-lying installations in Alexandria and Port Said would be threatened. Recreational tourism beach facilities would be endangered and essential groundwater would become salinated.

Sea level rise will only affect a small proportion of Africa's land mass, but in some locations the impact will be considerable. For example, Banjul, the capital city of Gambia, could be completely submerged in the next 50 years or so.[33,34] Although the areas inundated appear to be very small (Figure 9.17) they lie in, or near, many of

Figure 9.17 – Effects of a one metre sea level rise in West Africa. Inundated areas coloured in red[32]

the major cities. 40% of the population of West Africa live in coastal cities, and it is estimated that the 500 km of coastline, between Accra and the Niger delta, will become a continuous urban megalopolis of more than 50 million inhabitants by 2020.[35] By 2015, three coastal megacities of at least 8 million people will be located in Africa with many of the poorest populations living in the most flood prone districts.

In Ghana the coastal zone occupies less than 7% of the land area but contains 25% of the population and so even relatively small rises could have damaging effects on the economy (Box 9.8).

Box 9.8 Physical consequences of significant sea level rise in Ghana[36,37]

- Permanent connection of lagoons to the sea;

- Penetration of salt water inland;

- Increased coastal erosion;

- Salinisation of freshwater lagoons and aquifers;

- Increased depth of the water table in coastal areas

- Destruction of wetlands and associated industries;

- Accelerated loss of the capital, Accra.

A further say, six metre rise, resulting from a more rapid than expected acceleration in the melting of the Greenland and/or Antarctic ice caps, could have even more serious consequences. The effects on the south east coast of China are shown in Figure 9.18.

However, much of the damage is likely to come not just from the gradual rise in sea level itself but from the combined effect of such rises with the increasing magnitude and intensity of cyclonic and other storms. This will overwhelm defences and cause major surges of seawater to flow up rivers.

Coastal defences

In theory at least, it is possible to adapt to sea level rises and storm surges by building walls, dykes, barriers and other physical infrastructure. But these are likely to prove very costly and might have other unwelcome effects. In the Nile delta protective constructions would probably prevent the worst flooding up to a 50 cm sea level rise, but could cause considerable groundwater salinisation. Another problem is that new infrastructure built in one location may simply divert the rising sea to other locations in the region.

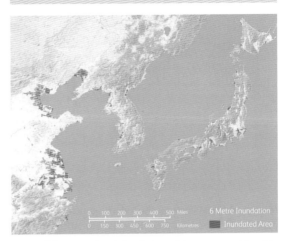

Figure 9.18 – A six metre sea level rise would produce extensive inundation in south-east China

These infrastructure measures do not confer much resilience. They may work for a number of years but are then overcome by a combination of the ongoing rise in sea level and an especially high storm surge. By then the communities behind the defences are unprepared and may have become complacent. Any hazard will have disastrous consequences.[38]

An alternative approach, which may prove less costly and more resilient, is to preserve and strengthen natural coastal protection which can be provided by coastal forests, such as mangroves, seagrass beds, coral reefs, dune systems, salt marshes, inter-tidal flats and lagoons (see Figure 9.20).

Figure 9.19 – Flooding in a village in Bangladesh

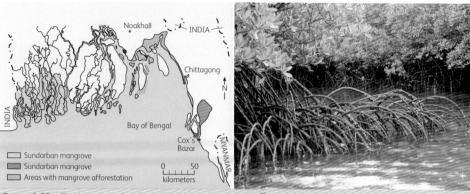

Figure 9.20 – The location of mangrove forests in Bangladesh[39] (left). Mangroves on Pangangan Island in the Philippines planted to help protect against typhoon damage (right)

Mangrove forests proved their worth in protecting coastal villages in India during the 1999 'super cyclone'. Researchers recently used statistical models to show that without mangroves, villages within ten kilometres of the coast would have suffered an average of 1.72 additional deaths. The forests are particularly helpful at reducing the wind energy and wave velocity of the storm surges caused by cyclones, which are typically up to eight metres high. Tsunami waves on the other hand can reach up to 20 metres, and it is still unclear if mangroves can be effective against such a large and fast-moving force.[40] Unfortunately there has been much clearance of these forests, mainly for rice and shrimp production. This can only be rectified by strict coastal zoning and its enforcement.

In developed countries there has been considerable experience with implementing the necessary regulations through Integrated Coastal Zone Management (ICZM) which is increasingly relevant to adapting to climate change. There has, however, been limited experience of coastal management in the developing countries.[41]

In the case of SIDS there are a number of ways they can prepare of rising sea levels. First, efforts can be made to decrease poverty and improve resilience through:

• Reforestation;

• Improved water management;

• Increased participation in trade;

• Strengthening institutions and monitoring and evaluation techniques.

SIDS can then develop specific actions to prepare for rising sea levels and changing weather patterns such as:

• Building sea defences and hurricane resistant buildings;

• Investigating drought and flood-tolerant crops and agronomic methods;

• Changing land zoning around coasts.

A number of global, regional and local efforts have already begun to help SIDS prepare. These include global action plans such as the Barbados Programme of Action[42] and the Mauritius Strategy Declaration.[43] The Eastern Caribbean[44] and the Pacific Islands[45] have also come together to make regional plans for adaptation.

4. Water resources

Climate change is likely to affect water resources more severely than any other environmental resource on which our lives depend. In Chapter 4 we showed the extent to which scarce water resources are under pressure. In some situations global warming may make water more available, but for much of the developing world the effect will be to make water scarcity even more acute.

The worldwide percentage of land in drought has risen dramatically in the last 25 years. In Africa, one-third of the people live in drought-prone areas. The Intergovernmental Panel on Climate Change (IPCC) estimates that, by the 2080s, the proportion of arid and semi-arid lands in Africa is likely to increase by 5-8 % . [35,46]

Glacier melting

A general retreat of glaciers began after 1800 and then accelerated in the latter part of the 20th century in all regions of the world (Figure 9.21). [47]

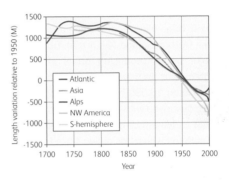

Figure 9.21 – Glacier retreat since about 1850 as measured by the length of glacier tonguesr [47]

The most significant area of glacial retreat is in the Himalayas. Here the glaciers cover about three million hectares, forming the largest body of ice outside the polar caps and storing some 12,000 km³ of freshwater. [48] They are receding faster than in any other part of the world and the likelihood of them disappearing by the year 2035 or sooner is very high if warming continues at the current rate.

One example is the 30 km long Gangotri glacier, located in Uttaranchal in the headwaters of the Ganges river. This has been receding at an alarming rate (Figure 9.22). Between 1842 and 1935, the glacier receded at an average of 7.3m every year; but between 1985 and 2001 the average rate of recession has increased to 23m per year. [49]

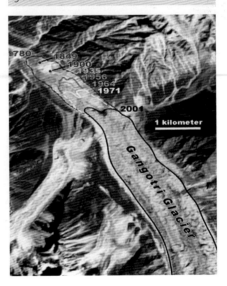

Figure 9.22 – The rapid retreat of the Gangotri glacier [48]

Some of the smaller glaciers, such as those shorter than four km in length in the Tibetan Plateau are projected to disappear altogether and the glaciated areas located in the headwaters of the Chang Jiang (Yangtze) River are likely to decrease by more than 60 % in area. [50]

In Africa the most spectacular glacier retreat has been on Mt. Kilimanjaro in Tanzania. The glaciers are receding and are expected to have disappeared by 2020 (see Figure 9.23). [51,52] However, the major change in hydrology on the mountain and its environs is not due to the glacier but to the dramatic shift in the vegetation zones on the mountain, as a result of climate change.

There are at least two consequences of glacier melting. First is the impact on river flows downstream. About 15,000 Himalayan glaciers form an unique reservoir that supports perennial rivers such as the Indus, Ganges and Brahmaputra which, in turn, are of vital importance to the lives of millions of people. The Gangetic basin alone is home to 500 million people, about 10 % of the total human population in the region.

The second, more immediate and very damaging consequence, will be the creation of very hazardous glacial lakes (Figure 9.24). As the glaciers retreat they leave voids which are filled by the melt water held in place by the original moraines (accumulated rock and soil debris). The latter may look sturdy but will frequently breach due to huge releases of water – a so-called Glacial Lake Outburst Flood (GLOF). In Tibet, one of the major barley producing areas of the Tibetan Plateau was destroyed by a GLOF in August 2000. More than 10,000 homes, 98 bridges and dykes

Figure 9.23 – The rapid receding of the glaciers on Mt Kilimanjaro, Tanzania[53]

were destroyed with an estimated cost of about US $75 million. The farming communities lost their grain and livestock and suffered serious food shortages.[54] One of the largest of the glacier lakes is Tsho Rolpa which has grown since the 1950s through amalgamation to over 1.76 km^2.[55]

Figure 9.24 – Dig Tsho Glacier Lake in Nepal, which burst in 1985, spilling an estimated 200 to 350 million cubic feet of icy water into the surrounding area

Adapting to glacial melt

Mitigating the hazard of damage from GLOFs is very difficult. It is possible, at least in theory, to reinforce the natural moraine dams, but this is expensive and is not likely to provide 100% protection. Another approach involves reducing the volume of lake water, such as through controlled breaching, pumping or siphoning of the water from the lake. It is also possible to tunnel through the moraine barrier. A range of technologies can also be employed to improve preparedness, including using satellite images to detect potentially dangerous lakes and ensuring local broadcast systems are ready to deliver early warnings.[56]

To address the risks associated with GLOFs, the United Nations Environment Programme (UNEP) is seeking to create an operational early warning system in the Hindu Kush Himalayan region.[57] The project is to be implemented by the Environment Assessment Program for Asia and the Pacific (EAP.AP) and the Asian Institute of Technology in Bangkok in partnership with the International Center for Integrated Mountain Development (ICIMOD) in Nepal.

River basins

It is difficult to predict with any certainty the future hydrological characteristics of major river basins. The IPCC points out that *'precipitation, a principal input signal to water systems, is not reliably simulated in present climate models.'*[58] However we do know that in glacier- or snowmelt-fed river basins (which nurture one sixth of the world's population), changes will be profound. The summer season melts that provide much of the water at that time of year will decrease and peak flows will move earlier in the year, with serious effects on agriculture. As the glaciers retreat, flows will increase, but then decrease over the next few decades as the amount of glaciated area is reduced.[58]

River flows elsewhere will be more dependent on changes in precipitation, rather than on snow or ice melt. A general conclusion is that seasonal flow will increase, with higher flows in the peak flow season and either lower flows during the low flow season or extended dry periods. Many semi-arid and arid areas will suffer decreased river flows (Figure 9.25).

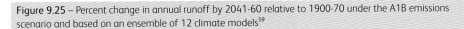

Figure 9.25 – Percent change in annual runoff by 2041-60 relative to 1900-70 under the A1B emissions scenario and based on an ensemble of 12 climate models[59]

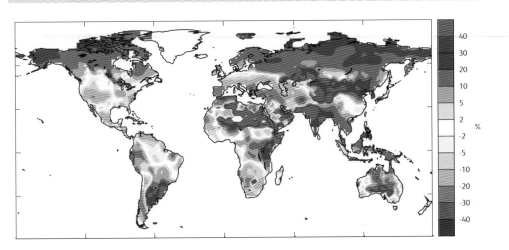

In Africa, these various impacts will be played out on a dozen major river basins where the impact of climate change is likely to depend on the rainfall regime, which varies from one river to another (Fig 9.26).

Because virtually none of these basins are dependent on glacier melt, the crucial factor is the rainfall regime. A recent study measured the effects of changes in precipitation on the 'perennial drainage density' of the river basin – or the length of streams which have continuous flow all the year round per unit of area in the basin. It was found that those basins which receive a low rainfall (below 400mm a year) have virtually no perennial drainage (coloured in red in Figure 9.27). Between 400 and 1,000 mm of precipitation, there exists an intermediate regime (coloured in yellow) in which the drainage density varies greatly with rainfall. Above 1,000 mm (coloured in green) there is a slight increase in drainage with increasing rainfall.

Figure 9.26 – The twelve major river basins of Africa[60]

1. Nile
2. Senegal
3. Niger
4. Volta
5. Lake Chad
6. Congo
7. Rufiji
8. Ganane
9. Zambez1
10. Okavango
11. Limpopo
12. Orange

Figure 9.27 – Rainfall and drainage regimes in Africa[60]

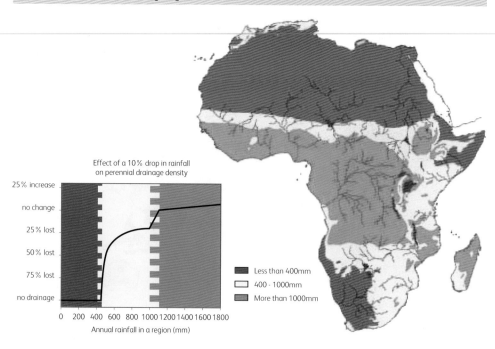

Effect of a 10% drop in rainfall on perennial drainage density

25% increase
no change
25% lost
50% lost
75% lost
no drainage

0   200 400 600 800 1000 1200 1400 1600 1800
Annual rainfall in a region (mm)

Less than 400mm
400 - 1000mm
More than 1000mm

Figure 9.28 – Waters flowing into the Okavango Delta, Botswana. This area of Africa is likely to be seriously affected if there are significant changes in precipitation in the region

© Moira Hart

The intermediate zone is likely to experience the greatest impact from climate change. For example, if a region is receiving 600 mm per year and the precipitation decreases to 550 mm, the drainage will be cut by 25 %, whilst a change from 500 mm year to 450 mm would cut the drainage by half. River flows will fall accordingly.

Most of southern Africa lies in either the unstable or the dry regime. The Orange River, the fifth largest river in Africa, and one of the 50 largest rivers globally, is likely to be severely affected. The river has run dry in the past and has experienced very low flows in recent years. On the other hand, rivers in eastern Africa may have increased drainage flows because of the higher predicted rainfall. The flow of the Nile is difficult to assess and current models vary considerably in their predictions, but some of the headwaters may experience greater rainfall.[61]

Water scarcity thresholds are based on estimates of the water requirements for the domestic, agricultural, industrial and energy sectors and the needs of the environment.[62] A country is assumed to experience water scarcity when the level available is below 1,000m^3 per capita per year – absolute scarcity is defined as below 500m^3. On this basis it will be north Africa that suffers most, although water availability may improve in northeast Africa (Figure 9.29).

Figure 9.29 – Change in water stress by 2085 using a Hadley Circulation model (HadCM3 A2a)[62]

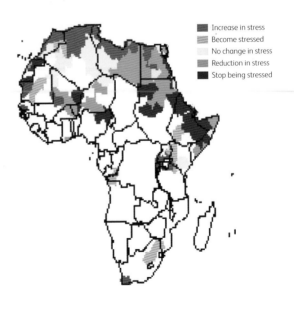

Increase in stress
Become stressed
No change in stress
Reduction in stress
Stop being stressed

River basin management

Water shortage in river basins can be addressed either through increasing supply or decreasing demand. Usually both are needed, but each has its advantages and disadvantages, and the relative benefits of different options depend on local circumstances (Table 9.2). For example, supply-side options will often have adverse environmental consequences, while demand-side measures, which rely on the cumulative actions of individuals, can be difficult to manage.

Table 9.2 Examples of supply- and demand-side water adaptations[58]

Supply-side	Demand-side
• Prospecting and extraction of groundwater	• Improvement of water-use efficiency by recycling water
• Increasing storage capacity by building reservoirs and dams	• Reduction in water demand for irrigation by changing the cropping calendar, crop mix, irrigation method and area planted
• Desalination of sea water	• Reduction in water demand for irrigation by importing agricultural products i.e. virtual water
• Expansion of rain-water storage	• Promotion of indigenous practices for sustainable water use
• Removal of invasive non-native vegetation from riparian areas	• Expanded use of water markets to reallocate water to highly valued uses
• Water transfer	• Expanded use of economic incentives including metering and pricing to encourage water conservation

Over the centuries engineers have developed a wide range of proven technologies for increasing water storage and water flows. While large-scale construction of dams, reservoirs and water transfer systems have fallen out of favour in some parts of the developing world – partly due to cost and the actual or perceived negative effects on human

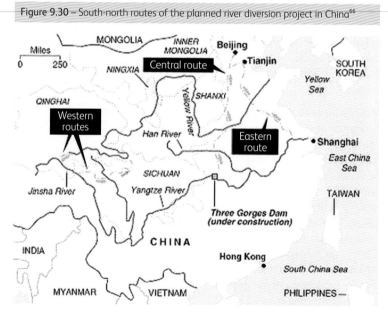

Figure 9.30 – South-north routes of the planned river diversion project in China[66]

populations and the environment – they are still being actively developed in some middle income countries such as China.[63,64] The Three Gorges Dam on the Yangtze River in China is primarily intended for hydropower generation but it will also help to regulate the flow of the river to the 1.5 million hectares of farmland in the Jianghan Plain and minimize the frequently disastrous flooding in the middle and lower parts of the river.[65] The Three Gorges Dam is also one of three origins for a major undertaking to divert river waters from the south to the north of the country (Figure 9.30). When completed in 2050, it will link China's four main rivers – the Yangtze, Yellow River, Huaihe and Haihe and eventually divert 44.8 billion m^3 of water annually to the drier north.

In the least developed countries more attention is now being paid to a variety of intermediate technologies, such as drip irrigation and treadle pumps, which will make more efficient use of available water (see Chapters 2 and 5).

There are also a large number of promising new technologies that can increase the supply of water, notably through desalination of salt and brackish water (Box 9.9).

Box 9.9   Making desalination cheaper

Over 97 % of the earth's water is salty, but it is currently too expensive and energy-intensive to convert it into fresh water. A number of recent technological breakthroughs may help to change that.

Using nanotechnology[67]

New nanotube membranes, developed by researchers at the Lawrence Livermore National Laboratory (LLNL), California, could reduce the cost of desalination by 75 %, compared to reverse osmosis methods used today.

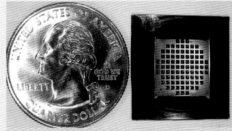

The carbon nanotubes are sheets of carbon atoms rolled so tightly that only seven water molecules can fit across their diameter. Their small size makes them good

Figure 9.31 – A carbon-nanotube membrane (quarter coin shown for scale)[68]

candidates for separating molecules. At the same time they allow water to flow at the same rate as with pores considerably larger, reducing the amount of pressure needed to force water through, and potentially saving energy and costs compared to reverse osmosis using conventional membranes.

The LLNL team measured water flow rates up to 10,000 times faster than would be predicted by classical equations. These surprising results might be due to the smooth interior of the nanotubes, or to the physics at this small scale – more research is needed to understand the mechanisms involved.

To make the membranes, the researchers started with a silicon wafer about the size of a quarter coin, coated with a metal nanoparticle catalyst for growing carbon nanotubes. The small particles allow the nanotubes to grow "like blades of grass – vertically aligned and closely packed." Once grown, the gaps between the nanotubes are filled with a ceramic material, silicon nitride, which provides stability and helps the membrane adhere to the underlying silicon wafer. The field of nanotubes functions as an array of pores, allowing water and certain gases through, while keeping larger molecules and clusters of molecules at bay.

The membranes could be brought to market within the next five to ten years.

Taking advantage of concentration gradients[69]

A team at Saltworks Technologies in Vancouver, Canada has discovered an energy-efficient way to produce drinking water from sea water by taking advantage of the natural properties of salt – specifically the positively charged sodium ion and the negatively charged chloride ion. They have constructed a simple unit which processes a stream of seawater made highly concentrated through evaporation, with three other streams of untreated water, connected by ion bridges. The treatment is fuelled by concentration gradients of salinity between the different vessels of brine. The only energy needed is that required to pump the streams of water through the apparatus, the rest is provided by the air and sun. It is estimated that this system will be able to produce 1,000 litres of fresh water with less than one kWh of electricity, compared to the normal 3.7 kWh needed by the best reverse-osmosis plants. The plant was set to open in November 2009.

Management practices and technologies to deal with increasing water demand have been developed throughout the years. As the IPCC points out *'adaptation to changing conditions in water availability and demand has always been at the core of water management.'*[58] For example, existing conventional and intermediate technologies have been created to improve uptake of water by crops and to increase water use efficiency through recycling. In the face of climate change all these technologies will be needed but in a new and more demanding context.

There has been an assumption that the natural resource base is constant and a relatively reliable supplier of water. Climate change, as in other areas of natural resource management, is undermining these assumptions leading to new management approaches and procedures. Traditionally water management has depended on probabilistic models of future hydrological changes, where the climatic parameters *'are assumed to fluctuate stochastically around means that can be quantified based on historical conditions.'*[70] In a changing climate such assumptions no longer apply. Moreover, in addition to the greater uncertainty, contemporary water management is complicated by demographic, economic, social and political changes.

For these reasons, attempts have been made to develop a more resilient and holistic approach often placed under the heading of Integrated Water Resources Management (IWRM).[71] This approach aims to coordinate land and water resource management, recognize water quantity and quality linkages, bring together surface and groundwater use, protect and restore natural systems, and reshape the planning process, in particular bringing in community input.[71-73] Approaches to water management must ultimately depend on the size and type of the river basin in question. Solutions to, for example, *'groundwater overdraft in the aquifers of northern Gujerat, where extraction by tens of thousands of individual farmers across thousands of square kilometres threatens the groundwater resource base,'*[74] may be quite different from a smaller stream which supplies a few communities. The challenge is to find a management approach that is resilient to future climate changes, and reflects both the priorities of the poor and the biophysical complexities and uncertainties.[75]

Floods and droughts

In addition to the gradual changes in river flow patterns, the increased intensity and variability of precipitation will increase the risks of major episodes of flooding and drought. Flooding leads to many direct and indirect negative consequences:

- Immediate deaths and injuries from drowning;
- Non-specific increases in mortality;
- Infectious diseases e.g. increased malaria;
- Exposure to toxic substances;
- Damage to infrastructure e.g. roads, dams, power generation;
- Damage to crops and livestock;
- Community breakdowns;
- Increased psychological stress;
- Increased demands on health systems and social security.

Disastrous floods will become more common in many parts of the developing world, because some regions will experience higher rainfalls, but even in drier regions there is likely to be a higher frequency of more intense downpours which may cause flooding. For example, 2007 saw heavy flooding in both eastern and western Africa (Box 9.10).

Box 9.10 The African floods of 2007

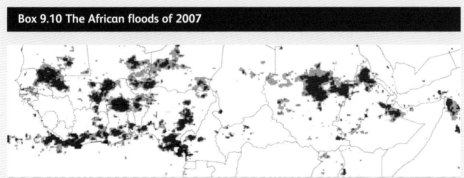

Figure 9.32 – Regions across Africa where the rainfall was a 1 in 20 year event or rarer (shown in blue) for July and August 2007[76]

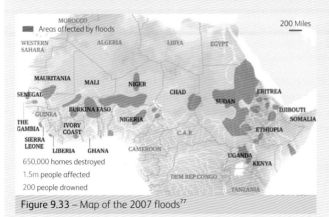

Areas affected by floods

650,000 homes destroyed
1.5m people affected
200 people drowned

Figure 9.33 – Map of the 2007 floods[77]

The floods that occurred in the summer of 2007 across the Sahel of Africa were caused by heavy rainfall and thunderstorms within the rain belt of the ITCZ which was further north than usual. Much of the land was dry from years of drought and the record rainfalls resulted in overwhelmingly high levels of run-off.

Several developing regions are also likely to experience greater cyclonic activity bringing torrential rain, high waves and damaging storm surges resulting in inland and coastal flooding (see Box 8.3). The devastating super cyclone that hit the Indian state of Orissa in 1999 was one of the worst disasters of the last decade. It affected the livelihoods of 12.9 million people and resulted in the loss of 1.6 million houses, nearly 2 million hectares of crops and 40,000 livestock.

The event raised several key questions about the role of science and technology in dealing with natural hazards:

- Can the hazard be predicted, at least probabilistically?
- Can we reduce or eliminate the probability of the hazard occurring?
- Can we reduce or eliminate its impact?
- Can communities adapt to disasters so the consequences are less severe?

Learning from previous natural disasters such as the Orissa super cyclone will be key to successfully dealing with future hazards.

Flooding, however in a more controlled manner, can be beneficial. Inundated floodplains provide soil moisture for agriculture, benefit flood plain fisheries, replenish groundwater aquifers for irrigation and contribute to increased soil fertility.[39]

Perhaps of even greater future importance for many developing countries will be the rising incidence of droughts, both short and long term. Most devastating will be situations where droughts occur for two or more successive years. The consequences of drought are similar to those for floods, with the most significant impact likely to be on agricultural production. Drought can have a catastrophic effect on rural communities. For example in North-Eastern Ethiopia, drought induced losses to crops and livestock between 1998 and 2000 were estimated at US $266 per household – greater than the annual average cash income for more than 75% of the households.[78]

Adapting to floods and droughts

Protection against floods depends on careful mapping of flood potential, avoidance of development activities that increase the risk of flooding, for example construction on flood plains, and a variety of standard engineering works (multi-purpose storage dams and reservoirs, weirs, barriers, dykes and embankments). Major examples include the flood diversion and detention basins already constructed for flood control along the Yangtze in China, with a storage capacity of over 50 billion cubic meters, and the thousands of kilometres of embankments and drainage canals constructed by the Bangladesh Water Development Board.

As in the case of sea level rises, as discussed above, the alternative to engineering approaches is to utilise forest, shrub and other vegetative barriers, especially along river banks. Loss of forests is a major cause of flooding. When land is deforested and the forest litter is removed interception of rainfall virtually stops, infiltration is reduced and soil erosion increases. There is also less evapotranspiration. The overall effect is increased run-off and a greater risk of flooding.[79]

Drought protection can be increased by creating water storage reservoirs and by the evolution of drought tolerant agricultural systems, discussed later in this chapter.

In the case of flooding from cyclones, resilience can be improved by better mapping and forecasting and by the provision of cyclone shelters. Shocks, such as floods and droughts, are best approached through the development of resilient forms of livelihood. Farmers need to increase the diversity of crops and livestock on their farm or, more generally, have a wider set of sources of income for the household. Local communities have often built resilience to disasters into their social networks and systems. For example, strategies for coping with drought may involve a diverse range of subsistence and income generating activities (Box 9.11).

© DFID

Figure 9.34 – A cyclone shelter in Bangladesh

Box 9.11 Drought coping mechanisms in Kenya[80]

The Kati District of eastern Kenya suffered from poor rainfall in 1995 and 1996 and ran out of food between the July 1996 harvest and the next harvest in February 1997. Only two out of a random sample of 52 households had a maize crop that lasted them through this period.

The farmers, when interviewed, listed a large number of coping activities:

- Skilled work;
- Selling land;
- Collecting honey for consumption and sale;
- Making bricks for sale;
- Engaging in food producing or money making group activities;
- Business, such as selling snacks;
- Burning charcoal for sale;
- Salaries of householder or remittances;
- Handicrafts for sale;
- Selling or consuming exotic fruits from the farm;
- Receiving credit;
- Borrowing food or money from relatives;
- Borrowing food or money from neighbours;
- Engaging in casual labour;
- Selling livestock;
- Collecting indigenous fruit for consumption or sale;
- Receiving food aid from government or other organisations.

Each household averaged about six activities during the drought. After the drought this dropped to three but diversity remains a common feature of their livelihoods.

There are clearly lessons to be learnt from people who have had to cope with regular stresses. But recently such resilience has been steadily eroded away in many places under the impact of migration, family breakdown, famine relief, poverty and disease, such that people have become more dependent on outside aid.[1] A major challenge for governments, donors and particularly for NGOs is to help communities rebuild their resilience mechanisms. Many of the activities in Box 9.11 rely on the informal sector; governments can help by creating links to the formal sector and by providing skills, knowledge and access to markets.

Women play a key role in creating resilient livelihoods. They may be primarily responsible for home gardens and for higher value vegetable and fruit crops that help to diversify the agricultural production. Skills such as weaving and handicraft can provide a source of income when agriculture fails. This stresses the importance of seeing livelihoods as a family affair involving both men and women and, as they grow older, the children. Any programme which enhances livelihoods has to take this wider holistic and more long-term approach.

5. Agriculture and natural resources

Agricultural production and food security are strongly affected by natural climate variability and are likely to be severely compromised by climate change, in particular high temperatures and the greater incidence of drought. Smallholder and subsistence farmers, pastoralists and artisanal fishers will especially suffer. As a result the area suitable for agriculture, the length of growing seasons and the yield potential of crops, particularly along the margins of semi-arid and arid areas, are expected to decrease. This is likely to further adversely affect food security and exacerbate undernutrition throughout the developing countries.[81]

Crop production

Many crops are grown close to their limits of thermal tolerance. We already know that just a few days of high temperature near flowering can seriously affect yields of crops such as wheat, fruit trees, groundnut and soybean.[82] In low-latitude regions, where most of the developing countries lie, even moderate temperature increases of 1-2°C can reduce yields of major cereals and the effects of adaptation are likely to be limited (Figure 9.36).

Figure 9.35 – Women planting rice in Nepal

© DFID

Figure 9.36 – Cereal yield responses to temperature change. (Results of 69 published studies at multiple simulation sites. Responses include cases without adaptation (red dots) and with adaptation (dark green dots). Adaptations include changes in planting, changes in cultivar, and shifts from rain-fed to irrigated conditions)[81]

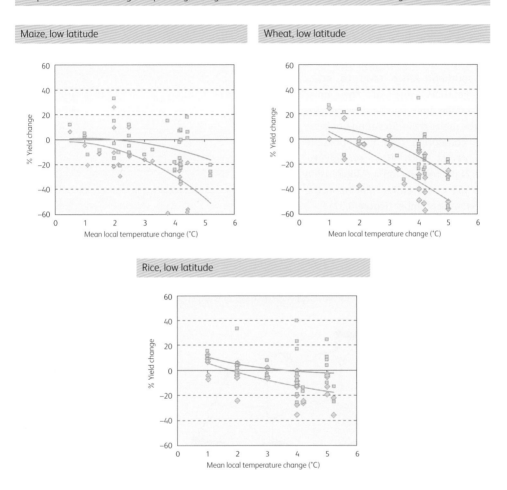

The most adverse conditions arise when high temperatures coincide with spells of drought. Such episodes of extreme weather are likely to become more frequent with global warming, creating high annual variability in crop production. Prolonged high temperatures and extended periods of drought will force large areas of marginal agriculture out of production.

The FAO reports that severe drought accounts for half of the world's food emergencies annually.[83] In 2003, the World Food Program spent US$565 million in response to drought in Sub-Saharan Africa.[84] The maize crop is particularly susceptible: some 20 million tonnes of potential tropical maize production is lost each year as a result of drought.[84] Maize crops in most parts of southern Africa already experience drought stress on an annual basis. The situation is likely to get worse with climate change and could result in maize production in many parts of Zimbabwe and South Africa becoming very difficult if not impossible. Wheat yields in northern Africa are also likely to be threatened.

Drought in southern Africa may be particularly severe in El Niño years. Maize yields in Zimbabwe have long been highly correlated with the ENSO cycle as measured by sea surface temperatures (SST) off the Peruvian coast. During El Niño years droughts in southern Africa tend to occur in February just at the most susceptible time for the development of the maize grain. So strong has been the correlation that it is possible to predict, with 70% probability, the Zimbabwean crop in March using the SST in the eastern Pacific in the previous September (Figure 9.37).[85]

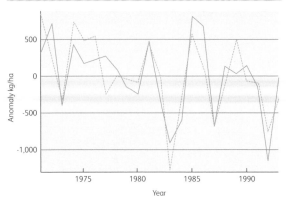

Figure 9.37 – The close correlation between SST and Zimbabwean maize yields (solid line – annual variations in maize yield, dashed line – SST anomalies in the eastern equatorial Pacific, scaled to corresponding units)[85]

In southern Africa and across western and north-central Africa lower rainfall may also cause the length of the growing season to shorten, threatening the probability of getting a second crop in some areas and even the viability of a single crop in others (Figure 9.38).

Figure 9.38 – Current length of the growing period (number of days) in Sub-Saharan Africa[86]

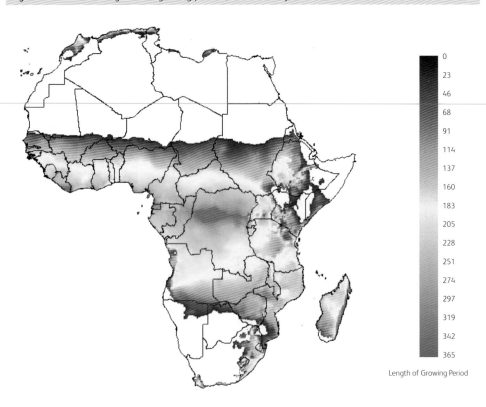

Length of Growing Period

In China, because of rising maximum and minimum temperatures, the length of the growing season is likely to increase throughout the country, and particularly in the west, although this may be restricted by declines in rainfall in some areas (Figure 9.39).

The rising minimum temperatures in northern China also reflect milder winters. This can be beneficial, for example in planting more winter wheat as is happening in the north of the Ningxia region of China. However, some crops, such as apples, need a winter cooling (a process known as vernalisation) to initiate flower bud formation. The milder winters in the Western Cape of South Africa are already adversely affecting the apple crop there.[88]

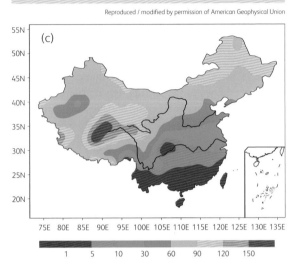

Figure 9.39 – Percentage increases in the length of the growing period by the end of the century in China for the IPCC B2 scenario.[87]

Reproduced / modified by permission of American Geophysical Union

Carbon fertilisation

Just how severe these various impacts on agriculture will be depends on the so-called "carbon fertilisation" effect. Carbon dioxide (CO_2) is the basic building block for plant growth and hence it would be assumed that rising levels will increase crop yields. In greenhouse and field chamber experiments plants with growth based on a so-called C3 metabolic pathway (such as wheat, rice and soybean) show this to be the case, whilst those with a C4 pathway (such as maize, millet, sorghum and sugar cane) are not responsive.

The latest analyses of more realistic field trials suggests that the benefits of CO_2 may be significantly less than initially thought – only an 8% to 15% increase in yield for a doubling of CO_2 for responsive C3 species and no significant increase for non-responsive species, such as maize and sorghum which are widely grown in Africa.[89,90] Hence this offsetting factor may be less than was previously assumed. Estimates produced for the IPCC of expected yield losses with a 3-4°C rise in temperature (with CO_2 fertilisation) for wheat are 18% in northern Africa and 22% for maize in southern Africa.[91]

Livestock and pasture production

Pastures are likely to respond to climate change with rapid alterations in the species composition and diversity. This may affect the quality of the forage and the grazing behaviour of the livestock.[81] Some of the most serious impacts will be in arid and semi-arid regions.

Increased temperatures often lead to lower physical activity by livestock and declines in eating and grazing.[92] High temperatures put a ceiling on dairy milk yield irrespective of feed intake. In the tropics this ceiling reaches between half and one-third of the potential of modern (Friesian) cow breeds.[93] Increases in air temperature and/or humidity also affect conception rates of livestock, particularly cattle that are not well adapted. A number of studies show a strong relationship between drought and livestock deaths.[81]

But the biggest effects are likely to be as a result of the increased variability in weather patterns and the impact this has on vegetation and water availability. In the 1980s protracted drought killed 20-62 % of cattle in countries as widespread as Botswana, Niger and Ethiopia.[94]

Fisheries

Increases in temperature may cause higher fish growth rates, but also higher mortality above a certain level. Climate change has been implicated in mass mortalities of many aquatic species including, plants, fish, corals and mammals, but it is difficult to reliably attribute the causes.[95] Regional changes in the distribution and productivity of particular fish species are expected to occur due to continued warming and local extinctions are likely at the edges of ranges.[81] Increased ocean acidification may also affect the nurseries of important fish stocks (see Box 9.17).

Pests, diseases and weeds

There is a strong likelihood that agricultural losses (in crops, livestock and forests) will increase as a result of more frequent or severe pest and disease attacks stimulated by higher temperatures and/or humidity.[81] Such threats already have a major effect on crop and livestock production. Countermeasures such as the use of pesticides may be expensive while integrated pest management systems may require increased labour and skills.

In some cases pests and disease may also extend their range as a result of climate change.

Weed growth may also be directly affected by increased CO_2 levels. Fourteen of the world's most serious weeds are C4 plants that grow in fields of C3 crops. Here the C3 crops may outcompete the weeds, but where the opposite is the case (C3 weeds in C4 crops) the C3 weeds may become much more damaging.[96]

Agricultural adaptation

The biggest challenge for agriculture in the developing countries is coping with increased heat and drought stress, which often act together.[97]

Drought resistance can be achieved in one of three ways: drought tolerant cropping systems, drought resistant crop varieties and provision of water resources.

One of the most significant recent successes in water and soil management, in the developed and developing countries, has been the substitution for a long-standing conventional technology, soil cultivation using a plough, with 'zero-tillage' regimes. Cultivation, especially using a plough, is frequently associated with high levels of soil erosion and water loss. There is now a range of no- or minimum- tillage systems in development and use that are grouped under the generic name of Conservation Agriculture (Box 9.12).

Box 9.12 Conservation farming in Zimbabwe

It has become common if not standard practice, since colonial times, to till the soil with a mole board plough before maize is sown. On poorer soils this destroys the soil structure and increases water loss. Many argue that the practice is responsible for the long term decline in Zimbabwe's soil fertility.

The alternative is to minimally till the soil and leave the crop residues in place as mulch for the next crop (Figure 9.40). Prior to seeding, farmers use hoes to prepare small basins in which fertiliser (inorganic and/or manure) is placed followed by one or two maize seeds. One or two selective weedings may be needed but that is all.

© Gordon Conway   © Gordon Conway

Figure 9.40 – Conservation farming in Zimbabwe. Use of the hoe to make holes for next year's seeds (left); remains of stalks as mulch on soil (right)

The benefits begin in year one. After three years they are dramatic. In one pair of plots in southern Zimbabwe the soils remain dry and sandy under conventional production but are moist and structured in the conservation plots (see Figure 9.41). Yields are doubled – in some cases the conventional will fail altogether.

© Gordon Conway

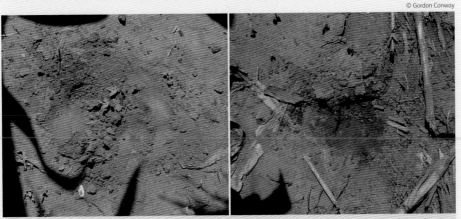

Figure 9.41 – Conservation plots in Zimbabwe after 3 years. Conventional tillage resulting in dry and sandy soil (left); minimum tillage producing moist and sticky soil (right)

Introducing drought tolerance into crops has been approached in two ways. First, natural variation in tolerance to drought and other stresses has been identified through trials of varieties in farmers' fields. Second, the biological basis of drought tolerance has been investigated across the range of staple cereal crops.

The growing understanding of breeding maize for drought-tolerance is now being put to use in a public-private breeding programme under the African Agricultural Technology Foundation (AATF) (Box 9.13).

Box 9.13 Water Efficient Maize for Africa (WEMA)[98]

WEMA is a public-private venture managed through the AATF. It involves one of the CGIAR centres – the International Maize and Wheat Improvement Center (CIMMYT), the private agricultural company Monsanto, and national agricultural research systems in eastern and southern Africa. The responsibilities are divided as follows:

- AATF is contributing its leadership, experience in public-private partnership management, technology stewardship and project management expertise;

- CIMMYT is providing high-yielding maize varieties that are adapted to African conditions and expertise in conventional breeding and testing for drought tolerance;

- Monsanto is providing proprietary germplasm, advanced breeding tools and expertise, and drought-tolerance transgenes developed in collaboration with BASF Chemical Company;

- The national agricultural research systems, farmers' groups, and seed companies are contributing their expertise in field testing, seed multiplication and distribution.

The varieties developed through the project will be distributed to African seed companies through AATF without royalty and made available to smallholder farmers as part of their seed business.

One of the keys to success in such a programme lies in the intimate involvement of the farmers – not just in assessing the final range of varieties but in the analytical trials themselves. A technique known as mother-baby trials has been developed in southern Africa to make this work (Box 9.14).

Box 9.14 Mother-baby trials for stress breeding

In recent years, with DFID funding, CIMMYT has cooperated with national agricultural research systems, the private sector and farmers themselves to breed over 50 new varieties of maize, currently planted on over one million hectares in southern and eastern Africa.

The varieties have been bred to be tolerant of drought, low soil fertility, parasitic weeds and other stresses. While some of the breeding can be done in the greenhouse or on an experimental farm, it will tend to focus on only one stress at a time. One of the advantages of carrying out the breeding trials on farmers' fields, with farmer participation, is to assess the tolerance of the varieties under a range of simultaneous stresses and to take advantage of the farmers' own knowledge and responses.

They were developed in a network of 'stress breeding sites' which involved 'mother-baby' trials. The mother trials, involving up to 12 varieties, were located close to the community and managed by schools, colleges or extension agents. The baby trials comprised four to six varieties in the fields of farmers who used their own inputs and equipment. This approach now needs replicating for other staple crops.

We have discussed the large-scale supply of water for irrigation above. There are, in addition, a number of small-scale technologies, widely adopted and well proven that provide efficient water supply for cropping. One example is the combination of simple, plastic tubed, drip irrigation with well constructed treadle pumps for raising water from shallow wells. Such systems usually lie in relatively small watersheds and rely on an intimate knowledge of the temporal and spatial pattern of the water supply by farm communities or individual farmers.

Among pastoralists, strategies for coping with drought have been developed over the centuries and in many cases have retained their resilience. This is now being tested by population pressures, increased degradation and the effects of climate change. Box 9.15 lists the coping strategies practised in northern Kenya and southern Ethiopia.

Box 9.15 Pastoralist adaptation strategies practised in recent years in Northern Kenya and Southern Ethiopia[79]

- *Mobility* remains the most important pastoralist adaptation to spatial and temporal variations in rainfall. In drought years many communities make use of fall-back grazing areas unused in 'normal' dry seasons because of distance, land tenure constraints, animal disease problems or conflict. But encroachment on, and fragmentation of, communal grazing lands, and the desire to settle in order to access human services and food aid, have severely limited pastoral mobility;

- Pastoralists engage in *herd accumulation* and most evidence now suggests that this is a rational form of insurance against drought;

- A small proportion of pastoralists now hold some of their wealth in bank accounts, and others use informal savings and credit mechanisms through shopkeepers;

- Pastoralists also use *supplementary feed* for livestock, purchased or lopped from trees, as a coping strategy; they intensify *animal disease management* through indigenous and scientific techniques; they pay for *access to water* from powered boreholes;

- *Livelihood diversification* away from pastoralism in this region predominantly takes the form of shifts into low-income or environmentally unsustainable occupations such as charcoal production, rather than an adaptive strategy to reduce vulnerability;

- A number of *intra-community mechanisms* distribute both livestock products and the use of live animals to the destitute, but these appear to be breaking down because of the high levels of covariate risk within communities.

© Kevin Heaton – Utah State University

Figure 9.42 – Pastoralists with their sheep in Ethiopia

6. Ecosystems and biodiversity

Climate change 'will alter the structure, reduce biodiversity and perturb functioning of most ecosystems, and compromise the services they currently provide.'[99]

The developing world is made up of a wide variety of ecosystems and their vital services, ranging from savannas and tropical forests to mountain ecosystems and from coral reefs to great inland lakes and rivers. African ecosystems are particularly rich; they are estimated to contain about one-fifth of all known species of plants, mammals, and birds, as well as one-sixth of amphibians and reptiles.[100]

One estimate suggests that, globally, 15 to 40% of land, plant and animal species will become extinct by 2050 as a result of climate change.[101] The ecosystems of dry and sub-humid lands are particularly at risk because quite small changes in temperature and rainfall patterns can have deleterious impacts on the viability of plants and animals. Most drylands are already under stress from cultivation, livestock grazing and other human activities.

For example, the succulent *karoo* of the west coast of South Africa and Namibia is home to about 3,000 species of plants that occur nowhere else. A large fraction of the world's succulent flora lives in the karoo thriving on its unique dry, winter-rainfall climate and the ecosystem is likely to shrink or completely disappear as a result of climate change.[102]

Many animal species would also be affected. Overall between 25 to 40% of animals in Sub-Saharan African national parks are endangered.

Corals

Marine ecosystems, especially coral reefs are very vulnerable. (Box 9.16).

© Martin Hart

Figure 9.43 – Many animal species in Sub-Saharan African national parks will be endangered as a result of climate change

---

Box 9.16 Increasing coral bleaching[103,104]

Seasonal increases in sea surface temperature (SST) and solar radiation often cause coral to bleach, because either symbiotic algae or pigments are lost. Corals will bleach white in response to abnormally high SST (~1°C above average seasonal maxima, often combined with high solar radiation). Sometimes the corals will recover their natural colour when temperatures fall but their growth rate and reproductive ability may be significantly reduced for a substantial period. If bleaching is prolonged, or if SST exceeds 2°C above average seasonal maxima, corals die. Branching species appear more susceptible than massive corals.[105]

Major bleaching events were observed in 1982-83, 1987-88 and 1994-95. Particularly severe bleaching occurred in 1998 (Figure 9.44), associated with pronounced El Niño events in one of the hottest years on record.[106] Since 1998 there have been several other extensive bleaching events. Reefs in the eastern Caribbean experienced a massive bleaching event in late 2005, another of the hottest years on record.

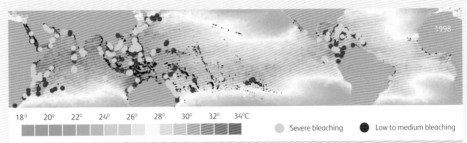

18° 20° 22° 24° 26° 28° 30° 32° 34°C

⬤ Severe bleaching   ⬤ Low to medium bleaching

Figure 9.44 – Coral bleaching and maximum monthly mean sea surface temperatures for 1998[103]

Global climate model results imply that thermal thresholds will be exceeded more frequently with the consequence that bleaching will occur more often than reefs can sustain.[107]

There is some evidence that corals may be able to adapt to rising temperatures, vulnerable species being replaced with others with different temperature tolerances.[108,109] Such natural adaptation or acclimatisation might result in an increase in the threshold temperature at which bleaching occurs, but whether this could happen with warming of more than a couple of degrees remains uncertain.

Ocean acidification

Such ecosystems are also likely to suffer damage from increasing acidification as a direct consequence of increased CO_2 concentrations.

Box 9.17 Ocean acidification

As much as one-half of anthropogenic CO_2 from the atmosphere is absorbed in our oceans. While this helps to reduce climate impacts, it also causes changes in marine ecosystems. When carbon dissolves in seawater it forms carbonic acid, which results in the pH of the water dropping from its slightly alkaline state of around 8 – 8.3 units, to something more acidic. The effects have been slowly accumulating since the beginning of industrialisation, and estimates are that pH has dropped by about 0.1 units since the mid-1700s.[110] This is significant, as a drop of just 0.3 pH units corresponds to a doubling of the hydrogen ion concentration, since pH is expressed on a logarithmic scale. A variety of studies have made predictions of further decreases, with estimates ranging from 0.3 to 0.5 units by 2100 depending on emissions and mitigation measures taken.[111-113]

© Carl Gustav – World Bank

Figure 9.45 – Coral reefs in Indonesia are vulnerable to ocean acidification

Changes in ocean pH are believed to have the greatest effect on calcifying organisms such as corals, molluscs and calcareous phytoplankton which use calcium carbonate ($CaCO_3$) to build their external skeletons or shells. Ocean acidification decreases the carbonate ion concentration in water, making it more difficult for organisms to build their shells, and leaving them vulnerable to dissolution if the seawater drops below a saturating concentration of

$CaCO_3$. While the exact effects that acidification will have on calcification in the future are still unknown, the possibility of disruption to such key marine species is cause for concern.[114,115]

Finally, increasing acidity may cause a broad range of small effects in other organisms, such as increasing the energy required to regulate internal pH, altering reproductive patterns, or changing food supply. Organisms may be able to adapt to such changes if they occur slowly enough, but with such large amounts of CO_2 entering the water, adaptation will be difficult if not impossible.[116]

A number of research teams in both Europe and the US are concentrating on learning more about this problem, including the National Oceanography Centre and the Natural Environment Research Council (NERC) in the UK, through such projects as Oceans 2025[117] and the European Project on Ocean Acidification.[118]

Forests

On land perhaps one of the biggest losses, with most widespread consequences, will be of forests, particularly in the Amazon and the Congo Basin. Natural and plantation forests are likely to be significantly affected by climate change, but it will be difficult to separate out the various factors that may be involved. Extreme events such as strong winds can severely damage and even kill trees. Insect outbreaks and wildfires can be equally damaging.[81] Positive feedbacks in the Amazon between deforestation, forest fragmentation, wildfire and increased frequency of droughts in a warmer and drier climate may trigger massive deforestation.[119-121]

We have few detailed assessments of land-use and land-cover changes in forested areas. Nonetheless deforestation is likely to result in:

1. Less biodiversity;

2. Less rainfall;

3. More soil erosion;

4. More floods;

5. Emergence of zoonotic diseases.

and, most important, more greenhouse gases (GHGs). Globally deforestation contributes to 20 % of GHGs. This in turn produces more droughts and hence creates a vicious circle.

Biodiversity adaptation

A number of options have been suggested for managing natural ecosystems in the face of climate change.[122] They include:

- Expansion of reserves to reduce the vulnerability of ecosystems;

- Design of reserve systems to accommodate long-term shifts in plant and animal distributions, natural disturbance regimes and the overall integrity of the protected species and ecosystems;

- Maintain viable, connected and genetically diverse populations;

- Reduce and manage the other stresses on species and ecosystems, such as habitat fragmentation and destruction, over-exploitation, eutrophication, desertification and acidification.

In general, actions to reduce the impact of other threats are very likely to enhance the resilience of natural ecosystems to climate change.

7. People and health

Not surprisingly there is a wide range of actual and potential impacts of climate change on health, some more serious than others (Figure 9.46).[123]

In 2000 an initial calculation was made of the disability adjusted life years (DALYs) lost through the effects of climate change. A DALY combines the time lived with disability and the time lost due to premature mortality. The calculation was based on deaths caused by cardiovascular diseases, diarrhoea, malaria, accidental injuries in coastal and inland floods and landslides, and the unavailability of recommended daily calorie intake as an indicator of malnutrition (Figure 9.47). Small increases in the risk for climate-sensitive conditions, such as diarrhoea and malnutrition, could result in very large increases in the total disease burden.[23]

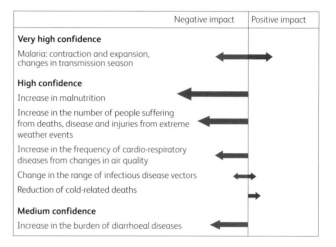

Figure 9.46 – Global estimates of the most serious impacts of climate change on human health[124]

	Negative impact	Positive impact
Very high confidence		
Malaria: contraction and expansion, changes in transmission season	←	→
High confidence		
Increase in malnutrition	←	
Increase in the number of people suffering from deaths, disease and injuries from extreme weather events	←	
Increase in the frequency of cardio-respiratory diseases from changes in air quality	←	
Change in the range of infectious disease vectors	←	→
Reduction of cold-related deaths		→
Medium confidence		
Increase in the burden of diarrhoeal diseases	←	

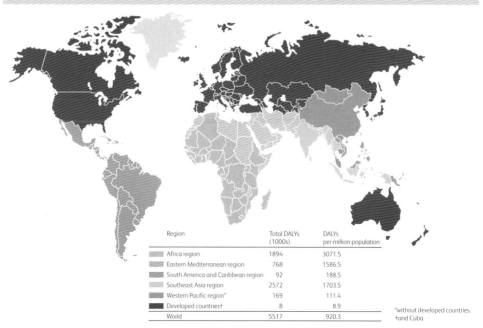

Figure 9.47 – Loss of Disability Adjusted Life Years (DALYs) in 2000 by WHO region[125]

Region	Total DALYs (1000s)	DALYs per million population
Africa region	1894	3071.5
Eastern Mediterranean region	768	1586.5
South America and Caribbean region	92	188.5
Southeast Asia region	2572	1703.5
Western Pacific region*	169	111.4
Developed countries†	8	8.9
World	5517	920.3

*without developed countries.
†and Cuba.

As with other climate change effects, adverse health outcomes are likely to be greatest in low-income countries and for poor people living in urban areas, elderly people, children, traditional societies, subsistence farmers, and coastal populations.[1,124] One prediction is that loss of healthy life years as a result of global environmental change (including climate change) is predicted to be 500 times greater in poor African populations than in European populations.[126]

Direct effects

High temperatures can cause mortality. In all urban areas, temperature rises above 30°C will result in significant loss of life (Figure 9.48). Most vulnerable are the elderly and those with existing diseases such as respiratory and cardiovascular diseases. The mortality typically occurs with lags of less than 3 days (over 3 days for mortality from extreme cold).[127] It is clear that populations adapt to their local climates; nevertheless as a recent comprehensive review suggests, populations in many cities in low- and middle-income countries are likely to have substantial vulnerability to the direct impacts of extremes of temperature.[128]

Indirect effects

Most other health effects are likely to be indirect. Diseases carried by insects and other vectors are especially susceptible to the effects of climate change. For example, the geographical distribution and the rates of development of mosquitoes are highly influenced by temperature, rainfall and humidity. The malaria vector *Anopheles arabiensis* has been observed in the central highlands of Kenya, where no malaria vectors have previously been recorded.[130] We can expect that increased temperatures and more prolonged rainy seasons will extend the transmission period of the disease.

We can also expect an extension of the range of malaria carrying mosquitoes and of malaria into higher elevations, particularly above 1,000m.[131,132] There have been resurgences of malaria in the

Figure 9.48 – Effect of high temperatures on human mortality in New Delhi[128,129]

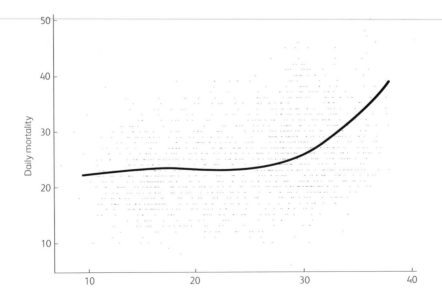

Daily mortality

Temperature, lag 0-2 days

highlands of East Africa in recent years. Many factors are probably involved – poor drug treatment implementation, drug resistance, land-use change, and various socio-demographic factors including poverty. But there is also a strong correlation with climate change.[133-138] Figure 9.49 reveals that the temperature in the highlands of East Africa has risen by 0.5°C since 1980 – much faster than the global average – and this is correlated with a sharp increase in mosquito populations.[139] There is also a trend towards greater rainfall in the September to November period and with the increased warmth this may accelerate mosquito larval development. One estimate suggests that 260-320 million more people will be affected by malaria by 2080 as a result of the geographic spread of transmission.[140]

Figure 9.49 – Temperature change (left) and mosquito population increases (right) at Kericho in Western Kenya[141]

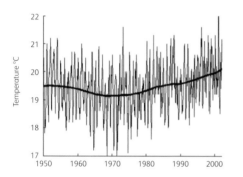
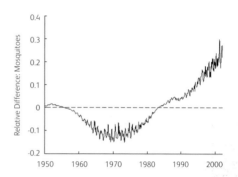

Dengue, another mosquito borne disease (carried principally by *Aedes aegypti*) is also likely to increase. Recent models, based on predicted rises in both relative humidity and in the human population, show a considerable expansion of the geographical range of the disease, particularly through Central and Eastern Africa (Figure 9.50). In 1990, almost 30 % of the world population, 1.5 billion people, lived in regions where the risk of dengue transmission was greater than 50 %. This is estimated to increase to five to six billion people (50-60 % of the projected global population) by 2085.

Figure 9.50 – Predicted expansion of Dengue worldwide (this projection uses an IPCC scenario that delivers a three-fold increase in CO_2 by 2100)[142]

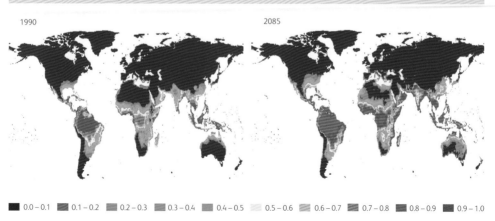

1990

2085

0.0 – 0.1   0.1 – 0.2   0.2 – 0.3   0.3 – 0.4   0.4 – 0.5   0.5 – 0.6   0.6 – 0.7   0.7 – 0.8   0.8 – 0.9   0.9 – 1.0

Dengue, like other vector borne diseases, is correlated with the El-Niño Oscillation, as measured by the Southern Oscillation Index (SOI).[143-145] When El Niño occurs, the SOI is negative: both temperature and rainfall are below average in the west Pacific, and above average in central and eastern areas. At the other extreme, La Niña, the SOI is positive, and the opposite climate

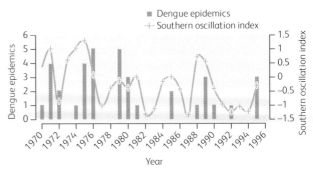

Figure 9.51 – Positive correlation between the SOI and the incidence of dengue epidemics. (SOI positive is La Niña; negative El Niño)[146]

pattern occurs. High temperatures and rainfall result in larger mosquito populations and the SOI is positively correlated with the number of dengue epidemics in a year (Figure 9.51).

The South Pacific islands are on the fringe of the present endemic zone for dengue, but since 1970 there have been several pan-Pacific epidemics, and the more serious dengue haemorrhagic fever has emerged for the first time.[147]

Other infectious diseases that may also increase in range and intensity include cholera and other water borne diseases. Cholera typically spreads along the continental margins and most of the major outbreaks occur along the coasts and in cities that lie on tidal rivers (Figure 9.52).

Figure 9.52 – Spread of Cholera along the continental coasts since 1960[148]

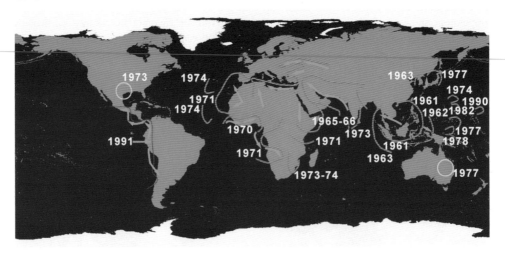

The bacterium is carried by small zooplankton, especially copepods, in the sea water and inland up tidal rivers. Figure 9.53 shows the correlation between cholera outbreaks, the surface temperature and the sea surface height. More recently correlation has been very close, but previously it was low because, although the temperature was high, the sea level was lower and hence the water did not reach up the inter-tidal rivers to cities like Dhaka and Calcutta. A major implication of this finding is that cholera outbreaks are going to become more frequent as a result of global warming.

Other climate correlations have been reported for rodent-borne diseases, meningococcal meningitis, Ross River virus and Rift Valley fever.[150,151] In addition, mortality from diarrhoeal diseases is likely to increase where climate change reduces the availability of adequate water resources so reducing the quality of drinking water and sanitation.

The impact of increased disease could be costly. One estimate puts the population at risk from malaria

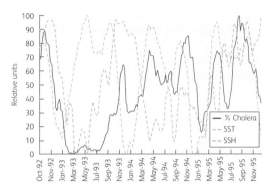

Figure 9.53 – Correlation between cholera outbreaks and sea surface temperatures (SSTs) and heights (SSH)[149]

in Africa as rising from 0.63 billion in 2005 to 1.15 billion by 2030.[152] The current economic burden of malaria already approximates to an average annual reduction in economic growth of 1.3 % for those African countries with the highest burden.[153]

Adaptations in health care

In 2008 the WHO set up an expert consultation to determine the priority research needs relating to the impact of climate change on health. One conclusion was that *'Proven interventions exist against most climate-sensitive risks, and expanding their coverage would reduce current and future health burdens.'*[154] Nevertheless, as is evident from Figure 9.54, adaptation is a complicated process because of the range of pathways of impact and of potential countermeasures.

Figure 9.54 – The complexity of adaptation to the health effects of climate change[155]

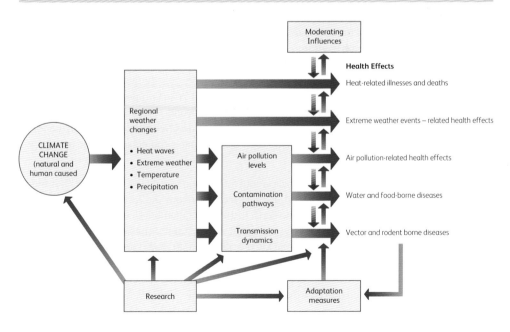

The WHO consultation also concluded that, among other priorities, more knowledge was needed of the risks involved, the cost-effectiveness of different interventions and the effectiveness of surveillance systems. *'Although existing disease surveillance systems already provide some coverage for most climate-sensitive diseases, there are gaps. The potential for using environmental information to enhance early warning, avoid health risks, and lower costs remains largely unproven. Additional research is needed to improve understanding of the kinds of information, dissemination methods, and participatory approaches that are most effective in engaging decision makers, including the general population.'*[154]

In particular information is needed on region-specific projections of changes in health-related exposures and projections of health outcomes under different future emissions and adaptation scenarios.[23]

An example of a surveillance system being developed for malaria in Botswana is described in Box 9.18).

Box 9.18 Improving malaria epidemic prediction in Botswana[156,157]

Malaria epidemics are closely associated with climate, in particular increases in temperature, precipitation and humidity, due to the positive effects these climate changes have on mosquito breeding, development and survival. For this reason improved climate prediction methods could have a significant impact on the ability of health practitioners to prepare and institute interventions which could greatly reduce the severity of oncoming epidemics.

© Georgina Goodwin – Vestergaard Frandsen

Figure 9.55 – A woman hangs out a mosquito net in preparation for the malaria season

In the semi-arid country of Botswana malaria is a top health concern. The country has in place a National Malaria Control Programme which supports control activities such as indoor residual spraying, preventative drugs for vulnerable groups and quick treatment for infected individuals. After a particularly bad epidemic in 1996 the government increased control measures, in particular developing an early warning system based on precipitation and sea-surface temperature data. Malaria epidemics peak in Botswana in March and April, shortly after the height of the rainy season, and weather data from the December to February period can successfully be used to provide predictions for an epidemic's characteristics one month in advance of their peak.

However, with recent advances in regional climate forecasting techniques, it was felt that this one-month lead time could be improved upon. Researchers from the International Research Institute for Climate and Society (IRI), the Earth Institute at Columbia University and Reading University worked with the team in Botswana to test recent state-of-the-art forecast methods developed in Europe. The system, called DEMETER, uses a multi-model ensemble forecast for seasonal-to-interannual climate variability. This allows users to see a 'probability distribution' of disease risk, which indicates not only the most likely upcoming climate, but also both the uncertainty in the prediction and how much it differs from the simpler climatology predictions.

The method successfully allows for predictions to be made up to five months ahead of the peak malaria season, four months earlier than previously used methods. This could allow officials in Botswana to make better informed early decisions about where to distribute and stockpile materials such as mosquito nets and medications and how to best inform the population about preventative measures. This ability will be increasingly important as temperatures and rainfall increase and intensify with the changing climate in the region.

8. Conclusion

The relatively poor state of knowledge of climate change highlights two key goals: first, as we discussed in the previous chapter, we urgently need more research, into the dynamics of the global drivers and into the detailed consequences at regional and local levels; second, we need to design and build on existing adaptation measures to cope with high levels of uncertainty.

The best assumption is that many regions will suffer from droughts *and* floods with greater frequency and intensity. The implication is that we have to plan for the certainty that more extreme events will occur in the future but with uncertain regularity.

Adaptation thus depends on developing resilience in the face of uncertainty. The conceptualisation of resilience presented above is similar in many respects to the approach that has been long used in the face of natural disasters such as earthquakes and tsunamis. It begins with anticipation, surveying and forecasting, moves to developing preventative measures and increasing tolerance, and subsequently after the event, or events, focuses on recovery and restoration. At the end is the importance of learning. In general, the more time and resources that are put into the earlier stages of this sequence, the better.

Resilience is important at the national, regional and local levels, involving not only technologies, but also appropriate economic policies and institutional arrangements. It is the poor who will be most vulnerable to the effects of climate change. To some extent, the process of development itself will help them to adapt. If people are better fed and in better health, and have access to education, jobs and markets they will have the capacity to be more resilient. Traditionally poor people have developed various forms of resilient livelihood strategies to cope with a range of natural and man-made stresses and shocks. But these may be inadequate in the future or may have been lost in the development process. The urgent need is for governments, NGOs and the private sector to work together with local communities to enhance the resilience of the poor.

Chapter 9 references and further reading

1 Toulmin, C., (2007) *Africa's development prospects up in smoke?* Colin Trapnell Memorial Lecture, Green College, Oxford.

2 UNEP. (2007) Global Environment Outlook 4, *Environment for development.* United Nations Environment Programme, Nairobi.

3 Climate Change and Agriculture in China. *Impacts of Climate Change on Chinese Agriculture.* Available at: www.china-climate-adapt.org. [Accessed 12 Dec 2009].

4 Erda, L., Agricultural vulnerability and adaptation to global warming in China. *Water, Air, & Soil Pollution,* **92**, 63-73.

5 NOAA. (nd). Risk and Vulnerability Assessment Tool. Available at: www.csc.noaa.gov/rvat/ [Accessed 12 Dec 2009].

6 Shukla, P. et. al., (eds) (2003) *Climate Change and India, Vulnerability Assessment and Adaption.* Universities Press, Hyderabad.

7 NATCOM India Available at: www.natcomindia.org [Accessed 12 Dec 2009].

8 Smit, B. et al., (2001) Adaptation to Climate Change in the Context of Sustainable Development and Equity. In: McCarthy, J. et al., eds. *Climate Change 2001: Impacts, Adaptation, and Vulnerability.* Contribution of Working Group II to the Third Assessment Report of the Intergovernmental Panel on Climate Change. Cambridge University Press, Cambridge.

9 Bicknell, J. Dodman, D. & Satterthwaite, D., (eds.) (2009). *Adapting Cities to Climate Change: understanding and addressing the development challenges.* London, Earthscan.

10 Taucer, F. Alarcon, J. & So, E., (2008) *Final Mission Report of the 15 August 2007 Magnitude 7.9 Earthquake near the Coast of Central Peru.* Luxembourg Office for Official Publications of the European Communities.

11 Stanekzai, M. & Cruickshank, H., (2008) Engineering, wealth creation and disaster recovery: The case of Afghanistan, In: Guthrie, P. Juma, C. & Sillem, H., (2008) *Engineering Change*, The Royal Academy of Engineering, London.

12 da Silva, J., Engineering Resilience: Disaster risk reduction in the developing world, In: Guthrie, P. Juma, C. and Sillem, H., (2008) *Engineering Change*, The Royal Academy of Engineering, London.

13 Juma, C., (2006) *Redesigning African Economies: The Role of Engineering in International Development.* 2006 Hinton Lecture, Royal Academy of Engineering.

14 Cumming, G. et al., (2005) An exploratory framework for the empirical measurement of resilience. *Ecosystems,* **8**, 975-987.

15 Walker, B. & Salt, D., (2006) *Resilience Thinking: Sustaining ecosystems and people in a changing world.* Island Press, Washington, DC.

16 Holling, C., (1973) Resilience and stability of ecological systems. *Annual Review of Ecology and Systematics,* **4**, 1-23.

17 Gladwell, M., (2000) *The Tipping Point: How Little Things Can Make a Big Difference*, Little Brown, New York.

18 ISDR. (2003) *Disaster Reduction in Africa – ISDR informs.* UN Secretariat of the International Strategy for Disaster Reduction, Nairobi, Kenya.

19 CIMMYT. *Atlas of Maize in Africa.* International Maize and Wheat Improvement Center (CIMMYT), Mexico.

20 ECMWF. (2009) *Seasonal Range Forecast Maps – Rain.* European Centre for Medium-Range Weather Forecasts. Available at: www.ecmwf.int/products/forecasts/d/charts/seasonal/forecast/seasonal_range_forecast/ [Accessed 12 Dec 2009].

21 Hui, J. et al., (2008) *Impacts of Climate Change on Chinese Agriculture – Phase II, Adaptation Framework and Strategy, Part 1: A Framework for Adaptation.* AEA Group, UK.

22   Tanner, T. et al., (forthcoming), "ORCHID: Piloting Climate Risk Screening in DFID Bangladesh", Research Report, Institute of Development Studies, Sussex.

23   Costello, A. et al., (2009) Managing the health effects of climate change. Lancet and University College London Institute for Global Health Commission. *Lancet*, **373**, 1693–733.

24   Meehl, G. et al., (2007) *Ch 10 - Global Climate Projections*. In: Solomon, S. et al., (eds). *Climate Change 2007*, The Physical Science Basis. Contribution of Working Group I to the Fourth Assessment Report of the IPCC. Cambridge University Press, Cambridge.

25   Center for Remote Sensing of Ice Sheets (CReSIS), University of Kansas, Available at: www.cresis.ku.edu [Accessed 12 Dec 2009].

26   Wassmann, R. et al., (2004) Sea level rise affecting the Vietnamese Mekong Delta: water elevation in the flood season and implications for rice production. *Climatic Change*, **66**, 89-107.

27   UNFCCC. (2007) *Vulnerability and Adaptation to Climate Change in Small Island Development States – Background paper for the expert meeting on adaptation for small island developing states.* United Nations Framework Convention on Climate Change. Available at: unfccc.int/files/adaptation/adverse_effects_and_response_measures_art_48/application/pdf/200702_sids_adaptation_bg.pdf [Accessed 12 Dec 2009].

28   Mimura, N. et al., (2007) Ch 16 – Small Islands. In: *Climate Change 2007: Contribution of Working Group II to the Fourth Assessment Report of the Intergovernmental Panel on Climate Change.* Cambridge University Press, Cambridge.

29   Small Island Developing States Network. (2007) *Climate Change & Sea Level Rise.* Available at: www.sidsnet.org/1f.html [Accessed 12 Dec 2009].

30   ACF. (2006) *Climate Change – Tuvalu.* ACF Newsource. Available at: www.acfnewsource.org/environment/Tuvalu.html [Accessed 12 Dec 2009].

31   UNEP/GRID-Arendal. (nd) *The Nile Delta Study.* Available at: www.grida.no/publications/vg/africa/page/3117.aspx [Accessed 12 Dec 2009].

32   Weiss and Overpeck, The University of Arizona.

33   Nicholls, R. & Leatherman, S., (1995) Global sea-level rise. In: Strzepek, K. & Smith, J., (eds.) *As Climate Changes; International Impacts and Implications.* Cambridge University Press, Cambridge, 92-123.

34   Jallow, B. Barrow, M. & Leatherman, S., (1996) Vulnerability of the coastal zone of The Gambia to sea level rise and development of response strategies and adaptation options, *Climate Research*, **6**, 165-177.

35   Boko, M. et al., (2007) Africa. In: Parry, M. et al., (eds) *Climate Change 2007: Impacts, Adaptation and Vulnerability. Contribution of Working Group II to the Fourth Assessment Report of the Intergovernmental Panel on Climate Change*, Cambridge University Press, Cambridge UK, 433-467.

36   Armah, A. Wiafe, G. & Kpelle, D., (2005) Sea-level rise and coastal biodiversity in West Africa: a case study from Ghana. In: Pak Sum Low (ed.) *Climate Change and Africa*, Cambridge University Press, 204-217.

37   Appeaning-Addo, K. Walkden, M. & Mills, J., (2008) Detection Measurement and Prediction of Shoreline Recession in Accra, Ghana. *ISPRS Journal of Photogrammetry & Remote Sensing*, **63**, 543-558.

38   White, G., (1973) Organising Scientific Investigations to deal with environmental impacts. In: Farvar, T & Milton, J., (eds). (1973) *The careless technology, ecology and international development.* Tom Stacy Ltd, London.

39   Mirza, M. et al., (2007) Flood and Storm Control. In: Chopra, K., (ed) *Ecosystems – and Human Well-being, vol 3. Policy Responses*, Island Press, Washington D.C.

40   Padma, T., (2009) *Mangroves 'protect coastal villages during cyclones.'* SciDev.net, 21 April Available at: www.scidev.net/en/news/mangroves-protect-coastal-villages-during-cyclones.html [Accessed 13 Dec 2009].

41   Harvey, N., (ed) (2006) *Global Change and Integrated Coastal Management. The Asia-Pacific Region.* Coastal Systems and Continental Margins. 10. Springer, New York.

42   Barbados Program of Action. (1994) Available at: www.sidsnet.org/docshare/other/BPOA.pdf [Accessed 13 Dec 2009].

43 Mauritius Strategy Declaration. (2005) Available at: www.sidsnet.org/MIM.html [Accessed 13 Dec 2009].

44 Organisation of Eastern Caribbean States, Environment and Sustainable Development Unit. Available at: www.oecs.org/esdu [Accessed 13 Dec 2009].

45 Pacific Islands Climate Change Program Available at: unfccc.int/resource/ccsites/marshall/activity/piccap.htm [Accessed 13 Dec 2009].

46 WorldWater Forum. (2000) *The Africa Water Vision for 2025: Equitable and Sustainable Use of Water for Socioeconomic Development.* UNWater/Africa.

47 Lemke, P. et al., (2007) Ch 4 – Observations: Changes in Snow, Ice and Frozen Ground. In: Solomon et al., (eds) *Climate Change 2007: The Physical Science Basis. Contribution of Working Group I to the Fourth Assessment Report of the Intergovernmental Panel on Climate Change,* Cambridge University Press, Cambridge.

48 Cruz, R. et al., (2007) Asia. *Climate Change 2007: Impacts, Adaptation and Vulnerability.* In: Parry, M.L. (eds) *Contribution of Working Group II to the Fourth Assessment Report of the Intergovernmental Panel on Climate Change,* Cambridge University Press, Cambridge

49 Hasnain, S., 2002) Himalayan glaciers meltdown: impacts on South Asian Rivers. In: van Lanen, H. & Demuth, S., (eds.) *FRIEND 2002-Regional Hydrology: Bridging the Gap between Research and Practice,* IAHS Publications,Wallingford, **274**, 417-423.

50 Shen,Y. et al., (2002) The impact of future climate change on ecology and environments in the Changjiang – Yellow Rivers source region. *Journal of Glaciology and Geocryology,* **24**, 308-313.

51 Hastenrath, S., (2010) Climatic forcing of glacier thinning on the mountains of equatorial East Africa. *Int. J. Climatol,* **30**, 146-152.

52 Thompson, L. et al., (2002) Kilimanjaro ice core records: evidence of Holocene change in tropical Africa. *Science,* **298**, 589-593.

53 Cullen, N. et al., (2006) Kilimanjaro glaciers; recent areal extent from satellite data and new interpretation of observed 20th century retreat rates. *Geophys. Res. Lett,* **33**, L16502. Copyright [2006] American Geophysical Union.

54 WWF. (2005) *An Overview of Glaciers, Glacier Retreat, and Subsequent Impacts in Nepal, India and China.* Available at: assets.panda.org/downloads/himalayaglaciersreport2005.pdf [Accessed 13 Dec 2009].

55 Shrestha, A., (2001) Tsho Rolpa glacier lake: Is it linked to climate change? In: Shrestha, K., (ed.) *Global Change and Himalayan Mountains,* Asia-Pacific Network for Global Change Research and Institute for Development and Innovation, Kathmandu, India, 85–95.

56 ICIMOD & UNEP. (2002) Ch 12 – Glacial Lake Outburst Flood Mitigation Measures, Monitoring and Early Warning System. In: Inventory of Glaciers, Glacial Lakes and Glacial Lake Outburst Floods. International Centre for Integrated Mountain Development and UNEP. Available at: www.rrcap.unep.org/issues/glof/glof/Nepal/Nepal/Report/chap12/chap12main.htm [Accessed 13 Dec 2009].

57 UNEP. (2009) Glacial Lake Outburst Flood Monitoring and Early Warning System, Available at: rrcap.unep.org/issues/glof/ [Accessed 13 Dec 2009].

58 Kundzewicz, Z. et al., (2007) Freshwater resources and their management. In: Parry, M. eds. *Climate Change 2007: Impacts, Adaptation and Vulnerability. Contribution of Working Group II to the Fourth Assessment Report of the Intergovernmental Panel on Climate Change,* Cambridge University Press, Cambridge.

59 Milly, P. Dunne, K. & Vecchia, A., (2005) Global pattern of trends in streamflow and water availability in a changing climate. *Nature,* **438**, 347-350.

60 De Wit, M. & Stankiewicz, J., (2006) Changes in Surface Water Supply with Predicted Climate Change, *Science,* **311**, 1917.

61 Strzepek, K. et al., (2001) Constructing "not implausible" climate and economic scenarios for Egypt. *Integrated Assessment,* **2**, 139–157.

62 Warren, R. et al., (2006) *Understanding the regional impacts of climate change. Research Report Prepared for the Stern Review on the Economics of Climate Change.* Tyndall Centre for Climate Change research, Working Paper 90.

63   Goldsmith, E. & Hildyard, N., (1984) *The Social and Environmental Impacts of Large Dams.* Wadebridge Ecological Centre, Cornwall.

64   World Commission on Dams. (2000) *Dams and Development: A New Framework for Decision Making.* Earthscan, London.

65   China Three Gorges Project. (2002) *Biggest Flood Control Benefit in the World.* Available at: www.ctgpc.com/benefifs/benefifs_a.php [Accessed 13 Dec 2009].

66   South-to-North Water Diversion Project, China. Available at: www.water-technology.net/projects/south_north/south_north1.html [Accessed 13 Dec 2009].

67   Risbud, A., (2006) *Cheap Drinking Water from the Ocean.* Technology Review, 12 June. Available at: www.technologyreview.com/energy/16977/ [Accessed 13 Dec 2009].

68   Holt, J. et al., (2006) Fast Mass Transport through Sub-2-Nanometer Carbon Nanotubes, *Science,* **312**, 1034-1037.

69   The Economist. (2009) Cheaper desalination. *The Economist* 29 Oct print edition. Available at: www.economist.com/sciencetechnology/displaystory.cfm?story_id=14743791 [Accessed 13 Dec 2009].

70   Moench, M. & Stapleton, S., (2007) *Water, Climate, Risk and Adaptation.* Working Paper, Institute for Social and Environmental Transition, Boulder Colorado.

71   Waterwiki. (2009) IWRM Available at: waterwiki.net/index.php/IWRM [Accessed 13 Dec 2009].

72   Global Water Partnership Technical Advisory Committee. (2000) *Integrated Water Management.* Stockholm, Global Water Partnership: 71.

73   World Bank. (1993) *Water Resources Management: A World Bank Policy Paper.* Washington DC, International Bank for Reconstruction and Development, 10.

74   Moench, M. et al., (2003) *The Fluid Mosaic: Water Governance in the Context of Variability, Uncertainty and Change – A Synthesis Paper.* Nepal Water Conservation Foundation, Kathmandu, Nepal and the Institute for Social and Environmental Transition, Boulder, Colorado.

75   Mehta, L. et al., (2007) Liquid Dynamics: challenges for sustainability in water and sanitation. STEPS Working Paper 6, STEPS Centre, Brighton.

76   JRC. (2007) *Floods in Northern Hemisphere Africa, 2007.* European Commission Joint Research Centre.

77   Guardian News & Media Ltd 2009

78   Carter, M., et al. (2004) *Shock, sensitivity and resilience: tracking the economic impacts of environmental disaster on assets in Ethiopia and Honduras.* BASIS, Wisconsin.

79   Singh, V., (1987) *Hydrologic Systems: Watershed Modelling, Vol. II,* Prentice Hall, NJ.

80   Eriksen, S., (2005) The role of indigenous plants in household adaptation to climate change: the Kenyan experience. In: Pak Sum Low (ed.) *Climate Change and Africa,* Cambridge University Press, 248-259.

81   Easterling, W., (2007) Ch 5 - Food, fibre and forest products. In: Parry, M. et al. eds *Climate Change 2007: Impacts, Adaptation and Vulnerability. Contribution of Working Group II to the Fourth Assessment Report of the Intergovernmental Panel on Climate Change,* Cambridge University Press, Cambridge, 273-313.

82   Challinor, A. et al., (2006) Assessing the vulnerability of crop productivity to climate change thresholds using an integrated crop-climate model, In: Schellnhuber, J. et al., (ed.), *Avoiding Dangerous Climate Change,* Cambridge University Press, 187-194.

83   FAO. (2004) *State of World Food Insecurity.* FAO, Rome.

84   Doering, D., (2005). *Public-private partnership to develop and deliver drought tolerant crops to food insecure farmers.* Winrock International.

85   Cane, M. Eshel, G. & Buckland, R., (1994) Forecasting Zimbabwean maize yields using eastern equatorial Pacific sea surface temperature. *Nature,* **370**, 204-205

86   ILRI. (2006) *Mapping climate vulnerability and poverty in Africa.* Report to Department for International Development. International Livestock Research Institute, Nairobi, Kenya.

87   Zhang, Y. et al., (2006) A future climate scenario of regional changes in extreme climate events over China using the PRECIS climate model. *Geophysical Research Letters,* **33**, L24702. Copyright [2006] American Geophysical Union.

88 Labuschagné, I., (2004) Budbreak number as selection criterion for breeding apples adapted to mild winter climatic conditions: A review. *Acta Horticulture* (ISHS), **663**, 775-782.

89 Long, S. et al., (2006) Food for thought: Lower-than-expected crop yield stimulation with rising CO_2 concentrations. *Science*, **312**, 1918-1921.

90 Long S. et al., (2007) Crop models, CO2, and climate change – Response. *Science*, **315**, 460-460.

91 Warren, R. et al., (2006) *Understanding the regional impacts of climate change*. Research Report Prepared for the Stern Review on the Economics of Climate Change. Tyndall Centre for Climate Change research, Working Paper 90.

92 Mader, T. & Davis, M., (2004) Effect of management strategies on reducing heat stress of feedlot cattle: feed and water intake. *J. Anim. Sci*, **82**, 3077-3087.

93 Parsons, D. et al., (2001) Integrated models of livestock systems for climate change studies.1. Grazing systems. *Glob. Change Biol*, **7**, 93-112.

94 Toulmin, C., (1985) Ch 2 – The effects of drought. In: *Livestock losses and post-drought rehabilitation in Sub-Saharan Africa*. LPU Working Paper No.9. International Livestock Centre for Africa, Addis Ababa. Available at: www.fao.org/Wairdocs/ILRI/x5439E/x5439e00.htm [Accessed 13 Dec 2009].

95 Harvell, C. et al., (1999) Emerging marine diseases – climate links and anthropogenic factors. *Science*, **285**, 1505-1510.

96 Akita, S. & Moss, D., (1973) Photosynthetic responses to CO_2 and light by maize and wheat leaves adjusted for constant stomatal apertures. *Crop Science*, **13**, 234-237.

97 Lobell, D. & Burke, M., (2008) Why are agricultural impacts of climate change so uncertain? The importance of temperature relative to precipitation, *Environmental Research Letters*, Vol. 3. Available at: foodsecurity.stanford.edu/publications/why_are_agricultural_impacts_of_climate_change_so_uncertain_the_importance_of_temperature_relative_to_precipitation/ [Accessed 13 Dec 20009].

98 Water Efficient Maize for Africa (WEMA). Available at: www.aatf-africa.org/aatf_projects.php?sublevelone=30&subcat=5 [Accessed 13 Dec 20009].

99 Fischlin, A. et al., (2007) Ecosystems, their properties, goods, and services. In: Parry, M. et al., (eds.) *Climate Change 2007: Impacts, Adaptation and Vulnerability. Contribution of Working Group II to the Fourth Assessment Report of the Intergovernmental Panel on Climate Change*, Cambridge University Press, Cambridge.

100 Siegfried, W., (1989) Preservation of species in southern African nature reserves. In: Huntley, B., (ed.) *Biotic Diversity in Southern Africa: Concepts and Conservation*. Oxford University Press, Cape Town, 186-201.

101 Thomas, C. et al., (2004) Extinction risk from climate change. *Nature*, **427**, 145-148.

102 Scholes, B., (2002) *The winds of change*. Science in Africa. Available at: www.scienceinafrica.co.za/2002/december/change.htm [Accessed 13 Dec 2009].

103 Nicholls, R. et al., (2007) Coastal systems and low-lying areas. In: Parry, M. et al., (eds) *Climate Change 2007: Impacts, Adaptation and Vulnerability. Contribution of Working Group II to the Fourth Assessment Report of the Intergovernmental Panel on Climate Change*, Cambridge University Press, Cambridge, UK, 315-356.

104 Buddemeier, R. Kleypas, J. & Aronson, B., (2004) *Coral Reefs and Global Climate Change: Potential Contributions of Climate Change to Stresses on Coral Reef Ecosystems*. Report prepared for the Pew Centre of Climate Change, Arlington, Virginia.

105 Douglas, A., (2003) Coral bleaching – how and why? *Mar. Pollut. Bull*, **46**, 385-392.

106 Lough, J., (2000) 1997-98: unprecedented thermal stress to coral reefs? *Geophys. Res. Lett.*, **27**, 3901-3904.

107 Donner, S. et al., (2005) Global assessment of coral bleaching and required rates of adaptation under climate change. *Glob. Change Biol*, **11**, 2251-2265.

108 Coles, S. & Brown, B., (2003) Coral bleaching - capacity for acclimatization and adaptation. *Adv. Mar. Biol.*, **46**, 183-224.

109 Rowan, R., (2004) Coral bleaching – Thermal adaptation in reef coral symbionts. *Nature*, **430**, 742.

110 Key, R. et al., (2004) A global ocean carbon climatology: Results from Global Data Analysis Project (GLODAP), *Global Biogeochem. Cycles*, **18**, GB4031.

111 Orr, J. et al., (2005) Anthropogenic ocean acidification over the twenty-first century and its impact on calcifying organisms. *Nature*, **437**, (7059), 681-686.

112 Caldeira, K. & Wickett, M., (2003) Anthropogenic carbon and ocean pH. *Nature*, **425**, (6956), 365-365.

113 Raven, J. et al., (2005) *Ocean acidification due to increasing atmospheric carbon dioxide*. Royal Society, London, UK.

114 EUR-OCEANS. (2007) *Ocean Acidification – the other half of the CO$_2$ problem*. EUR-OCEANS Knowledge Transfer Unit Fact Sheet 7. Available at: www.eur-oceans.eu/WP9/Factsheets/FS7/FS7_webprint.pdf [Accessed 13 Dec 2009].

115 Atkinson, M. & Cuet, P., (2008) Possible effects of ocean acidification on coral reef biogeochemistry: topics for research. *Marine Ecology Progress Series*, **373**, 249-256.

116 Harris, R., (2009) *Acid In The Oceans: A Growing Threat To Sea Life by Richard Harris*. National Public Radio – All Things Considered, 12 August. Available at: www.npr.org/templates/transcript/transcript.php?storyId=111807469 [Accessed 13 Dec 2009].

117 Oceans 2025. Available at: www.oceans2025.org [Accessed 13 Dec 2009].

118 EPOCA. Available at: www.epoca-project.eu [Accessed 13 Dec 2009].

119 Laurance, W. & Williamson, G., (2001) Positive feedbacks among forest fragmentation, drought, and climate change in the Amazon. *Conserv. Bio.*, **15**, 1529-1535.

120 Laurance, W. et al., (2004) Deforestation in Amazonia. *Science*, **304**, 1109.

121 Nepstad, D. et al., (2004) Amazon drought and its implications for forest flammability and tree growth: a basin-wide analysis. *Glob. Change Bio.*, **10**, 704-717.

122 Fischlin, A. et al., (2007) Ecosystems, their properties, goods, and services. In: Parry, M. et al., (eds) *Climate Change 2007: Impacts, Adaptation and Vulnerability. Contribution of Working Group II to the Fourth Assessment Report of the Intergovernmental Panel on Climate Change*, Cambridge University Press, Cambridge, 211-272.

123 McMichael, A. et al., (eds) (1996) *Climate Change and Human Health: an assessment*. WHO, Geneva.

124 Confalonieri, U. et al., (2007) Ch 8 - Human health. In: Parry, M. et al., (eds) *Climate Change 2007: Impacts, Adaptation and Vulnerability*. Contribution of Working Group II to the Fourth Assessment Report of the Intergovernmental Panel on Climate Change, Cambridge University Press, Cambridge.

125 Campbell-Lendrum, D. Corvalán, C. & Prüss Ustün, A., (2003) How much disease could climate change cause? In: McMichael, A. et al., (eds.) *Climate change and human health: risks and responses*. WHO, Geneva.

126 McMichael, A. et al., (2008) Global environmental change and health: impacts, inequalities, and the health sector. *British Medical Journal*, **336**, 191-94.

127 Gosling, S., (2008) Associations between elevated atmospheric temperature and human mortality: a critical review of the literature. *Climatic Change*, **92**, 299-341.

128 McMichael, A. et al., (2008) International study of temperature, heat and urban mortality: the 'ISOTHURM' project. *International Journal of Epidemiology*, **37**, 1121-1131.

129 Kovats, S., (forthcoming). *The effect of temperature on daily mortality in Delhi, India*.

130 Chen, H. et al., (2006) New records of *Anopheles arabiensis* breeding on the Mount Kenya highlands indicate indigenous malaria transmission. *Malaria Journal*, **5**, 17.

131 Tanser, F. Sharp, B. & le Sueur, D., (2003) Potential effect of climate change on malaria transmission in Africa. *Lancet*, **362**, 1792-1798.

132 Beniston, M., (2002) Climatic change: possible impacts on human health. *Swiss Med Wkly*, **132**, 332-337.

133 Githeko, A. & Ndegwa, W., (2001) Predicting malaria epidemics in the Kenyan highlands using climate data: a tool for decision makers. *Global Change & Human Health*, **2**, 54-63.

134 Abeku, T. et al., (2004) Malaria epidemic early warning and detection in African highlands. *Trends in Parasitology*, **20**, 400-405.

135 Patz, J. et al., (2002) Regional warming and malaria resurgence. *Nature*, **420**, 627-8.

136 Patz, J. & Olson, S., (2006) Malaria risk and temperature: Influences from global climate change and local land use practices. *PNAS*, **103**, 5635-5636.

137 Zhou, G. et al., (2004) Association between climate variability and malaria epidemics in the East African highlands. *PNAS*, **101**, 2375-2380.

138 Hay, S. et al., (2002) Climate change and the resurgence of malaria in the East African highlands. *Nature*, **415**, 905-909.

139 Schreck, C. & Semazzi, F., (2004) Variability of the Recent Climate of Eastern Africa. *International Journal of Climatology*, **24**, 681-701.

140 Lindsay, S. & Martens, W., (1998) Malaria in the African highlands: past, present and future. *Bull World Health Organ*, **76**, 33-45.

141 Pascual, M. et al., (2006) Malaria resurgence in the East African highlands: Temperature trends revisited. *PNAS*, **103**, 5829-5834.

142 Hales, S. et al., (2002) Potential effect of population and climate changes on global distribution of dengue fever: an empirical model. *Lancet*, **360**, 830-834.

143 Hales, S. Weinstein, P. & Woodward, A., (1996) Dengue fever epidemics in the South Pacific: driven by El Nino Southern Oscillation? *Lancet*, **348**, 1664.

144 Nicholls, N., (1993) El Nino Southern Oscillation and vector-borne disease. *Lancet*, **342**, 1284-1285.

145 Bouma, M. & Van der Kaay, H. (1996) The El Nino Southern Oscillation and the historic malaria epidemics on the Indian subcontinent and Sri Lanka: an early warning system for future epidemics?, *Trop Med Int Health*, **1**, 86-96.

146 Hales, S. Weinstein, P. & Woodward, A., (1996) Dengue fever epidemics in the South Pacific: driven by El Nino Southern Oscillation? *Lancet*, **348**, 1664-5.

147 Gubler, D. & Clark, G., (1995) Dengue/dengue haemorrhagic fever: the emergence of a global health problem, *Emerg Infect Diseases*, **1**, 55-57.

148 Colwell, R., (nd) *From Cholera to Complexity to Society: A Journey on Many Dimensions*. Presentation. Available at: dimacs.rutgers.edu/Workshops/Opening/Slides/Colwell.ppt [Accessed 13 Dec 2009].

149 Lobitz, B. et al., (2000) Climate and infectious disease. *PNAS*, **97**, no.4.

150 Molesworth, A. et al., (2003) Environmental risk and meningitis epidemics in Africa. *Emerg. Infect. Diseases*, **9**, 1287-1293.

151 Baylis, M., (2006) *T7.1: Climate change and diseases of plants, animals and humans: an overview.* Prepared for the Foresight Project Detection and Identification of Infectious Diseases. Office of Science and Innovation, London. Available at: www.foresight.gov.uk/Infectious%20Diseases/t7_1.pdf [Accessed 13 Dec 2009].

152 Snow, B. Hay, S. & Marsh, K., (2006) *T5.8: Malaria in Africa: sources, risks, drivers and disease burden 2005-2030.* Prepared for the Foresight Project Detection and Identification of Infectious Diseases. Office of Science and Innovation, London. Available at: www.foresight.gov.uk/Infectious%20Diseases/t5_8.pdf [Accessed 13 Dec 2009].

153 Gallup, J. & Sachs, J., (2001) The economic burden of malaria. *American Journal of Tropical Medicine and Hygiene*, **64**, 85-96.

154 Campbell-Lendrum, R. et al., (2009) Health and climate change: a roadmap for applied research. *Lancet*, **373**, 1663-1665.

155 Patz, J., (2002) A human disease indicator for the effects of recent global climate change. *PNAS*, 1206-1209, based on Patz, J. et al., (2000) *Environ. Health Perspect.* **108**, 367-376.

156 Thomson, M. et al., (2006) Malaria early warnings based on seasonal climate forecasts from multi-model ensembles. *Nature*, **439**, 576-579.

157 WMO. (nd) *Climate Applications – Health Sector.* World Meteorological Organization Available at: www.wmo.int/pages/themes/climate/applications_health.php [Accesed 13 Dec 2009].

Part 4

10

Conclusion

Trachoma testing and diagnosis in Tanzania
© Wellcome Images

We have used the Millennium Development Goals (MDGs) to frame our exploration of science and innovation for development. The MDGs stand out as the most comprehensive, results-focused and influential set of international development priorities so far developed. The breadth of their targets for the reduction of poverty and improvement of human welfare has allowed us to examine the contributions of science over a range of development challenges.

1. Science and innovation in the MDGs

From our consideration of MDGs relating to agriculture, health and the environment, we can draw the following general conclusions about science and innovation for development.

Firstly, *science innovation for development is not just about technological solutions.* As importantly, it is about establishing a scientific understanding of problems that will guide development policy and investment. This role for science is particularly clear with environmental challenges. Understanding ecosystem function has given us tools to value ecosystem services in development decision-making, while the growing scientific understanding of climate change has not only made this a development priority, but identified the targets around which policies and agreements for mitigation and adaptation need to be built.

Secondly, *successful science innovation for development draws on the full range of sources of science and technology.* We frequently found that conventional, intermediate and new platform technologies are all making valuable contributions to a single development challenge. For instance, we saw for malaria management the complementary development of medicines based on traditional products like artemisinin, conventional mosquito nets improved with persistent and safe pesticides, and cutting edge vaccine technology. Similarly, we saw how the conservation of natural resources for agriculture could benefit from traditional dryland water and nutrient capture methods, on the one hand, and biotechnological research to improve the efficiency of water and nutrient use by crops on the other.

This observation challenges deep-seated and extreme views. At one extreme is the naïve perception of new technologies as stand alone, "silver bullet" solutions for development problems. At the other extreme is the belief that traditional or intermediate technologies are the only legitimate, fair and appropriate technologies in a development context. A new generation of science innovators needs to replace these prejudices with the understanding that being "appropriate" is not about where innovation comes from but about how useful it is.

Finally, *there are specific needs and opportunities for **new** science innovation for development*, not simply the modification and wider application of existing, conventional technologies. New platform technologies have a key role here, and it will be particularly important that scientists in developing countries participate in the global innovation systems which exploit them.

Specific areas of new science innovation, which we have identified in our study include the use of biotechnologies for increasing agricultural productivity and sustainability through plant and animal breeding, the development of new vaccines and medicines against diseases of the poor and the synthesis of remote sensing, modelling and GIS for measuring environmental change.

Important as science innovation may be to development objectives in agriculture, health and environment, we must stress that these areas are only a fraction of those covered by the MDGs.

Specifically, we have not considered MDGs for education (MDG 2) and gender equity (MDG 3), nor have we considered development priorities identified in the Millennium Declaration but left out of the MDGs, notably peace, security, human rights and good governance. Science innovation makes a contribution towards these priorities as well, particularly in the form of advances in data gathering, communication and analysis associated with new platform ICTs.[1] Education in developing countries is already benefiting from innovation in online learning technology. Technologies, ranging from innovative mobile phone networks to satellite-based remote sensing, have considerable potential to improve monitoring, analysis and reporting of political events such as elections, as well as conflicts and wars.

2. Beyond the MDGs

The MDGs have five more years to run to their target delivery date. We will miss many targets and indicators, particularly in the poorest countries. As we approach 2015, considerable discussion has begun on whether the MDGs have proven a good model for progressing international development.[2,3] There are concerns about their conceptualization, about ownership and about the use of targets. For instance, in seeking MDG impact, efforts are frequently focused on those most easily helped, which may actually contribute to inequity. Proposals for the future range from extending the time period for the MDGs, to modifying them, to starting again from scratch.

Towards this discussion, we contribute three observations which emerge from our consideration of science and innovation for development. They relate to the linkages between MDGs, the convergence of MDG challenges and to the anticipation of shocks.

Breaking down MDG silos

As explained in Chapter 4, the MDGs were not developed from a zero base through a process of collective priority setting. Rather, they were assembled from different, independent, often long-standing sectoral initiatives, with their existing priorities and targets. This explains their patchiness in coverage between sectors, as well as within sectors such as health. Each MDG represents years of development thinking in separate sectoral silos.

This isolation of development initiatives is not unique to the MDGs. It is a phenomenon born in the disciplinary structure of university education, and realized in the specialization of governmental and inter-governmental organisations and, consequently, their development programmes. For all of the benefits which specialization brings to the rapid advancement of understanding and delivery of results, it is often ill-suited to addressing complex development challenges.

Throughout this book, the inter-connectedness of the MDGs, and the importance of these connections to their achievement, has been revealed through exploration of their underpinning scientific basis. In Chapter 9, for instance, we saw how climate change impacts on agriculture, health and other development goals. In Chapter 6 we began by highlighting nutrition, which is not an MDG target, but because a good diet is critical to the baseline of health on which the three health MDGs build – improving child health, maternal health and reducing infectious disease. The lack of integration of international development investment between agriculture, health and the environment, perpetuated in the MDG structure, needs particularly urgent attention, as illustrated in Box 10.1.

Box 10.1   Agriculture, health and environment – inter-linked development goals?

The link between agriculture and health is surely straightforward, is it not? Agriculture produces food which is necessary for the maintenance of health. The focus of the Green Revolution on the improvement of cereal production – maize, wheat and rice – had a strong health driver. In the 1960s, when developing countries like India were facing famine, increasing the availability of calories to the poor was critical.

© DFID

Figure 10.1 – The livestock revolution – an agricultural, health or environmental issue?

Subsequent yield improvements and intensification contributed to a global reduction in the cost of cereals and vegetable oils. By contrast, vegetables and fruits, sources of important micronutrients, have had comparatively little development and promotion, and access to meat and dairy products by many poorer households has remained low. The relatively low cost of commodities like cereals, combined with globalisation of food processing and distribution, and creeping urbanisation, have made a cheap, energy-dense, nutrient-poor diet available and affordable to millions of increasingly less active people.

This is fuelling a global obesity crisis.[4,5] Steady growth in the body mass index (BMI) of populations has been linked to a range of diseases: including diabetes, stroke, hypertension, osteoarthritis, cardiovascular disease and a number of cancers. Diabetes and cardiovascular disease, historically a major cause of ill health in wealthy countries, are now growing most rapidly in poor countries, even amongst the urban and rural poor.[6] At the same time, as incomes increase in some developing countries, we are seeing a rapid growth in the consumption of meat, providing important nutrients, particularly to children, but also contributing to chronic disease risk in adults through consumption of saturated fats.

The concept of malnutrition must now embrace both under- and over-nutrition, a "double burden" of food-related diseases. Thus how we invest in future research for agricultural development will affect future patterns of price, consumption, diet and therefore health. It will also affect how we address environmental challenges. Agriculture contributes substantially to anthropogenic greenhouse gas (GHG) emissions – four fifths of this contribution can be associated with animal production systems which generate GHGs from the production of crops to feed animals, from forest conversion to create pasture and through methane production by ruminants. Getting the right balance of agriculture, health and environmental investment is challenging, but it can have substantial benefits.

For instance, a recent study on how to achieve climate change targets for the agricultural sector in the UK has concluded that a 50 % reduction in GHGs from animal production by 2030 could be achieved by a combination of improvements in agricultural technology and a 30 % reduction in the overall amount of livestock produced. Were this reduction to translate directly into a proportionate reduction in consumption of saturated fats from animal sources, we could see a reduction in the total health burden from ischaemic heart disease by 15 % in disability-adjusted life-years (DALYs), by 16 % in years of life lost, and by 17 % in number of premature deaths.[7]

Another predictive exercise, the Agrimonde Project conducted by the French institutes CIRAD and INRA, has constructed two possible future scenarios for the relationship between agriculture, health and the environment: one focused on increasing food calorie production through technological innovation and increased trade, and the other on changing regional production, consumption and diet to specifically address under- and over-nutrition. The first scenario, because it focuses on agricultural intensification, has low environmental sustainability, while the second, because it shifts food consumption patterns to benefit populations, generates less environmental stress.[8]

Linking international development policy on agriculture, health and the environment is important, because of considerable interactions between these, including substantial co-benefits. As it stands, the MDG targets for hunger focus on dietary energy consumption and do not consider diet quality. Neither nutrition nor chronic disease enter into targets for health MDGs, and the MDG targets for environment do not identify agricultural, or indeed, any other specific indicators for GHG reduction. Continuing in our existing MDG silos will not address this cross-cutting issue effectively. Inter-disciplinary scientific research in these areas, which is just now beginning[†], may help to frame better future development goals and policies.

† These initiatives include the Agriculture Health Research Platform (programs.ifpri.org/ahrp/ahrp.asp) a collaboration between the CGIAR, WHO and other partners, and the new Leverhulme Centre for Integrative Research on Agriculture and Health (LCIRAH) established at the London International Development Centre (www.lidc.org.uk). Both of these focus particularly on international development dimensions of the agriculture, health and environment interaction.

Convergent future challenges

Besides revealing the inter-connectedness of development goals, scientific research reveals likely trajectories of development progress. We are now able to develop increasingly sophisticated models which predict how key development parameters like population growth, use of natural resources, and agricultural productivity change over time and interact. This in turn helps us to visualise the timetable over which progress in development goals is required. For instance, John Beddington, the UK Chief Scientist, has highlighted how scientific models predict the convergence of a number of inter-connected development demands by the year 2030. As Beddington explains, "It is predicted that by 2030 the world will need to produce 50 % more food and energy, together with 30 % more available fresh water, whilst mitigating and adapting to climate change. This threatens to create a 'perfect storm' of global events."[9] Figure 10.2 illustrates the crucial connections which drive this process.

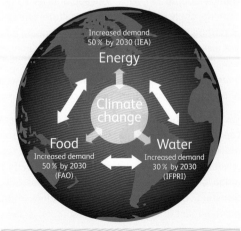

Figure 10.2 – Interacting elements of the Perfect Storm scenario[9]

Beddington's analysis is a wake-up call to those preparing timetables for future development goals. This timetable is likely to vary between regions and the convergence may come sooner in many developing countries due to more rapid population growth or more rapid environmental degradation.

Preparing for shocks

Across the range of MDG challenges which we have surveyed, we have found that scientific research points to a future pattern of agricultural, health-related and environmental shocks which may increase in intensity and frequency.

Climate change predictions suggest an increase in the frequency and severity of extreme weather events, for instance, droughts, extreme temperatures, flooding and tropical storms. Globalisation of trade and travel has contributed to the rapid movement of new pests and diseases of crops and livestock, leading to more frequent outbreaks that threaten agricultural production and trade. The same process of globalisation is increasing the risks of human infectious disease pandemics.

A recent UK Foresight study on *Infectious Diseases: Preparing for the Future* has shown how quite similar processes are operating today to increase the movement and risk of disease for humans, animals and plants, both in the developed and developing world. Changes in trade, travel, transport and tourism have increased the rate and distance of spread of human, animal and plant species, while more protected and rapid transport has increased pathogen survival over these longer distances. In addition, this movement of pathogens enables more mixing of species and strains, sometimes generating new and virulent forms.[10]

For human diseases, we have seen the emergence of new pathogens to be particularly associated with greater mixing of human and animal pathogens. Of 173 emerging or re-emerging human pathogens (pathogens that have appeared for the first time, or whose incidence has increased, over the past two decades), 130 or 73% are zoonotic, having moved from animal to human hosts, usually from livestock or other animals used for food.[11]

How can the design of future development goals prepare for the environmental, agricultural and health-related shocks that are the inevitable consequence of globalisation and our impact on climate? In Chapter 9 we explored the concept of resilience as a development objective for climate change adaptation. This concept and its components: anticipation, prevention, tolerance and learning, apply equally well to agricultural and health shocks arising from movement and evolution of pathogens. For these problems, developing countries are not only the most vulnerable, but they are likely to be the "weakest links" in building a system of global resilience. Due to a lack of surveillance and response capacity, new disease shocks are most likely to emerge and spread undetected in these countries. Once detected, wealthy countries are likely to restrict the movement of people and goods from poorer countries, thus damaging their economies.

We suggest that future international development priorities should include strengthening national capacity for resilience to shocks. While these shocks may be varied, the processes underpinning resilience are similar. They include building a technical capacity to monitor populations and the environment so as to detect shocks, a capacity for predictive modelling and anticipation, and a range of responses that help communities and nations to prevent, tolerate and recover from disasters. Development itself, including improving food security, human health and the management of environmental resources, is the necessary foundation for building this capacity

These steps all point to a need for investment in science and technology. Before we do that, however, we might ask whether recent development investment in this area has been successful?

For instance,

- East Africa has suffered between the 1980s and the present a series of disastrous new plant pest and disease outbreaks on cassava, coffee, banana and wheat (see Box 5.14). Has East African national and regional capacity to respond to such agricultural shocks improved over this period as a result of technological development assistance directed at these outbreaks?

- In the Indian Ocean and Pacific, the terrible tsunami of 2004 led to the expansion of a network of satellite-linked sensors that monitor tsunami development across the world's oceans, the Deep-ocean Assessment and Reporting of Tsunamis (DART) system.[12] Has this improved national resilience to subsequent shocks, such as those in Indonesia and the Pacific in October 2009?

- With human infectious disease, have we seen an improvement in the speed and efficacy of response to the threat of swine flu in developing countries as a result of surveillance and diagnostic technology developed in response to SARS and avian flu outbreaks in 2003 and 2004, respectively?

Has science and technology improved the capacity of poorer countries to deal with these successive agricultural, health and environmental shocks? Evaluating examples such as these might be a first step in understanding the role of science innovation in preparing developing countries for future shocks.

3. Conclusions

In this book we have explored the potential of science innovation for international development. We have written the book particularly for those who have little experience of science in a development context. Necessarily, we have therefore focused on scientific aspects of development, and placed less emphasis on the other factors critical to successful progress, including good governance, infrastructure, economic growth and lack of conflict. Science does not provide wholesale solutions for development; it only makes contributions to those solutions. Further, we have not explored in detail the importance of linking natural and social science research in addressing development problems, a key feature of modern innovation systems.

We are very positive about the role of science in international development. Our confidence is based on its long history of success and the clear indication that problems encountered in the past when applying science to development are being addressed.

This timeliness derives from three emerging trends. First, the problems of rich and poor are increasingly shared problems. Wealthy countries no longer represent a model of successful technological achievement, towards which less wealthy countries can target their technological growth. We are all needing to change, and we are all on new trajectories for sustainable growth and stability, seeking paths towards agricultural security, control of global infectious and chronic disease threats, a low carbon economy and adaptation to climate change. While different paths will be taken by rich and poor, common problems will have elements of common solutions, particularly in science and technology.

Second, we are experiencing today in science a growth in new platforms that have the flexibility to be turned quickly and easily towards the problems of rich or poor alike. Biotechnology has given us a tool to accelerate the development of improved crops or new vaccines which, because of its reliance on fundamental genetic and molecular processes, is easily directed towards the crops and diseases of the poor. Scientific progress in these biological areas is less dependent today on marginal advances on a body of accumulated knowledge for a particular target species. Instead, we can understand and study valuable traits in new species quickly by exploiting complementarity between species in genomes and physiological processes. Similarly, new scientific platforms for nano-, energy, information and communication technologies are much more flexible than earlier engineering technologies which depended on established infrastructures and big industry.

Finally, we are experiencing a revolution in information and communication technology that increases our capacity to communicate and participate globally in science innovation, and to engage stakeholders and beneficiaries in this process, across historical boundaries of developed and developing countries.

Shared challenges, shareable technologies and improved opportunities for communication and collaboration – all very recent trends – greatly improve the prospects of effective science innovation for development. What actions will best secure these new opportunities and accelerate development? We close by suggesting five priorities for action, drawn from the experience of preparing this book, and the examples which we have gathered:

Train and empower scientists who can work internationally on science innovation for development. This involves first and foremost investment in science in developing countries. Building good science training into school systems, supporting universities to develop undergraduate and postgraduate science degree programmes, and supporting both universities and government research institutions to provide attractive career paths for bright scientists are all part of this priority. Development institutions which fund science need to shift their programmes from supporting national scientists on short term research grants to funding national research grant systems that make possible longer term research programmes driven by developing country institutions.

But empowering scientists to work internationally on science innovation for development also means raising the awareness of scientists in developed countries of developing country problems and improving their skills in being effective participants in international development research.

Strengthen science innovation systems in developing countries. National science innovation systems are needed to bring together scientists, entrepreneurs, regulators and other stakeholders who will support and deliver research and its benefits. At the same time, we need to help scientists from developing countries participate in global innovation systems through research with experts in other countries, working South-North and South-South. These research partnerships need to be more equitable and empowering for developing country scientists, supporting their careers in national institutions through opportunities for longer term research, publication and building research groups.

Ensure that new technologies are accessible to science for development. Besides engagement of scientists from developing countries in global innovation systems, we need to ensure continuous and sufficient resourcing for international public goods (IPG) research, so that the full potential of science innovation is available to address poverty reduction. This means supporting research institutions which focus on developing country problems and generate IPGs available to all. But it also means making imaginative partnerships with the private sector to make proprietary technologies available to research for development.

Design and deliver research for impact, by building results based frameworks for development research which ensures the "impact pathway" between the generation of scientific research outputs, the outcomes which they will achieve, and the *impact* which they will have on reducing poverty and improving well being. This means involving stakeholders in the framing of research questions, so that they are prepared to be involved as partners in the execution, application and scaling up of research outputs and outcomes. This will encourage development of appropriate technologies, drawing upon both international and local knowledge, and conventional and new platform science. At the same time, we must never forget the value of curiosity driven or "blue sky" research and we must ensure that some research investment is left to explore new ideas without the need to deliver specific impacts.

Raising the profile of science in governments, by helping governments and industry to understand the value of investing in science innovation systems to their poverty reduction and economic growth agendas. This includes demonstrating the societal value of support to science education and research, and to the establishment of independent scientific societies and advisory groups which can help governments make more informed policy decisions at the national and international level.

Chapter 10 references and further reading

1   Unwin, T., (ed.) (2009) *ICT4D*. Cambridge University Press, Cambridge.

2   Manning, R., (2009) *Using Indicators to Encourage Development: Lessons from the Millennium Development Goals*, Copenhagen, Danish Institute for International Studies. Available at: www.isn.ethz.ch/isn/Digital-Library/Publications/Detail/?ots591=0C54E3B3-1E9C-BE1E-2C24-A6A8C7060233&lng=en&id=96406. [Accessed 13 Dec].

3   Sumner, A., (2009) Rethinking Development Policy: Beyond 2015, *The Broker* **14**, 8-12. Available at: www.thebrokeronline.eu/en/articles/Beyond-2015 [Accessed 13 Dec 2009].

4   Uauy, R. Corvalan, C. & Dangour, A., (2009) Global nutrition challenges for optimal health and well-being. Rank Prize Lecture. *Proceedings of the Nutrition Society*, **68**: 1-9.

5   Uauy, R., (2005) Defining and addressing the nutritional needs of populations. *Public Health Nutrition*, **8**, 773-780.

6   Popkin, B., (2006) Technology, transport, globalization and the nutrition transition food policy. *Food Policy*, **31**, 554-569.

7   Friel, S. et al., (2009) Public health benefits of strategies to reduce greenhouse-gas emissions: food and agriculture. *Lancet*, **374**, 2016-2025.

8   INRA/CIRAD. (2009) *Agrimonde: Scenarios and Challenges for Feeding the World in 2050*. INRA and CIRAD. Available at: www.international.inra.fr/the_institute/foresight/agrimonde [Accessed 13 Dec 2009].

9   Beddington, J., (2009) *Food, Energy, Water and the Climate: A Perfect Storm of Global Events?* Government Office for Science, London.

10 Brownlie, J. et al., (2006). Foresight. Infectious diseases: preparing for the future. Future Threats. Office of Science and Innovation, London.

11 Woolhouse, M. Gowtage-Sequeria, S. & Evans, B., (2006) Quantitative analysis of the characteristics of emerging and re-emerging human pathogens. In: *Infectious Diseases: Preparing for the Future*. Office of Science and Innovation, Foresight Programme, Department of Trade and Industry, UK.

12 NDBC. (2009) *Deep-ocean Assessment and Reporting of Tsunamis (DART) Description*. National Data Buoy Center, NOAA. Available at: www.ndbc.noaa.gov/dart/dart.shtml [Accessed 13 Dec 2009].

Index

Index

Rabies 191, 192

Radar 230

Radiative forcing 273

Raw Solar 248

Recombinant DNA technology (definition) 46

Rede de Informações para o Terceiro Setor (RITS) 40

Reducing Emissions for Deforestation and Forest Degradation (REDD) 234

Regional Initiative in Science and Education (RISE) 65

Regulation 6, 10, 17, 28, 41, 54, 55, 62, 64, 77, 82, 83, 143, 154, 225, 236, 307, 308, 318

Remote sensing 230, 233–235, 239, 305, 358, 359

Renewable energy 82, 246, 247, 249, 253, 257

Rensselaer Nanotechnology Center 44

Resilience 131, 174

Retrovirus 198

Rice 7, 18, 19, 21, 22, 29, 30, 67, 68, 72, 76, 77, 125, 128, 130, 132, 133, 135–137, 140–142, 145, 149, 150, 152, 159, 160, 163, 241, 242, 252

Rice brown planthopper 149, 241

Rice-Wheat Consortium 159

Rice-wheat system 159

Rinderpest 7, 52, 55, 156, 181

Rio Declaration on Environment and Development 222

Roche Pharmaceuticals 179

Rockefeller Foundation 21, 47, 55, 67, 80, 142

Royal Society (UK) 11

Royal Society Pfizer African Academies Programme 11

Rwanda 17, 44, 63, 92, 104, 140, 187

SACRED-Africa 143

Saltworks Technologies 326

Sandia National Laboratories 247

Sanitation 74, 75, 91–93, 101, 107, 115, 116, 174, 178, 182, 195, 215, 222–224, 258, 259, 261, 263, 264, 307, 345

Satellite imagery 146, 230–235, 248, 255, 274, 321, 359, 363

Science (definition) 4

Science, Technology and Innovation for Results (STIR) programme 17

Scientifically advanced country (definition) 16

Scientifically developing country (definition) 16

Scientifically lagging country (definition) 16

Scientifically proficient country (definition) 16

SCORE project 255

Sea-level rise 275, 276, 278, 280, 287, 291, 295, 302, 307, 308, 310, 314–318, 328, 344

Sea-surface temperature (SST) 280, 281, 285, 287, 310, 332, 338, 339, 345, 346

Seed 19, 26, 48, 51, 69–71, 77, 81, 125, 127, 128, 134, 135, 141, 146, 151, 152, 159, 226, 242, 256, 257, 335, 336

Seldon Laboratories 44

Senegal 20, 92

Sexual behaviour 104, 186, 187

Sheep 138–140, 157, 337

Shock (definition) 308, 131, 303, 308–310, 312, 313, 328, 347, 359, 362, 363

Slum 38, 91, 107, 116, 222, 223, 262, 263, 304, 308

Small and medium-sized enterprises (SME) 62, 77